D0270748

GRAIG LIBRARY

CLASS 620·11

STRENGTH OF MATERIALS

This book is to be returned on or before
the last date stamped below.

17 FEB 1994 ▮3 MAY 200▮

-2 MAR 1994 ▮17

CARMARTHENSHIRE COLLEGE OF TECHNOLOGY AND ART
LLANELLI CAMPUS
LIBRARY

STRENGTH OF MATERIALS
THEORY AND EXAMPLES

BY

R. C. STEPHENS
M.Sc.(Eng.), C.Eng., M.I.Mech.E.

FORMERLY PRINCIPAL LECTURER IN MECHANICAL ENGINEERING,
WEST HAM COLLEGE OF TECHNOLOGY

Edward Arnold
A division of Hodder & Stoughton
LONDON   NEW YORK   MELBOURNE   AUCKLAND

© R. C. Stephens 1970

First published in Great Britain 1970
Reprinted
1971, 1974, 1975, 1978, 1979, 1982, 1986, 1988, 1990, 1993

ISBN 0–7131–32116

All rights reserved. No part of this publication may be reproduced or
transmitted in any form or by any means, electronically or
mechanically, including photocopying, recording or any information
storage or retrieval system, without either prior permission in writing
from the publisher or a licence permitting restricted copying. In the
United Kingdom such licences are issued by the Copyright Licensing
Agency: 90 Tottenham Court Road, London W1P 9HE.

Printed and bound in Great Britain for Edward Arnold, a division
of Hodder and Stoughton Limited, Mill Road, Dunton Green,
Sevenoaks, Kent TN13 2YA by Athenaeum Press Ltd, Newcastle
upon Tyne.

00098123

PREFACE

This book is intended to cover the basic Strength of Materials of the first two years of an engineering degree or diploma course; it does not attempt to deal with the more specialized topics which usually comprise the final year of such courses.

The work has been confined to the mathematical aspect of the subject and no descriptive matter relating to design or materials testing has been included.

Each chapter consists of a concise but thorough statement of the theory, followed by a number of worked examples in which the theory is amplified and extended. A large number of unworked examples, with answers, are also included.

The majority of examples have been taken, with permission, from examination papers set by the University of London and the Institutions of Mechanical and Civil Engineers; these have been designated U.Lond., I.Mech.E. and I.C.E. respectively. All questions were originally set in Imperial units; they have now been converted to equivalent S.I. units but are otherwise unchanged.

Over 500 questions have been solved and some errors in solutions are inevitable. Notification of these would be gratefully acknowledged.

R. C. STEPHENS

NOTE ON S.I. UNITS

The fundamental units in the *Système International d'Unités* are the metre, kilogramme and second, with the newton as the derived unit. Where mixed quantities are involved in a problem, the solution has generally been worked throughout in the basic units, e.g. for a given stress of 200 MN/m^2, the figure 200×10^6 N/m^2 has been substituted and for a density of 7·8 Mg/m^3, the figure $7·8 \times 10^3$ kg/m^3 has been substituted.

In many examples of stress analysis or thick cylinders, however, it has been possible to work throughout in MN/m^2 (or the identical unit N/mm^2) and in the calculation of second moment of area of beam sections, etc, preliminary calculations have often been made in mm where this unit has been more appropriate.

The cm is not approved in S.I. units and has therefore not been used.

CONTENTS

CHAPTER 1

SIMPLE STRESS AND STRAIN

1.1 Introduction. When a load is applied to a member of a machine or structure, the material distorts. The *stress intensity* (usually abbreviated to *stress*) is the load transmitted per unit area of cross-section and the *strain* is a measure of the resulting distortion.

Assuming that the load is insufficient to cause rupture, it is resisted by the force of attraction between the molecules of the material and the deformation is the result of the slight re-orientation of the molecules.

If the material returns to its former shape when the load is removed, it is said to be *elastic*; if the strain is permanent, it is said to be *plastic*. Most engineering materials are elastic up to a certain stress (referred to as the *elastic limit*), after which they are partly elastic and partly plastic. The transition is not always abrupt, but for the purposes of calculation it is usually assumed to be so, an assumption which is reasonably justified for common mild steel.

In the simple theory of Strength of Materials, it is assumed that the material is *isotropic* (i.e. displays the same properties in all directions) and that it is equally rigid in tension and compression. It is further assumed that the stress is uniformly distributed over the area resisting the load; this is approximately true, except in the near vicinity of the point of application of the load or a sudden change of section (St Venant's Principle).

1.2 Tensile and compressive stress and strain. If a piece of material of cross-sectional area a is subjected to equal and opposite forces P, either tensile, as in Fig. 1.1(a) or compressive, as in Fig. 1.1(b), then

$$\text{stress} = \frac{\text{force}}{\text{cross-sectional area}}$$

i.e.
$$\sigma = \frac{P}{a} \qquad . \qquad . \qquad . \qquad . \qquad . \qquad . \quad (1.1)$$

If the original length of the bar is l and under the effect of the force P it extends or compresses a distance x, then

$$\text{strain} = \frac{\text{change in length}}{\text{original length}}$$

i.e.
$$\varepsilon = \frac{x}{l} \qquad . \qquad . \qquad . \qquad . \qquad . \qquad . \quad (1.2)$$

The deformed shapes of the bars are as shown dotted in Fig. 1.2; the strain in directions perpendicular to that of the load is proportional to that in the direction of the load and is of the opposite sign.

The ratio $\dfrac{\text{lateral strain}}{\text{axial strain}}$ is called *Poisson's Ratio* and is denoted by ν.

Thus if the axial strain is ε, the lateral strain is $-\nu\varepsilon$.

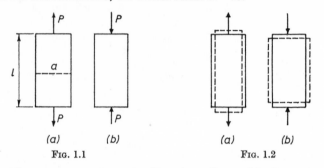

(a)   (b)   (a)   (b)

FIG. 1.1   FIG. 1.2

1.3   Shear stress and strain. If a piece of material of cross-sectional area a is subjected to equal and opposite forces P which produce a state of shear, as shown in Fig. 1.3, then

$$\text{shear stress} = \frac{\text{force}}{\text{cross-sectional area}}$$

i.e.
$$\tau = \frac{P}{a} \qquad \qquad \qquad (1.3)$$

If the deformation in the direction of P is x and the perpendicular distance between the applied forces is l, then

$$\text{shear strain} = \frac{\text{deformation}}{\text{couple arm}}$$

i.e.
$$\phi = \frac{x}{l} \qquad \qquad \qquad (1.4)$$

ϕ is the angular displacement in radians, since $\dfrac{x}{l}$ is very small.

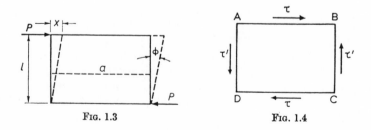

FIG. 1.3   FIG. 1.4

When a shear stress τ is applied to the faces AB and CD of an element of the material, Fig. 1.4, a clockwise couple $(\tau \times AB \times t) \times BC$ is applied to the element, t being the thickness of the material. Since it does not rotate, however, an equal anticlockwise couple must be applied by means of shear stresses induced on faces AD and BC.

If the magnitude of these stresses is τ', then for equilibrium,

$$(\tau \times AB \times t) \times BC = (\tau' \times BC \times t) \times AB$$

$$\therefore \tau' = \tau$$

Thus a shear stress in one plane is always accompanied by an equal shear stress (called the *complementary shear stress*) in the perpendicular plane.

1.4 Hooke's Law. Hooke's Law states that when a load is applied to an elastic material, the deformation is directly proportional to the load producing it. Since the stress is proportional to the load and the strain is proportional to the deformation, it follows that the stress is proportional to the strain, i.e. the ratio stress/strain is a constant for any given material.

For tensile or compressive stresses, this constant is known as the *Modulus of Elasticity* (or *Young's Modulus*) and is denoted by E.

Thus
$$E = \frac{\sigma}{\varepsilon} = \frac{P/a}{x/l} = \frac{Pl}{ax} \qquad . \qquad . \qquad . \qquad (1.5)$$

For shear stress, this constant is known as the *Modulus of Rigidity* and is denoted by G.

Thus
$$G = \frac{\tau}{\phi} = \frac{P/a}{x/l} = \frac{Pl}{ax} \qquad . \qquad . \qquad . \qquad (1.6)$$

1.5 Factor of safety. The maximum stress used in the design of a machine or structure is considerably less than the ultimate stress (i.e. the stress at failure), to allow for possible overloading, non-uniformity of stress distribution, shock loading, faults in material and workmanship, corrosion, wear, etc.

The ratio $\dfrac{\text{breaking stress}}{\text{maximum design stress}}$ is called the *factor of safety*.

Instead of basing this factor on the stress at failure, it is sometimes based on the stress at the yield point (where the material suddenly becomes plastic) or, for materials which have no well-defined yield point, on the stress at which the extension is a certain percentage (e.g. 0·1 per cent) of the original length.

1.6 Stresses in thin cylindrical shells. When a thin cylinder is subjected to internal pressure, stresses are induced on the longitudinal section XX, Fig. 1.5, due to the force tending to separate the top and bottom halves, and on the circumferential section YY due to the force tending to separate the right- and left-hand ends of the cylinder.

The stress on the longitudinal section is termed the circumferential stress and that on the circumferential section is termed the longitudinal stress; the type of stress is determined by the direction of the arrows.

In determining the stresses induced, it is assumed that the thickness is small in comparison with the diameter so that the stress on a cross-section may be taken as uniform* and also that the ends give no support to the sides, an assumption which would be appropriate to a long cylinder such as a pipe.

Let the internal diameter and length be d and l respectively, the thickness of metal be t and the internal pressure be p.

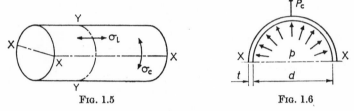

Fig. 1.5   Fig. 1.6

Circumferential stress. The force tending to separate the top and bottom halves is the pressure multiplied by the projected area in a direction perpendicular to the diametral plane,† Fig. 1.6,

i.e. $$P_c = pdl$$

This is resisted by the stress acting on the longitudinal section, XX,

i.e. $$\sigma_c = \frac{pdl}{2tl} = \frac{pd}{2t} \qquad . \qquad . \qquad . \qquad . \qquad (1.7)$$

If the cylinder is made up from riveted plates and the efficiency of the longitudinal joints is η_l then the average stress in the joint is given by

$$\sigma_c = \frac{pd}{2t\eta_l} \qquad . \qquad . \qquad . \qquad . \qquad (1.8)$$

* See Chapter 14.

† The radial force on an element subtending an angle $d\theta$, Fig. 1.7, is $p \times \dfrac{d}{2} d\theta \times l$. The vertical component of this force is $\dfrac{pdl}{2} d\theta . \sin \theta$ so that the total force normal to XX is $\displaystyle\int_0^\pi \frac{pdl}{2} \sin \theta \, d\theta = pdl$.

Fig. 1.7

Longitudinal stress. The force tending to separate the right- and left-hand halves is the pressure multiplied by the area of one end, Fig. 1.8,

i.e.
$$P_l = p \times \frac{\pi}{4} d^2$$

This is resisted by the stress acting on the circumferential section, YY,

i.e.
$$\sigma_l = \frac{p \times \dfrac{\pi}{4} d^2}{\pi dt} = \frac{pd}{4t} \qquad . \qquad . \qquad . \qquad (1.9)$$

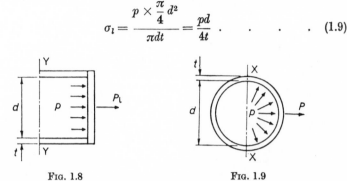

FIG. 1.8   FIG. 1.9

If the cylinder is made up from riveted plates and the efficiency of the circumferential joints is η_c then the average stress in the joint is given by

$$\sigma_l = \frac{pd}{4t\eta_c} \qquad . \qquad . \qquad . \qquad . \qquad (1.10)$$

It is evident from equations (1.8) and (1.10) that the efficiency of the circumferential joints need only be half that of the longitudinal joints.

1.7   Stress in thin spherical shells. Let the internal diameter be d, the thickness of metal be t and the internal pressure be p, Fig. 1.9. Then the force tending to separate the two halves on a section XX is the pressure multiplied by the projected area in the direction perpendicular to XX,

i.e.
$$P = p \times \frac{\pi}{4} d^2$$

This is resisted by the stress acting on the section XX,

i.e.
$$\sigma = \frac{p \times \dfrac{\pi}{4} d^2}{\pi dt} = \frac{pd}{4t} \qquad . \qquad . \qquad . \qquad (1.11)$$

If the shell is made up from riveted plates and the efficiency of the joints is η, then

$$\sigma = \frac{pd}{4t\eta} \qquad . \qquad . \qquad . \qquad . \qquad (1.12)$$

1.8   Stress in thin rotating rims. Let a thin rim (one in which the radial depth is small in comparison with the mean radius) of cross-sectional area a, mean radius r and density m rotate at a tangential speed v, Fig. 1.10. Then the centrifugal force, F, on an element subtending an angle $d\theta$ is

$$m \times a \times r\, d\theta\, \frac{v^2}{r}$$

This is resisted by the radial components of the forces on the ends of the element. If the stress induced is σ, then

$$mav^2 d\theta = 2 \times \sigma a \times \frac{d\theta}{2}$$

from which $$\sigma = mv^2 \qquad . \qquad . \qquad . \qquad . \qquad . \quad (1.13)$$

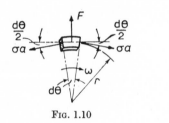
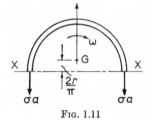

FIG. 1.10   FIG. 1.11

Alternatively, the centre of gravity of the half of the rim above the diametral plane XX, Fig. 1.11, is at a distance $\dfrac{2r}{\pi}$ from XX. The centrifugal force on this part is then resisted by the stress σ acting on the section XX,

i.e. $$m \times a \times \pi r \times \omega^2 \times \frac{2r}{\pi} = 2\sigma a$$

from which $$\sigma = m\omega^2 r^2 = mv^2$$

1.9   Stresses in composite bars. A composite bar is a load-resisting member which is made up of two different materials.

Let the cross-sectional areas of the two materials be a_1 and a_2, the moduli of elasticity be E_1 and E_2 and the coefficients of expansion be α_1 and α_2.

Stresses due to external load. If the ends through which the load is applied are rigid, Fig. 1.12, the change in length of each part is the same,

i.e. $$x_1 = x_2$$

i.e. $$\frac{\sigma_1 l_1}{E_1} = \frac{\sigma_2 l_2}{E_2} . \qquad . \qquad . \qquad . \qquad . \quad (1.14)$$

Also the sum of the loads carried by each part is equal to the applied load,

i.e. $$P_1 + P_2 = P$$

or $$\sigma_1 a_1 + \sigma_2 a_2 = P \qquad . \qquad . \qquad . \qquad . \qquad (1.15)$$

σ_1 and σ_2 can then be obtained from equations (1.14) and (1.15).

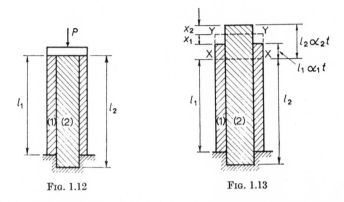

FIG. 1.12   FIG. 1.13

Stresses due to change in temperature. Let XX, Fig. 1.13, be the initial level of the top of the composite bar and let YY be its final level after a temperature rise t. If both parts were free to expand, the extension of material (1) would be $l_1 \alpha_1 t$ and that of material (2) would be $l_2 \alpha_2 t$; if, however, the two materials are rigidly connected at the top, material (1) is forced to extend a distance x_1 and material (2) is forced to compress a distance x_2. It is only these forced changes in length, x_1 and x_2, which produce stresses in the materials.

From Fig. 1.13, it will be seen that

$$x_1 + x_2 = l_2 \alpha_2 t - l_1 \alpha_1 t$$

i.e. $$\frac{\sigma_1 l_1}{E_1} + \frac{\sigma_2 l_2}{E_2} = (l_2 \alpha_2 - l_1 \alpha_1)t \qquad . \qquad . \qquad . \qquad (1.16)$$

Also, since no external force is applied to the bar,

tensile force in material (1) = compressive force in material (2),

i.e. $$\sigma_1 a_1 = \sigma_2 a_2 \qquad . \qquad . \qquad . \qquad . \qquad (1.17)$$

σ_1 and σ_2 can then be obtained from equations (1.16) and (1.17).

If the bar is subjected to an external load P, Fig. 1.14, as well as to a temperature rise t, then, from the equilibrium of the end plate,

$$P + P_1 = P_2$$

or $$\sigma_1 a_1 - \sigma_2 a_2 = P \qquad . \qquad . \qquad . \qquad (1.18)$$

assuming P to be compressive and $\alpha_2 > \alpha_1$.

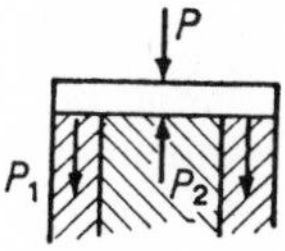

FIG. 1.14

Equation (1.16) will still be applicable and hence σ_1 and σ_2 may be calculated. In many instances, however, it may be simpler to determine the stresses due to the external load and temperature change separately and then combine these values to obtain the resultant stresses, particular care being taken over the nature of the separate stresses.

1.10   Strain energy. When a body is stressed, it distorts and work is done on it. This energy is stored in the material and is recoverable when the stress is relieved, provided that the material remains elastic. The energy is termed *strain energy* or *resilience* and that stored when the material is stressed to the elastic limit is termed the *proof resilience*.

Gradually applied load. If an axial load P is gradually applied to a bar and produces an extension x, then the work done, or strain energy, is represented by the area under the load/extension diagram, Fig. 1.15,

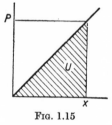

i.e. $\qquad\qquad U = \frac{1}{2}Px$

But $\qquad\qquad P = \sigma \times a$ and $x = \dfrac{\sigma l}{E}$

$$\therefore\ U = \frac{\sigma^2}{2E} \times al$$

$$= \frac{\sigma^2}{2E} \times \text{volume} \qquad . \qquad . \ (1.19)$$

FIG. 1.15

The expression $\dfrac{\sigma^2}{2E} \times$ volume represents the strain energy in the material when the stress is σ and however this stress is caused, the strain energy will always be given by the same expression.

Suddenly applied load. Let a mass M be dropped from a height h on to a collar at the lower end of a bar, Fig. 1.16, producing an instantaneous extension x and an instantaneous stress σ. Then the loss of potential energy of the weight is $Mg(h + x)$, so that, ignoring any loss of energy at impact,

$$Mg(h + x) = \frac{\sigma^2}{2E} \times \text{volume}$$

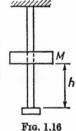

i.e. $\qquad Mg\left(h + \dfrac{\sigma l}{E}\right) = \dfrac{\sigma^2}{2E} \times \text{volume} \ . \qquad . \ (1.20)$

This is a quadratic from which σ can be found; the positive solution will represent the tensile stress at the point of maximum extension and the negative solution will represent the compressive stress at the end of the rebound. The oscillation of the weight will die away due to internal

FIG. 1.16

friction in the material and its final position will be the same as when gradually applied.

When $h = 0$, $\qquad Mg \times \dfrac{\sigma l}{E} = \dfrac{\sigma^2}{2E} \times$ volume

from which $\qquad\qquad\qquad \sigma = 2\dfrac{Mg}{a}$

i.e. the maximum stress is twice that due to a gradually applied load of the same magnitude.

1.11 Shear strain energy. Referring to Fig. 1.3, the work done by the shearing force P is $\frac{1}{2}Px$, assuming it to be gradually applied.

But $\qquad\qquad P = \tau \times a$ and $x = \dfrac{\tau l}{G}$

$$\therefore U = \dfrac{\tau^2}{2G} \times al$$

$$= \dfrac{\tau^2}{2G} \times \text{volume} \quad . \qquad . \qquad . \quad (1.21)$$

1. *A tension specimen of circular cross-section tapers uniformly from 20 mm to 16 mm diameter over a gauge length of 200 mm. When an axial load of 40 kN is applied, the extension measured on this gauge length is 0·4 mm. Find the modulus of elasticity of the material.*

Compare the strain energy in this specimen with that in a specimen of the same material of uniform diameter 18 mm carrying the same load. (U. Lond.)

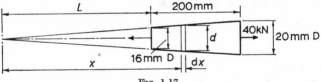

FIG. 1.17

Referring to Fig. 1.17,

$$\dfrac{0·016}{L} = \dfrac{0·02 - 0·016}{0·2} \qquad\qquad \therefore L = 0·8 \text{ m}$$

$$\dfrac{d}{x} = \dfrac{0·016}{L} \qquad\qquad\qquad \therefore d = 0·02x \text{ m}$$

Stress on element $= \dfrac{40 \times 10^3}{\dfrac{\pi}{4} \times (0·02x)^2} = \dfrac{127·4 \times 10^6}{x^2} \text{ N/m}^2$

$\therefore$ extension of element $= \dfrac{\sigma l}{E} = \dfrac{127·4 \times 10^6}{x^2} \times \dfrac{dx}{E}$

$$\therefore \text{ total extension of bar} = \frac{127\cdot4 \times 10^6}{E} \int_{0\cdot8}^{1\cdot0} \frac{dx}{x^2} = \frac{31\cdot85 \times 10^6}{E}$$

$$= 0\cdot000\ 4 \text{ m}$$

$$\therefore E = \frac{31\cdot85 \times 10^6}{0\cdot000\ 4} \text{ N/m}^2 \ = \underline{79\cdot6 \text{ GN/m}^2}$$

For a bar of uniform diameter 0·018 m, extension under a load of 40 kN

$$= \frac{Pl}{aE} = \frac{40 \times 10^3 \times 0\cdot2}{\dfrac{\pi}{4} \times 0\cdot018^2 \times 79\cdot6 \times 10^9} = 0\cdot000\ 395 \text{ m}$$

$\therefore$ ratio of strain energies = ratio of extensions for the same load

$$= \frac{0\cdot000\ 4}{0\cdot000\ 395} = \underline{1\cdot012}$$

2. *A steel ball, radius r, has equal and parallel flats machined on opposite sides so that the thickness across the faces is 1·6r. Calculate the decrease in thickness when an axial load W is applied to these faces.*

Referring to Fig. 1.18,

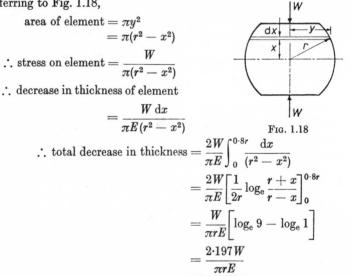

$$\text{area of element} = \pi y^2$$
$$= \pi(r^2 - x^2)$$

$$\therefore \text{ stress on element} = \frac{W}{\pi(r^2 - x^2)}$$

$\therefore$ decrease in thickness of element

$$= \frac{W\ dx}{\pi E(r^2 - x^2)}$$

Fig. 1.18

$$\therefore \text{ total decrease in thickness} = \frac{2W}{\pi E} \int_0^{0\cdot8r} \frac{dx}{(r^2 - x^2)}$$

$$= \frac{2W}{\pi E} \left[\frac{1}{2r} \log_e \frac{r+x}{r-x} \right]_0^{0\cdot8r}$$

$$= \frac{W}{\pi r E} \left[\log_e 9 - \log_e 1 \right]$$

$$= \underline{\frac{2\cdot197 W}{\pi r E}}$$

3. *A straight steel bar of uniform cross-section, 1 m long, rotates at 2 500 rev/min about an axis at mid-length perpendicular to the length of the bar. Find the maximum stress and total extension if E = 200 GN/m² and steel density = 7·8 Mg/m³.* (U. Lond.)

Tensile force on element

= centrifugal force on part of bar to right of element, Fig. 1.19

$= M\omega^2 r$

$$= 7\cdot8 \times 10^3 \times a \times (0\cdot5 - x) \times \left(2\,500 \times \frac{2\pi}{60}\right)^2 \times \frac{0\cdot5 + x}{2}\ \text{N}$$

where a is the cross-sectional area

$$= 267\cdot5a(0\cdot25 - x^2)\ \text{MN}$$

The maximum stress is at the axis of rotation (i.e. where $x = 0$)

i.e.   maximum stress $= \dfrac{267\cdot5a \times 0\cdot25}{a} = \underline{66\cdot88\ \text{MN/m}^2}$

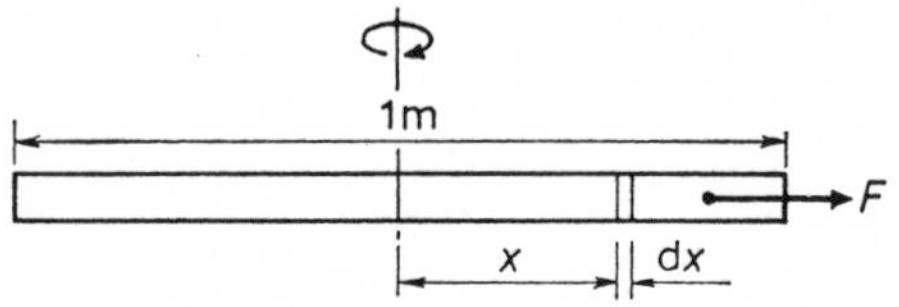

FIG. 1.19

Extension of element $= \dfrac{Pl}{aE}$

$$= \frac{267\cdot5 \times 10^6\, a\, (0\cdot25 - x^2)\ \mathrm{d}x}{a \times 200 \times 10^9}$$

$$= 1\cdot338 \times 10^{-3}(0\cdot25 - x^2)\ \mathrm{d}x$$

$\therefore$ total extension $= 2 \times 1\cdot338 \times 10^{-3} \displaystyle\int_0^{0\cdot5} (0\cdot25 - x^2)\ \mathrm{d}x$

$$= 0\cdot229 \times 10^{-3}\ \text{m}\quad\text{or}\quad \underline{0\cdot229\ \text{mm}}$$

4. *Explain the meaning of the term 'efficiency of a riveted joint'.*

A cylindrical vessel having a diameter of 2 m is subjected to an internal pressure of 1·25 MN/m². The vessel is made of steel plates 15 mm thick which have an ultimate tensile strength of 450 MN/m². If the efficiencies of the longitudinal and circumferential joints are 80 and 60 per cent respectively, what is the factor of safety? (U. Lond.)

The efficiency of a riveted joint is the ratio $\dfrac{\text{strength of riveted joint}}{\text{strength of undrilled plate}}$.

From equation (1.8), $\sigma_c = \dfrac{pd}{2t\eta_l}$

$$= \frac{1\cdot25 \times 2}{2 \times 0\cdot015 \times 0\cdot80} = 104\ \text{MN/m}^2$$

From equation (1.10) $\sigma_l = \dfrac{pd}{4t\eta_c}$

$$= \frac{1\cdot25 \times 2}{4 \times 0\cdot015 \times 0\cdot60} = 69\cdot5\ \text{MN/m}^2$$

Therefore factor of safety $= \dfrac{450}{104}\qquad\qquad = \underline{\underline{4\cdot32}}$

5. *Derive an expression for the tensile strength of a thin rotating ring.*

Find the greatest speed in rev/min for a rotor so that the stress due to rotation does not exceed 120 MN/m². The rotor may be treated as equivalent to a ring of 1 m mean diameter, and the material has a density of 7·8 Mg/m³.

(U. Lond.)

From equation (1.13), $\sigma = mv^2$

i.e. $$120 \times 10^6 = 7\cdot8 \times 10^3 v^2$$

$$\therefore v = 124\cdot2 \text{ m/s}$$

$$\therefore N = \frac{v}{r} \times \frac{60}{2\pi}$$

$$= \frac{124\cdot2}{0\cdot5} \times \frac{60}{2\pi} = \underline{2\ 370 \text{ rev/min}}$$

6. *A brass rod 6 mm diameter and 1 m long is joined at one end to a rod of steel 6 mm diameter and 1·3 m long. The compound rod is placed in a vertical position with the steel rod at the top and connected top and bottom to rigid fixings in such a way that it is carrying a tensile load of 3·5 kN.*

An attachment is fixed at the junction of the two rods and to this a vertical axial load of 1·3 kN is applied downwards. Calculate the stresses in the steel and brass.

The temperature is then raised 30 deg C. What are the final stresses in the steel and brass?

$$E_s = 200 \text{ GN/m}^2;$$
$$\alpha_s = 12 \times 10^{-6}/\text{deg C};$$
$$E_b = 85 \text{ GN/m}^2;$$
$$\alpha_b = 19 \times 10^{-6}/\text{deg C. (U. Lond.)}$$

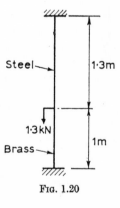

Fig. 1.20

Let the forces in the steel and brass be P_s and P_b respectively, Fig. 1.20. Then, equating upward and downward forces at the junction,

$$P_s = P_b + 1\ 300 \quad . \quad . \quad (1)$$

The tension in the steel increases by $(P_s - 3\ 500)$ N and that in the brass decreases by $(3\ 500 - P_b)$ N. Since the overall length of the rod remains unaltered, the increase in length of the steel is equal to the decrease in length of the brass,

i.e. $$\frac{(P_s - 3\ 500) \times l_s}{a_s E_s} = \frac{(3\ 500 - P_b) \times l_b}{a_b E_b} \quad . \quad . \quad (2)$$

Substituting for P_s from equation (1), equation (2) becomes

$$(P_b - 2\ 200) \times \frac{1 \cdot 3}{200} = (3\ 500 - P_b) \times \frac{1}{85}$$

from which $\qquad P_b = 3\ 040 \text{ N} \quad \text{and} \quad P_s = 4\ 340 \text{ N}$

$$\therefore \sigma_b = \frac{3\ 040}{\dfrac{\pi}{4} \times 0 \cdot 006^2}\ \text{N/m}^2 = \underline{107 \cdot 5\ \text{MN/m}^2}$$

and

$$\sigma_s = \frac{4\ 340}{\dfrac{\pi}{4} \times 0 \cdot 006^2}\ \text{N/m}^2 = \underline{153 \cdot 5\ \text{MN/m}^2}$$

Let the compressive stress in the rod due to the increase in temperature be σ (which will be the same in the steel and brass since they both have the same cross-sectional area). The reduction in overall length due to σ must be the same as the free expansion due to the temperature increase, since the ends remain fixed,

i.e. $\qquad \dfrac{\sigma l_s}{E_s} + \dfrac{\sigma l_b}{E_b} = l_s \alpha_s t + l_b \alpha_b t$

i.e. $\quad \sigma \left(\dfrac{1 \cdot 3}{200 \times 10^9} + \dfrac{1}{85 \times 10^9} \right) = (1 \cdot 3 \times 12 \times 10^{-6} + 1 \times 19 \times 10^{-6}) \times 30$

from which $\qquad \sigma = 56 \cdot 9\ \text{MN/m}^2$

$\therefore$ resultant stress in steel $= 153 \cdot 5 - 56 \cdot 9 = \underline{96 \cdot 6\ \text{MN/m}^2}$

and the resultant stress in brass $= 107 \cdot 5 - 56 \cdot 9 = \underline{50 \cdot 6\ \text{MN/m}^2}$

7. *Fig.* 1.21 *shows a round steel rod supported in a recess and surrounded by a coaxial brass tube. The upper end of the rod is* 0·1 *mm below that of the tube and an axial load is applied to a rigid plate resting on the top of the tube.*

(a) *Determine the magnitude of the maximum permissible load if the compressive stress in the rod is not to exceed* 110 *MN/m² and that in the tube is not to exceed* 80 *MN/m².*

(b) *Find the amount by which the tube will be shortened by the load if the compressive stress in the tube is the same as that in the rod.*

$E_{\text{steel}} = 200\ \text{GN/m}^2;$
$E_{\text{brass}} = 100\ \text{GN/m}^2.$ (U. Lond.)

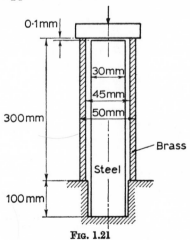

Fig. 1.21

The sum of the loads carried by the brass and steel is equal to the total load,

i.e.
$$P_b + P_s = P$$

i.e.
$$\sigma_b \times \frac{\pi}{4}(0.05^2 - 0.045^2) + \sigma_s \times \frac{\pi}{4} \times 0.03^2 = P$$

i.e.
$$0.000\,373\,\sigma_b + 0.000\,707\,\sigma_s = P \qquad (1)$$

After the plate has made contact with the top of the rod, the compression of the brass exceeds that of the rod by $0.000\,1$ m,

i.e.
$$x_b = x_s + 0.000\,1$$

i.e.
$$\frac{\sigma_b \times 0.3}{100 \times 10^9} = \frac{\sigma_s \times 0.4^*}{200 \times 10^9} + 0.000\,1$$

or
$$\sigma_b = 0.667\,\sigma_s + 33.3 \times 10^6. \qquad . \qquad . \qquad (2)$$

The maximum stresses of 110 MN/m² and 80 MN/m² in the steel and brass respectively will not occur simultaneously. Equation (2) shows that if $\sigma_b = 80$ MN/m², $\sigma_s = 70$ MN/m² and if $\sigma_s = 110$ MN/m², $\sigma_b = 106.7$ MN/m². Hence the maximum permissible load is that which will produce stresses of 80 MN/m² and 70 MN/m² in the brass and steel respectively.

Therefore, from equation (1),

$$P = 0.000\,373 \times 80 \times 10^6 + 0.000\,707 \times 70 \times 10^6 \text{ N} = \underline{79.33 \text{ kN}}$$

When $\sigma_s = \sigma_b$, equation (2) becomes

$$\sigma_b = 0.667\,\sigma_b + 33.3 \times 10^6 \text{ N/m}^2$$

from which $\sigma_b = 100$ MN/m²

$$\therefore x_b = \frac{100 \times 10^6 \times 0.3}{100 \times 10^9} = 0.000\,3 \text{ m} \quad \text{or} \quad \underline{0.3 \text{ mm}}$$

8. *A mass of 150 kg is suspended by three vertical wires. The two outer wires are of steel and the middle one of aluminium, each of area 8 mm². The lengths are adjusted so that each wire carries an equal share of the load. If the temperature is raised by 50 deg C, find the stresses in the wires.*

Find also what rise of temperature would just cause the aluminium wire to become slack.

	Steel	Aluminium
$E(GN/m^2)$	210	70
Coefficient of expansion per deg C	12×10^{-6}	24×10^{-6}

(U. Lond.)

Initial stress in steel = initial stress in aluminium

$$= \frac{50 \times 9.81}{8 \times 10^{-6}} \text{ N/m}^2 = 61.3 \text{ MN/m}^2 \text{ (tensile)}$$

---

* Allowance for the $0.000\,1$ m in the original length of the rod will have a negligible effect on the answers.

Let σ_s and σ_a be the stresses in the steel and aluminium respectively due to the temperature rise only. Then

$$2\sigma_s a_s = \sigma_a a_a \ . \quad \text{from equation (1.17)}$$

i.e.
$$2\sigma_s = \sigma_a \quad . \qquad . \qquad . \qquad . \qquad (1)$$

Also
$$\frac{\sigma_s l}{210 \times 10^9} + \frac{\sigma_a l}{70 \times 10^9} = l\,(24 - 12) \times 10^{-6} \times 50$$
$$\text{from equation (1.16)}$$

from which
$$\sigma_s + 3\sigma_a = 126 \text{ MN/m}^2$$

Substituting for σ_s from equation (1), $\sigma_a = 36\!\cdot\!0 \text{ MN/m}^2$ (compressive)

and
$$\sigma_s = 18\!\cdot\!0 \text{ MN/m}^2 \text{ (tensile)}$$

∴ resultant stress in aluminium $= 61\!\cdot\!3 - 36\!\cdot\!0$

$$= \underline{25\!\cdot\!3 \text{ MN/m}^2 \text{ (tensile)}}$$

and resultant stress in steel $= 61\!\cdot\!3 + 18\!\cdot\!0$

$$= \underline{79\!\cdot\!3 \text{ MN/m}^2 \text{ (tensile)}}$$

When aluminium wire becomes slack, $\sigma_a = 61\!\cdot\!3 \text{ MN/m}^2$ (compressive). Therefore, since σ_a is proportional to the change in temperature,

$$\text{temperature rise} = \frac{61\!\cdot\!3}{36\!\cdot\!0} \times 50$$

$$= \underline{85\!\cdot\!1 \text{ deg C}}$$

9. *It is estimated that the loads to be carried by a lift may be dropped through a distance of* 100 *mm on to the floor. The cage itself has a mass of* 100 *kg and it is supported by* 25 *m of wire rope of mass* 0·8 *kg/m, consisting of* 49 *wires each* 1·6 *mm diameter. The maximum stress in the wire is not to exceed* 90 *MN/m² and E for the rope may be taken as* 75 *GN/m². Find the maximum safe load that can be carried, neglecting loss of energy at impact.* (U. Lond.)

Stress in wire due to dead weight of lift and rope

$$= \frac{(100 + 25 \times 0\!\cdot\!8) \times 9\!\cdot\!81}{49 \times \dfrac{\pi}{4} \times 0\!\cdot\!001\,6^2} \text{ N/m}^2 = 12 \text{ MN/m}^2$$

∴ stress due to falling load $= 90 - 12 \qquad\qquad = 78 \text{ MN/m}^2$

If M is the mass of the falling load, then, from equation (1.20),

$$9\!\cdot\!81M\!\left(0\!\cdot\!1 + \frac{78 \times 10^6 \times 25}{75 \times 10^9}\right) = \frac{(78 \times 10^6)^2}{2 \times 75 \times 10^9} \times 49 \times \frac{\pi}{4} \times 0\!\cdot\!001\,6^2 \times 25$$

from which
$$M = \underline{80\!\cdot\!8 \text{ kg}}$$

10. *A solid steel bar, 200 mm long, is 10 mm square over part of its length. The remainder is circular, and alone has a volume of 24×10^{-6} m^3. The bar is subjected to a pull of 20 kN. Find the dimensions of the circular portion so that the total strain energy may be a minimum, and find its value. $E = 200$ GN/m^2.* (U. Lond.)

Let suffices 1 and 2 refer to the square and circular portions respectively, Fig. 1.22.

Then

$$\sigma_1 = \frac{20 \times 10^3}{0 \cdot 01^2} \text{ N/m}^2 = 200 \text{ MN/m}^2$$

and

$$\sigma_2 = \frac{20 \times 10^3}{\frac{\pi}{4} d^2} \text{ N/m}^2 = \frac{0 \cdot 08}{\pi d^2} \text{ MN/m}^2$$

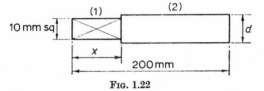

FIG. 1.22

$$U = \frac{\sigma_1^2}{2E} \times V_1 + \frac{\sigma_2^2}{2E} \times V_2$$

$$= \frac{1}{2E}\left\{(200 \times 10^6)^2 \times x \times 0 \cdot 01^2 + \left(\frac{0 \cdot 08 \times 10^6}{\pi d^2}\right)^2 \times 24 \times 10^{-6}\right\}$$

But

$$\frac{\pi}{4} d^2 (0 \cdot 2 - x) = 24 \times 10^{-6}$$

$$\therefore \pi d^2 = \frac{96 \times 10^{-6}}{0 \cdot 2 - x}$$

$$\therefore U = \frac{1}{2E}\left\{4x \times 10^{12} + \left[\frac{0 \cdot 08}{96}(0 \cdot 2 - x) \times 10^{12}\right]^2 \times 24 \times 10^{-6}\right\}$$

$$= \frac{10^{12}}{12E}\{100x^2 - 16x + 4\}$$

For the strain energy to be a minimum, $\dfrac{\mathrm{d}U}{\mathrm{d}x} = 0$,

i.e. $$200x - 16 = 0$$
or $$x = 0 \cdot 08 \text{ m}$$
$$\therefore \text{ length of circular portion} = \underline{0 \cdot 12 \text{ m}}$$

$$\pi d^2 = \frac{96 \times 10^{-6}}{0 \cdot 2 - 0 \cdot 12}$$

$$\therefore \; d = 0 \cdot 025\;5 \text{ m} \quad \text{or} \quad \underline{25 \cdot 5 \text{ mm}}$$

$$U = \frac{10^{12}}{12 \times 200 \times 10^9} \{100 \times 0 \cdot 08^2 - 16 \times 0 \cdot 08 + 4\}$$

$$= \underline{1 \cdot 4 \text{ J}}$$

11. The maximum safe compressive stress in a hardened steel punch is limited to 1 GN/m^2 and the punch is used to pierce circular holes in mild steel plate 20 mm thick.

(*a*) If the ultimate shearing stress of the plate is 300 MN/m^2, calculate the smallest diameter of hole that can be pierced.

(*b*) If the effective length of the punch is 75 mm, calculate the maximum strain energy stored in the punch during the piercing operation. Assume the modulus of elasticity for the material of the punch to be 200 GN/m^2. (*Ans.:* 24 mm; 84·8 J)

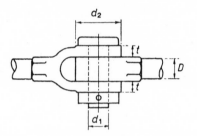

Fig. 1.23

12. Fig. 1.23 shows a knuckle joint in a tie bar. Allowing stresses of 105, 75 and 150 MN/m^2 for tension, shearing and bearing respectively, obtain suitable dimensions for D, d_1, t and d_2 if the load on the rod is 125 kN.

(*Ans.:* 39 mm; 32·5 mm; 12·8 mm; 79 mm)

13. A steel bar 40 mm diameter and 4 m long is raised in temperature through 60 deg C, after which its ends are firmly secured. After cooling to normal temperature again, the length of the bar is found to be 1·2 mm less than when at its highest temperature. Determine the total pull exerted by the cold bar and the intensity of stress in it. $E = 200$ GN/m^2 and $\alpha = 0 \cdot 000\;011$/deg C.

(*Ans.:* 90·5 kN; 72 MN/m^2)

14. A mild steel rod, 600 mm long, is 25 mm in diameter for 150 mm of its length and 50 mm for the rest of its length. It carries an axial tensile pull of 18 kN. With the axial pull applied, the ends of the rod are secured by rigid fixings. Find the temperature through which the rod must be raised to reduce the axial pull by two thirds. $\alpha_{steel} = 11 \times 10^{-6}$/deg C; $E_{steel} = 200$ GN/m^2. (*U. Lond.*)

(*Ans.:* 4·86 deg C)

15. A uniform rectangular slab of concrete, 2·5 m by 1·5 m, of mass 1 200 kg rests on vertical columns at the four corners. One of these columns may be regarded as rigid and the others as three identical columns of the same length, cross-section and elasticity. Assuming that the slab may be treated as rigid and that it remains sensibly horizontal when the elastic columns are slightly compressed under load, determine the reaction at each support. (*U. Lond.*)

(*Ans.:* 3 924 N; 3 924 N; 1 962 N; 1 962 N)

16. A flat steel bar, 10 m long and 10 mm thick tapers from 60 mm at one end to 20 mm at the other. Determine the change in length of the bar when a tensile force $P = 12$ kN is acting along its axis. $E = 200$ GN/m^2. (*U. Lond.*)

(*Ans.:* 1·648 mm)

17. A boiler shell, 2 m mean diameter, is constructed of steel plate having an ultimate tensile strength of 450 MN/m^2. If the thickness of the shell plates is 20 mm, calculate the maximum internal gauge pressure to which the boiler may be subjected, assuming a factor of safety of 6 and a longitudinal joint efficiency of 80 per cent. (*Ans.:* 1·2 MN/m^2)

18. Derive formulae to give the longitudinal and circumferential tensions in a thin boiler shell, stating the assumptions made in your argument.

A cylindrical compressed air drum is 2 m in diameter with plates 12·5 mm thick. The efficiencies of the longitudinal and circumferential joints are respectively 85 and 45%. If the tensile stress in the plating is to be limited to 100 MN/m^2, find the maximum safe air pressure. (*U. Lond.*) (*Ans.:* 1·063 MN/m^2)

19. Derive an expression for the tensile stress in a thin spherical shell of thickness t and internal diameter d when subjected to an internal pressure p.

A thin spherical pressure vessel is required to contain 18 000 l of water at a gauge pressure of 700 kN/m^2. Assuming the efficiency of all riveted joints to be 75 per cent, determine the diameter of the vessel and the thickness of the plate. The stress in the material must not exceed 140 MN/m^2. (*Ans.* 3·248 m; 5·41 mm)

20. Derive a formula for the hoop stress in a thin cylinder having a mean radius R and made of material of density m when rotating at ω rad/s about its axis. What is the most important assumption you make?

Apply this theory to find the maximum allowable speed in rev/min for a flywheel 1·25 m external diameter and 50 mm thick. The material has a density of 7·3 Mg/m^3 and the hoop stress is limited to 20 MN/m^2. (*U. Lond.*)

(*Ans.:* 834 rev/min)

21. Deduce an expression for the centrifugal stress induced in a thin rotating rim.

A thin rim 1·5 m mean diameter rotates at 600 rev/min. The cross-section of the rim is rectangular, 125 mm $\times$ 12·5 mm thick, and the density of the material of which it is constructed is 7·8 Mg/m^3. Calculate the stress and force produced in the rim. (*Ans.:* 17·34 MN/m^2; 27·15 kN)

22. A thin rim, 1·5 m diameter and 150 mm wide, is made of steel plate 12·5 mm thick. The rim is made in two halves with the joints parallel to the axis. Determine the centrifugal stress produced in the material at a speed of 420 rev/min. Density of steel = 7·8 Mg/m^3.

The two halves are fastened by three bolts on each side of each joint. The bolts are 20 mm diameter and are in single shear. Determine the shear stress in each bolt when the rim is rotating at 420 rev/min. (*Ans.:* 8·5 MN/m^2; 16·9 MN/m^2)

23. State Hooke's Law. Comment briefly on its limitations.

A straight rod of steel, 1 m long, of constant section, rotates at 1 200 rev/min about an axis at one end, perpendicular to its length. Calculate (*a*) the maximum stress in the rod, (*b*) the extension. Density of steel = 7·8 Mg/m^3; $E = 200$ GN/m^2. (*U. Lond.*) (*Ans.:* 61·65 MN/m^2; 0·205 5 mm)

24. Two elastic rods, A and B, of equal free length hang vertically 0·6 m apart and support a rigid bar horizontally. The bar remains horizontal when a vertical load of 60 kN is applied to the bar 0·2 m from A. If the stress in A is 100 MN/m^2, find the stress in B and the cross-sectional areas of the two rods; $E_A = 200 \text{ GN/m}^2$; $E_B = 130 \text{ GN/m}^2$. (*I.C.E.*) (*Ans.*: 65 MN/m²; 400 mm²; 307·5 mm²)

25. A wire strand consists of a steel wire 2·7 mm diameter, covered by six bronze wires each of 2·5 mm diameter. The tensile modulus for the steel is 200 GN/m² and for the bronze 85 GN/m².

If the working stress for the bronze is 60 MN/m², calculate the strength of the strand, also the equivalent tensile modulus for the complete strand. (*U. Lond.*)
(*Ans.*: 2 575 N; 104 GN/m²)

26. A round steel bar, 28 mm diameter and 400 mm long, is placed concentrically within a brass tube which has an outside diameter of 40 mm and an inside diameter of 30 mm; the length of the tube exceeds that of the bar by 0·12 mm. Rigid plates are placed on the ends of the tube through which an axial compressive force is applied to the compound bar. Determine the compressive stresses in the bar and tube due to a force of 60 kN. $E_{steel} = 200 \text{ GN/m}^2$; $E_{brass} = 100 \text{ GN/m}^2$. (*U. Lond.*) (*Ans.*: 48·2 MN/m²; 54·1 MN/m²)

27. A steel bolt, 20 mm external diameter, is inserted into a copper sleeve, 21 mm internal and 27 mm external diameter, one end of the tube being in contact with the shoulder of the bolt-head. A rigid washer is placed on the other end of the sleeve and a nut is screwed on the bolt until the compressive stress in the sleeve is 80 MN/m². It may be assumed that the washer slides freely on the end of the sleeve and consequently that torsional stresses are negligible. Find the range of external axial load that can be applied to the assembly if the stress in the sleeve is never to be zero and that in the bolt never to be compressive. $E_{steel} = 200 \text{ GN/m}^2$; $E_{copper} = 90 \text{ GN/m}^2$. (*U. Lond.*)
(*Ans.*: 80 kN (tensile) to 19·5 kN (compressive))

28. A steel rod of 320 mm² cross-sectional area and a coaxial copper tube of 800 mm² cross-sectional area, are rigidly bonded together at their ends. An axial compressive load of 40 kN is applied to the composite bar, and the temperature is then raised by 100 deg C.

Determine the stresses then existing in both steel and copper. The moduli of elasticity for steel and copper at 200 GN/m² and 100 GN/m², and the coefficients of linear expansion 12×10^{-6}/deg C and 16×10^{-6}/deg C respectively. (*I.C.E.*)
(*Ans.*: 11·11 MN/m²; 45·55 MN/m², both compressive)

29. A copper tube of mean diameter 120 mm, and 6·5 mm thick, has its open ends sealed by two rigid plates connected by two steel bolts of 25 mm diameter, initially tensioned to 20 kN at a temperature of 30°C, thus forming a pressure vessel. Determine the stresses in the copper and steel at freezing point, and the temperature at which the vessel would cease to be pressure tight.

$E_{steel} = 200 \text{ GN/m}^2$; $\alpha_{steel} = 11 \times 10^{-6}$/deg C.
$E_{copper} = 100 \text{ GN/m}^2$; $\alpha_{copper} = 18 \times 10^{-6}$/deg C. (*U. Lond.*)
(*Ans.*: 7·0 MN/m²; 17·4 MN/m²; −22·4°C)

30. A bar of brass 25 mm diameter is enclosed in a steel tube 50 mm external diameter and 25 mm internal diameter. The bar and tube are both initially 1 m long and are rigidly fastened together at both ends. Find the stresses in the two materials when the temperature rises from 15°C to 95°C.

If the composite bar is then subjected to an axial tensile load of 50 kN, find the resulting stresses and the increase in length from the initial state.

$E_{steel} = 200 \text{ GN/m}^2$; $\alpha_{steel} = 11·6 \times 10^{-6}$/deg C.
$E_{brass} = 100 \text{ GN/m}^2$; $\alpha_{brass} = 18·7 \times 10^{-6}$/deg C. (*U. Lond.*)
(*Ans.*: 48·7 MN/m² (comp); 16·23 MN/m² (tensile); 34·17 MN/m² (comp);
45·3 MN/m² (tensile); 1·115 mm)

31. A steel tie-rod 25 mm diameter is placed concentrically in a brass tube 3 mm thick and 60 mm mean diameter. Nuts and washers are fitted on the tie-rod so that the ends of the tube are enclosed by the washers. The nuts are initially tightened to give a compressive stress of 30 MN/m^2 in the tube, and a tensile load of 45 kN is then applied to the tie-rod. Assuming the rod and tube to have the same effective length, find the resultant stresses in the tie-rod and tube; (i) when there is no change of temperature; (ii) when the temperature increases by 60 deg C.

$$E_{steel} = 200 \text{ GN/m}^2; \alpha_{steel} = 1 \cdot 1 \times 10^{-5}/\text{deg C.}$$
$$E_{brass} = 80 \text{ GN/m}^2; \alpha_{brass} = 1 \cdot 89 \times 10^{-5}/\text{deg C.} \quad (U. \text{ Lond.})$$

(*Ans.:* 97·2 MN/m^2 (tensile); 4·9 MN/m^2 (comp); 127·1 MN/m^2 (tensile); 30·9 MN/m^2 (comp))

32. A wagon, of mass 5 t, is attached to a steel wire rope, the other end of which is wound round a brake drum. The wagon is descending a slope at a uniform speed of 5 km/h and the rope is taut. By the action of the brake the drum is suddenly stopped and the wagon is brought to rest. If the length of the rope between the wagon and the drum at that instant was 250 m and its cross-sectional area is 300 mm^2, find the maximum stress in the rope. $E = 200$ GN/m^2. (*U. Lond.*)

(*Ans.:* 160 MN/m^2)

33. A bar of certain material, 40 mm diameter and 1·2 m long, has a collar securely fitted to one end. It is suspended vertically with the collar at the lower end and a mass of 2 000 kg is gradually lowered on to the collar, producing an extension in the bar of 0·25 mm. Find the height from which this load could be dropped on to the collar if the maximum tensile stress in the bar is to be 100 MN/m^2. (*U. Lond.*)

(*Ans.:* 3·58 mm)

34. A bar 10 mm diameter and 3 m long is fixed at the top and hangs vertically. At the lower end is fixed a disc and on to this disc a mass of 10 kg is allowed to fall freely through a distance of 50 mm. Calculate the maximum stress induced in the rod, stating any assumptions made and proving any formula used. $E = 200$ GN/m^2. (*U. Lond.*)

(*Ans.:* 92·5 MN/m^2)

35. A steel wire 2·5 mm diameter is firmly held in a clamp from which it hangs vertically. An anvil, the weight of which may be neglected, is secured to the wire 1 m below the clamp. The wire is to be tested by allowing a mass bored to slide over the wire to drop freely from 0·5 m above the anvil. Calculate the mass required to stress the wire to 1·2 GN/m^2 assuming the wire to be elastic to this stress. $E = 200$ GN/m^2. (*U. Lond.*)

(*Ans.:* 3·56 kg)

36. Define Resilience. Show how to calculate the resilience in a rod of uniform section under a uniform direct stress.

A vertical tie, rigidly fixed at the top end, consists of a steel rod 2·5 m long and 20 mm diameter encased throughout in a brass tube 20 mm internal diameter and 25 mm external diameter. The rod and casing are fixed together at both ends. The compound rod is suddenly loaded in tension by a mass of 1 Mg falling freely through 3 mm before being arrested by the tie. Calculate the maximum stresses in the steel and brass. $E_{steel} = 200$ GN/m^2; $E_{brass} = 100$ GN/m^2. (*U. Lond.*)

(*Ans.:* 135 MN/m^2; 67·5 MN/m^2)

CHAPTER 2

SHEARING FORCE AND BENDING MOMENT

2.1 Shearing force and bending moment. The *shearing force* at a section of a beam is the algebraic sum of all the forces to one side of the section.

The *bending moment* at a section of a beam is the algebraic sum of the moments of all the forces to one side of the section.

At the point P in the cantilever shown in Fig. 2.1(a), the shearing force is $W_1 + W_2$, which is tending to shear the beam as shown in Fig. 2.1(b). This is opposed by the shearing resistance of the part of the beam to the left of P.

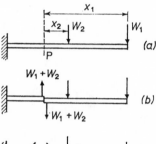
(a)

(b)

(c)

Fig. 2.1

The bending moment at the point P is $W_1x_1 + W_2x_2$, which is tending to bend the beam as shown in Fig. 2.1(c). This is opposed by the bending resistance of the part of the beam to the left of P.

In the case of the simply supported beam shown in Fig. 2.2, the shearing force at P is either $R_1 - W_1$ or $W_2 - R_2$. These terms are equal since, equating upward and downward forces on the beam,

$$R_1 + R_2 = W_1 + W_2.$$

The bending moment at P is either $R_1a - W_1x_1$ or $R_2b - W_2x_2$. These terms are equal since, equating clockwise and anticlockwise moments about P,

$$R_1a + W_2x_2 = R_2b + W_1x_1.$$

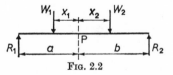
Fig. 2.2

It is evident that it is immaterial which side of the section is chosen for the calculation of the shearing force or bending moment. When calculating the bending moment due to a distributed load, the part of the load to one side of the section may be considered as a concentrated load acting at the centre of gravity of that part.

If the bending moment at a section of a beam changes sign, that point is called a point of *inflexion* or *contra-flexure*.

Sign convention. If the resultant force to the right of a section is upward (or to the left is downward), this will be regarded as a positive shearing force and the opposite kind of shearing will be regarded as negative, Fig. 2.3(a).

21

If the resultant bending moment to the right of a section is clockwise (or to the left is anticlockwise), this will be regarded as a positive bending moment and the opposite kind of bending will be regarded as negative, Fig. 2.3(b). Thus a positive bending moment bends the beam convex upward and a negative bending moment bends it convex downward.*

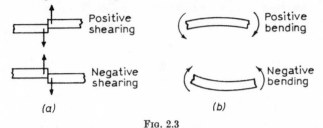

FIG. 2.3

2.2 Shearing force and bending moment diagrams. These are diagrams which show the value of the shearing force and bending moment at all points along a beam. The most common cases are as follows:

(a) Cantilever with concentrated end load, W, Fig. 2.4:

S.F. at P $= -W$
B.M. at P $= Wx$
Maximum S.F. $= -W$
Maximum B.M. $= Wl$

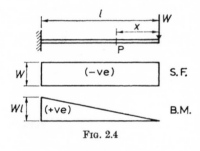

FIG. 2.4

(b) Cantilever with uniformly distributed load, w per unit length, Fig. 2.5:

S.F. at P $= -wx$

B.M. at P $= wx \cdot \dfrac{x}{2}$

$= \dfrac{wx^2}{2}$

Maximum S.F. $= -wl$

Maximum B.M. $= \dfrac{wl^2}{2}$

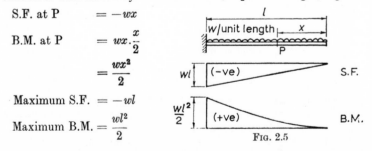

FIG. 2.5

---

* The advantages of this convention are:

(a) If the B.M. diagram is drawn directly on the beam, the diagram is on the tension flange, which corresponds with the usual structural convention;

(b) Minus signs are avoided in the relation $w = \dfrac{\mathrm{d}F}{\mathrm{d}x} = \dfrac{\mathrm{d}^2M}{\mathrm{d}x^2}$ and in all deflection formulae (Chap. 5).

(c) Simply supported beam with central concentrated load, W, Fig. 2.6:

S.F. at P $= \dfrac{W}{2}$

B.M. at P $= -\dfrac{W}{2}\left(\dfrac{l}{2} - x\right)$

Maximum S.F. $= \dfrac{W}{2}$

Maximum B.M. $= -\dfrac{W}{2}\cdot\dfrac{l}{2}$

$\qquad\qquad = -\dfrac{Wl}{4}$

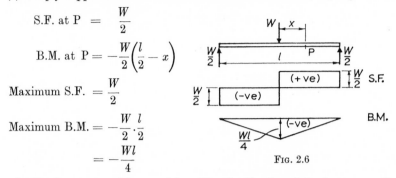

Fig. 2.6

(d) Simply supported beam with uniformly distributed load, w per unit length, Fig. 2.7:

S.F. at P $\quad = \dfrac{wl}{2} - w\left(\dfrac{l}{2} - x\right) = wx$

B.M. at P $\quad = -\dfrac{wl}{2}\left(\dfrac{l}{2} - x\right) + \dfrac{w}{2}\left(\dfrac{l}{2} - x\right)^2$

$\qquad\qquad = -\dfrac{w}{2}\left(\dfrac{l^2}{4} - x^2\right)$

Maximum S.F. $= \dfrac{wl}{2}$

Maximum B.M. $= -\dfrac{wl^2}{8}$

Where both concentrated and distributed loads act on a beam, the S.F. and B.M. may be calculated separately for each type of loading and added together algebraically or they may be calculated directly for all the loads acting together.

2.3 Relation between intensity of loading, shearing force and bending moment. Consider a short length, dx, of a beam, Fig. 2.8, carrying a uniformly distributed load w per unit length. Over this length, let the shear force change from F to $F + dF$ and the bending moment change from M to $M + dM$.

Equating vertical forces on the element,

$$F + w\,dx = F + dF$$

or $\qquad\qquad\qquad w = \dfrac{dF}{dx}$ . . . . . . (2.1)

B

Taking moments about the right-hand end of the element,

$$M + F\,\mathrm{d}x + w\,\mathrm{d}x.\frac{\mathrm{d}x}{2} = M + \mathrm{d}M$$

i.e. $F\,\mathrm{d}x = \mathrm{d}M$, ignoring the second order
of small quantities,

i.e. $$F = \frac{\mathrm{d}M}{\mathrm{d}x}$$.   .   .   .   .   (2.2)

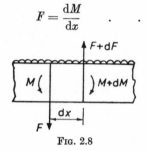

FIG. 2.8

Thus intensity of loading is the rate of change of shearing force and shearing force is the rate of change of bending moment. This latter relation shows that the maximum bending moment occurs where the shearing force is zero.*

Combining equations (2.1) and (2.2),

$$w = \frac{\mathrm{d}F}{\mathrm{d}x} = \frac{\mathrm{d}^2M}{\mathrm{d}x^2}$$.   .   .   .   (2.3)

2.4 Graphical construction of S.F. and B.M. diagrams. To construct the S.F. and B.M. diagrams for the beam shown in Fig. 2.9(a), first letter the spaces using Bow's Notation and then draw the load line bcd, Fig. 2.9(b), so that $bc = W_2$ and $cd = W_1$. Project across from the points b, c and d to form part of the S.F. diagram.

Choose any pole o and join ob, oc and od. Across space B, Fig. 2.9(c), draw a line parallel to ob, across space C a line parallel to oc and across space D a line parallel to od. Join the two ends to complete the B.M. diagram. Draw through o a line parallel to this closing line to obtain the point a and then project across from a to complete the S.F. diagram.

The *vertical* ordinate at any point in the B.M. diagram represents the B.M. at that point. This diagram may be corrected to a horizontal baseline

---

* This relation gives the position of the *mathematical* maximum bending moment, i.e. the point at which the tangent to the bending moment diagram is horizontal. In many cases there is no such point and the position of the *greatest* bending moment must be found by inspection. In other cases, such as with an overhanging load, the *mathematical* maximum is not necessarily the *greatest* bending moment (see Ex. 2).

Under a 'point' load, such as in Fig. 2.6, the load must actually be distributed over a short length of the beam. The vertical line in the S.F. diagram should therefore have a slight slope and the apex of the B.M. diagram should be rounded, the point of zero slope corresponding with the point at which the S.F. diagram cuts the base line.

by drawing through a a horizontal line ao' and then reconstructing the B.M. diagram from this new pole.

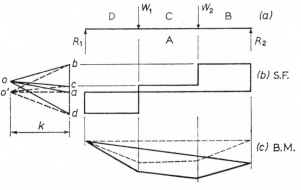

FIG. 2.9

For a distributed load, Fig. 2.10(a), divide the load into strips (not necessarily of equal width) and replace the load in each strip by a concentrated load of the same magnitude, acting through the centre of gravity of that strip. Draw the S.F. and B.M. diagrams, Figs. 2.10(b) and (c) respectively, for these concentrated loads as before. Project the bounding lines of the strips to intersect the approximate diagrams obtained. The points of intersection with these diagrams then give points on the true S.F. and B.M. diagrams, which can then be connected by a smooth curve.

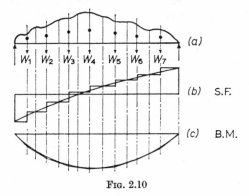

FIG. 2.10

Scales. The scale for the S.F. diagram is the same as the load scale.

If $k = 1$ m, the load scale is 1 m $= p$ N and the length scale is 1 m $= q$ m, then the B.M. scale is 1 m $= pq$ N m. If $k = 2$ m, the slope of the lines in the diagram are halved and hence the scale is 1 m $= 2pq$ N m. Thus in general, 1 m $= kpq$ N m.

1. *A beam* 4 *m long is simply supported over a span of* 2*m and overhangs both supports by the same amount. The right-hand overhanging portion carries a uniformly distributed load of* 80 *kN/m and a concentrated load of* 20 *kN at the extreme end; the left-hand overhanging portion carries a uniformly distributed load of* 40 *kN/m and a concentrated load of* 30 *kN at the extreme end; in addition a load of* 160 *kN is concentrated at mid-span.*

Draw to scale the shear force and bending moment diagrams and find how much may be added to the load at mid-span without increasing the maximum bending moment on the beam. (U. Lond.)

Taking moments about R_2, Fig. 2.11(*a*),

$$30 \times 3 + 40 \times 2 \cdot 5 + 160 \times 1 = 2R_1 + 20 \times 1 + 80 \times 0 \cdot 5$$
$$\therefore R_1 = 145 \text{ kN}$$
$$\therefore R_2 = 185 \text{ kN}$$

The S.F. diagram is shown in Fig. 2.11(*b*).

$$\text{B.M. at } R_1 = 30 \times 1 + 40 \times 0 \cdot 5$$
$$= 50 \text{ kNm}$$
$$\text{B.M. at } R_2 = 20 \times 1 + 80 \times 0 \cdot 5$$
$$= 60 \text{ kNm}$$
$$\text{B.M. at centre} = 30 \times 2 + 40 \times 1 \cdot 5 - 145 \times 1$$
$$= -25 \text{ kN m}$$

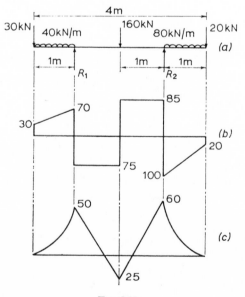

Fɪɢ. 2.11

The B.M. diagram is shown in Fig. 2.11(c).

If an additional load W is added at the centre, the bending moments at the supports remain unchanged. The reactions are each increased by $W/2$, so that the central B.M. is increased by

$$-1 \times \frac{W}{2} = -0.5W \text{ kN m}$$

Therefore, when the central B.M. is increased to equal (numerically) the B.M. at the right-hand support,

$$25 + 0.5W = 60$$
$$\therefore W = \underline{70 \text{ kN}}$$

2. *A horizontal beam AB, 8 m long, carries a total uniformly distributed load of 300 kN. The beam is supported at the end A and at a point C distant x from the other end B. Determine the value of x if the mid-point of the beam is to be a point of inflexion, and for this arrangement draw the S.F. and B.M. diagrams, indicating the principal numerical values on each.* (U. Lond.)

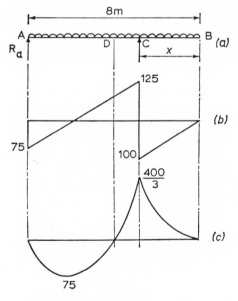

FIG. 2.12

Taking moments about C, Fig. 2.12(a),

$$R_a(8 - x) = 300(4 - x)$$
$$\therefore R_a = 300\left(\frac{4 - x}{8 - x}\right) \text{ kN}$$

$$\text{B.M. at centre} = -300\left(\frac{4-x}{8-x}\right) \times 4 + 150 \times 2$$

$$= 0$$

if the centre is to be a point of inflexion.

$$\therefore x = \underline{8/3 \text{ m}}$$

$$\therefore R_a = 300\left(\frac{4-\frac{8}{3}}{8-\frac{8}{3}}\right) = 75 \text{ kN}$$

$$\text{B.M. at C} = \frac{300}{8} \times \frac{\left(\frac{8}{3}\right)^2}{2} = \frac{400}{3} \text{ kN m}$$

$$\text{and B.M. at centre of AD} = -75 \times 2 + \frac{300}{8} \times \frac{2^2}{2}$$

$$= -75 \text{ kN m}$$

The S.F. and B.M. diagrams are shown in Figs. 2.12(*b*) and (*c*).

3. *A beam ABC is continuous over two spans, being supported as shown in Fig. 2.13(a). A hinge, capable of transmitting shearing force but not bending moment, is placed at the centre of span AB. The loading consists of a distributed load, of total weight 20 kN, spread over the span AB, and a concentrated load of 30 kN at the centre of span BC. Sketch the shearing force and bending moment diagrams, indicating the magnitude of all important values.*

(I.C.E.)

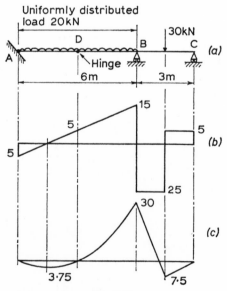

Fig. 2.13

The section of the beam AD is simply supported at A and D and hence exerts a downward force of 5 kN on DBC at the point D.

Considering the section DBC as a simply supported beam with the overhanging portion carrying a concentrated load of 5 kN at D in addition to the distributed load, the reaction at C is given by

$$R_c \times 3 + 5 \times 3 + 10 \times 1\cdot5 = 30 \times 1\cdot5,$$

taking the moments about B,

$$\therefore R_c = 5 \text{ kN}$$
$$\therefore R_b = 45 - 5$$
$$= 40 \text{ kN}$$
$$\text{B.M. at 30-kN load} = -5 \times 1\cdot5$$
$$= -7\cdot5 \text{ kN m}$$
$$\text{B.M. at B} = -5 \times 3 + 30 \times 1\cdot5$$
$$= 30 \text{ kN m}$$
$$\text{B.M. at centre of AD} = -5 \times 1\cdot5 + 5 \times 0\cdot75$$
$$= -3\cdot75 \text{ kN m}$$

The S.F. and B.M. diagrams are shown in Figs. 2.13(*b*) and (*c*).

4. *A girder* 10 *m long, carrying a uniformly distributed load of w N /m, is to be supported on two piers* 6 *m apart so that the greatest bending moment on the girder shall be as small as possible. Find the distances of the piers from the ends of the girder and the maximum bending moment.* (U. Lond.)

Let the positions of the reactions be as shown in Fig. 2.14.

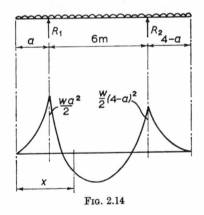

FIG. 2.14

Then B.M. at $R_1 = \dfrac{wa^2}{2}$

and B.M. at $R_2 = \dfrac{w}{2}(4 - a)^2$

Taking moments about R_2,

$$6R_1 = 10w(1 + a)$$

$$\therefore R_1 = \frac{5}{3}w(1 + a)$$

$\therefore$ B.M. at a section distance x from L.H. end

$$= \frac{wx^2}{2} - \frac{5}{3}w(1 + a)(x - a)$$

The maximum B.M. between supports occurs when

$$\frac{\mathrm{d}M}{\mathrm{d}x} = 0$$

i.e.　　　　when $x = \frac{5}{3}(1 + a)$

∴ maximum B.M. between supports

$$= \frac{w}{2}\left\{\frac{5}{3}(1 + a)\right\}^2 - \frac{5}{3}w(1 + a)\left(\frac{5}{3} + \frac{2}{3}a\right)$$

$$= \frac{5}{18}w(1 + a)(a - 5)$$

For the greatest B.M. on the beam to be as small as possible,
　　　　B.M. at supports = maximum B.M. between supports

i.e.　　　　　　$\frac{wa^2}{2} = -\left[\frac{5}{18}w(1 + a)(a - 5)\right]^*$

from which　$14a^2 - 10a - 15 = 0$

i.e.　　　　　　　　$a = \underline{2\cdot23 \text{ m}}$

$$\therefore M_{\max} = w \times \frac{2\cdot23^2}{2} = \underline{2\cdot486w \text{ N m}}$$

5. *A beam, 8 m long, is simply supported at two points and loaded with two concentrated loads, two uniformly distributed loads and a couple, as shown in Fig. 2.15(a). Draw the S.F. and B.M. diagrams.*　　　　(U. Lond.)

Taking moments about R_1,

$25 \times 2 \times 5 + 50 \times 2 \times 7 + 40 \times 4 + 10 \times 6$
$$= 6R_2 + 100$$
$$\therefore R_2 = 178\cdot5 \text{ kN}$$
$$\therefore R_1 = 200 - 178\cdot5$$
$$= 21\cdot5 \text{ kN}$$

B.M. at $R_2 = 50 \times 2 \times 1 = 100 \text{ kN m}$
B.M. at 40-kN load $= 50 \times 2 \times 3 + 25 \times 2 \times 1 - 168\cdot5 \times 2$
$$= 13 \text{ kN m}$$

B.M. immediately to left of couple
$$= -21\cdot5 \times 2$$
$$= -43 \text{ kN m}$$

The S.F. and B.M. diagrams are shown in Figs. 2.15(b) and (c).

Note that there is no discontinuity in the S.F. diagram at the point of application of the couple but the shape of the diagram is affected by it due to its effect on the reactions.

In going from right to left of the point of application of the couple, there is a sudden change in B.M. of -100 kN m.

* The B.M.s at these points are of opposite sign.

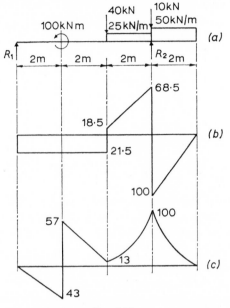

Fig. 2.15

6. *A brake cross-shaft is carried at its ends in short bearings 4 m apart which may be assumed to give point support. At 1 m from one end, it carries a horizontal arm 1·5 m long which is subject to a vertical force of 2 kN at its free end, and at 1 m from the other end of the cross-shaft there is a vertical arm 1 m long, to the free end of which is attached a horizontal rod which actuates the brake gear.*

Draw the resultant bending moment diagram for the shaft and calculate the position and magnitude of the least bending moment between the arms.

(U. Lond.)

The arrangement is shown diagrammatically in Fig. 2.16. For rotational equilibrium,

$$P \times 1 = 2 \times 1\cdot5$$
$$\therefore P = 3 \text{ kN}$$

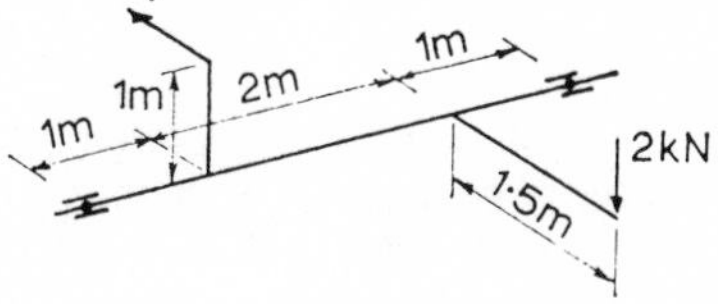

In the vertical plane, Fig. 2.17,

$$V_1 = 0\cdot5 \text{ kN}$$
and $$V_2 = 1\cdot5 \text{ kN}$$

Fig. 2.16

Therefore at a distance x from the L.H. end,

$M = 0\cdot5x$ kN m	for $0 < x < 3$ m
and $M = 1\cdot5(4 - x)$ kN m	for $3 < x < 4$ m

In the horizontal plane, Fig. 2.18,

$$H_1 = 2\cdot25 \text{ kN}$$

and

$$H_2 = 0\cdot75 \text{ kN}$$

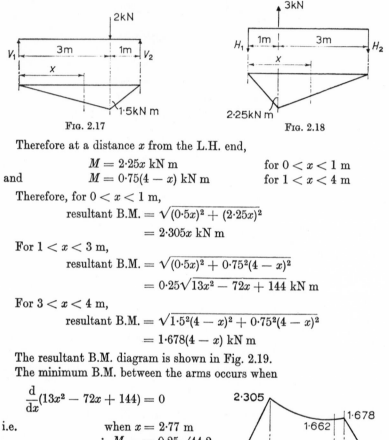

FIG. 2.17

FIG. 2.18

Therefore at a distance x from the L.H. end,

$$M = 2\cdot25x \text{ kN m} \qquad \text{for } 0 < x < 1 \text{ m}$$

and

$$M = 0\cdot75(4 - x) \text{ kN m} \qquad \text{for } 1 < x < 4 \text{ m}$$

Therefore, for $0 < x < 1$ m,

$$\text{resultant B.M.} = \sqrt{(0\cdot5x)^2 + (2\cdot25x)^2}$$

$$= 2\cdot305x \text{ kN m}$$

For $1 < x < 3$ m,

$$\text{resultant B.M.} = \sqrt{(0\cdot5x)^2 + 0\cdot75^2(4 - x)^2}$$

$$= 0\cdot25\sqrt{13x^2 - 72x + 144} \text{ kN m}$$

For $3 < x < 4$ m,

$$\text{resultant B.M.} = \sqrt{1\cdot5^2(4 - x)^2 + 0\cdot75^2(4 - x)^2}$$

$$= 1\cdot678(4 - x) \text{ kN m}$$

The resultant B.M. diagram is shown in Fig. 2.19.
The minimum B.M. between the arms occurs when

$$\frac{\mathrm{d}}{\mathrm{d}x}(13x^2 - 72x + 144) = 0$$

i.e.

$$\text{when } x = 2\cdot77 \text{ m}$$

$$\therefore M_{\min} = 0\cdot25\sqrt{44\cdot2}$$

$$= \underline{1\cdot662 \text{ kN m}}$$

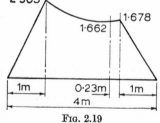

FIG. 2.19

7. *A beam ABC is 8 m long and simply supported at A and B, 6 m apart. A triangularly distributed load acts on the span AB, varying linearly in intensity from 0 at A to 30 kN/m at B, and a concentrated load of 10 kN acts at C.*

Sketch the shearing force and bending moment diagrams, giving critical values, and determine the position and magnitude of the maximum bending moment. (I.C.E.)

Fig. 2.20(*a*) shows the loading system on the beam. Taking moments about B,

$$(\tfrac{1}{2} \times 6 \times 30) \times \tfrac{1}{3} \times 6 = 6R_a + 10 \times 2$$

$$\therefore R_a = \frac{80}{3} \, \text{kN}$$

and

$$R_b = 100 - \frac{80}{3} = \frac{220}{3} \, \text{kN}$$

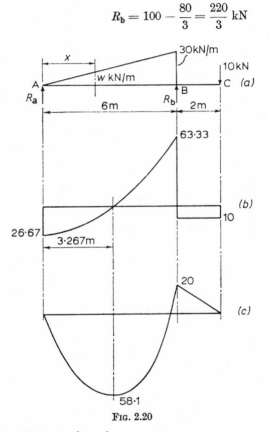

FIG. 2.20

At a section distance x from A,

$$\text{S.F.} = \frac{1}{2} wx - R_a$$

$$= \frac{1}{2} \times \frac{x}{6} \times 30 \times x - \frac{80}{3} = \frac{5}{2}x^2 - \frac{80}{3} \, \text{kN}$$

$$\text{B.M.} = \frac{1}{2} wx \times \frac{x}{3} - R_a x$$

$$= \frac{1}{2} \times \frac{x}{6} \times 30 \times x \times \frac{x}{3} - \frac{80}{3}x \quad = \frac{5x}{6}(x^2 - 32) \text{ kN m}$$

The S.F. and B.M. diagrams are shown in Figs. 2.20(*b*) and (*c*). The maximum B.M. occurs when the S.F. $= 0$,

i.e.   when $x = 3 \cdot 267$ m

$$\therefore M_{max} = \frac{5 \times 3 \cdot 267}{6}(3 \cdot 267^2 - 32)$$

$$= -58 \cdot 1 \text{ kN m}$$

8. *Fig. 2.21(a) shows the curve of upward distributed water pressure reaction on a pontoon. This reaction is uniformly distributed over the central 9 m and decreases to zero at the two ends, the equation of this curve being* $y = kx^2$, *where k is a constant.*

The pontoon carries a uniformly distributed load of 50 kN/m run over the central 7 m.

Sketch the S.F. and B.M. diagrams due to this loading and find the maximum values of S.F. and B.M.   (U. Lond.)

If p is the uniform upward force per metre on the central part of the pontoon,

total upthrust $= 9p + 2 \times \frac{2}{3} \times 3p$

i.e. $50 \times 7 = 13p$

$$\therefore p = 26 \cdot 9 \text{ kN/m}$$

Upthrust on parabolic part of curve $= 26 \cdot 9 - kx^2$

When $x = 3$ m, upthrust $= 0$, $\therefore k = \frac{26 \cdot 9}{9}$

$$\therefore \text{ intensity of loading, } w = -26 \cdot 9\left(1 - \frac{x^2}{9}\right)$$

$$F = \int w \, dx = -26 \cdot 9\left(x - \frac{x^3}{27}\right) + A$$

When $x = 3$ m, $F = 0$, $\therefore A = 26 \cdot 9 \times 2$

$$\therefore F = -26 \cdot 9\left(x - \frac{x^3}{27} - 2\right)$$

$$M = \int F \, dx$$

$$= -26 \cdot 9\left(\frac{x^2}{2} - \frac{x^4}{108} - 2x\right) + B$$

When $x = 3$ m, $M = 0$,
$$\therefore B = 26.9 \times 2.25$$

$$\therefore M = -26.9\left(\frac{x^2}{2} - \frac{x^4}{108} - 2x + 2.25\right)$$

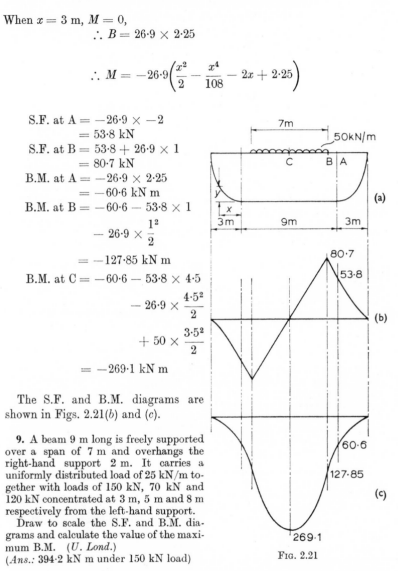

S.F. at A $= -26.9 \times -2$
        $= 53.8$ kN
S.F. at B $= 53.8 + 26.9 \times 1$
        $= 80.7$ kN
B.M. at A $= -26.9 \times 2.25$
        $= -60.6$ kN m
B.M. at B $= -60.6 - 53.8 \times 1$
        $- 26.9 \times \frac{1^2}{2}$
        $= -127.85$ kN m
B.M. at C $= -60.6 - 53.8 \times 4.5$
        $- 26.9 \times \frac{4.5^2}{2}$
        $+ 50 \times \frac{3.5^2}{2}$
        $= -269.1$ kN m

The S.F. and B.M. diagrams are shown in Figs. 2.21(b) and (c).

9. A beam 9 m long is freely supported over a span of 7 m and overhangs the right-hand support 2 m. It carries a uniformly distributed load of 25 kN/m together with loads of 150 kN, 70 kN and 120 kN concentrated at 3 m, 5 m and 8 m respectively from the left-hand support. Draw to scale the S.F. and B.M. diagrams and calculate the value of the maximum B.M. (*U. Lond.*)
(*Ans.:* 394.2 kN m under 150 kN load)

Fig. 2.21

10. A beam ABCD, 10 m in length, is simply supported at B and C, which are 5 m apart, and overhangs the support B by 3 m. The overhanging part AB carries a total load of 180 kN, uniformly distributed, and the part BD carries a total load of 210 kN uniformly distributed. Draw to scale the S.F. and B.M. diagrams for the beam. *Calculate* the position and magnitude of the least value of the B.M. between the supports. (*U. Lond.*)   (*Ans.:* 41.85 kN m at 1.1 m from C)

11. A beam ABCD is simply supported at B and C, 6 m apart, and the over-hanging parts AB and CD are 2 m and 4 m long respectively. The beam carries a uniformly distributed load of 60 kN/m between A and C and there is a concentrated load of 40 kN at D.

Draw to scale the S.F. and B.M. diagrams. Calculate the position and magnitude of the maximum B.M. between B and C. (*U. Lond.*)

(*Ans.:* 130 kN m at 2·89 m from B)

12. A horizontal beam is 16 m long, has supports 10 m apart, the overhangs being 2 m and 4 m at the left and right-hand ends respectively. The beam supports vertical loads of 60 kN at the left and 80 kN at the right extremity, with a uniformly spread load of 15 kN/m over the whole length. Draw to scale diagrams of S.F. and B.M., giving maximum values and stating where these operate. (*U. Lond.*)   (*Ans.:* 140 kN at R.H. support; 440 kN m at R.H. support)

13. A log of wood 5 m in length and of square cross-section 0·4 m by 0·4 m rendered impervious to water, floating in a horizontal position in fresh water, is loaded at the centre with a weight just sufficient to immerse it completely. Plot, on squared paper, careful diagrams of S.F. and B.M., stating their maximum values. Take the specific gravity of wood as 0·8. (*U. Lond.*)

(*Ans.:* 785 N at centre; 981 N m at centre)

14. A beam 2·4 m long is simply supported at one end and at a point 0·6 m from the other. The beam carries a series of point loads at intervals of 0·2 m starting 0·1 m from the overhanging end with a load of 5 N and increasing by increments of 5 N to a load of 60 N. In addition there is a uniformly distributed load of 40 N/m. Find the position and magnitude of the maximum B.M. (*U. Lond.*)   (*Ans.:* 91·35 N m at 0·768 m from simply supported end)

15. A horizontal beam AD, 10 m long, carries a uniformly distributed load of 200 N/m run, together with a concentrated load of 500 N at the left-hand end A. The beam is supported at a point B which is 1 m from A and at C which is in the right-hand half of the beam and x m from the end D.

Determine the value of x if the mid-point of the beam is a point of inflexion (or contra-flexure) and for this arrangement draw the B.M. diagram, indicating the principal numerical values.

Locate any other points of inflexion. (*U. Lond.*)

(*Ans.:* 3 m; 600 and 900 N m at supports, 156·25 N m at 3·75 m from A; 2·5 m from A)

16. A beam is 10 m long and carries a uniformly distributed load of 15 kN/m over its whole length. Find from first principles the position of two supports to keep the maximum B.M. on the beam as low as possible. Give the corresponding maximum S.F. and maximum B.M. acting on the beam. (*U. Lond.*)

(*Ans.:* 2·07 m from each end; 43·95 kN; 32·2 kN/m)

17. Two slings are to be used in raising a newly-cast reinforced concrete pile of length l and uniform cross-section, the pile remaining horizontal during the lift.

Determine the most suitable positions for the slings and sketch the S.F. and B.M. diagrams. It may be assumed that the damage to the pile due to the S.F. is negligible and that failure would be by bending of the pile under its own weight. (*U. Lond.*)   (*Ans.:* 0·207 l from ends)

18. A beam AB, 10 m long, carries a uniformly distributed load of 20 kN/m run, together with concentrated loads of 50 kN at the left-hand end A and 80 kN at the end B. The beam is to be supported on the two props at the same level, 6 m apart, so that the reaction is the same on each. Determine the position of the beam and draw diagrams of B.M. and S.F. State the value of the maximum B.M. (*U. Lond.*)   (*Ans.:* Supports 2·455 m and 8·455 m from A; 183 kN m)

19. A beam 7 m long rests on two level supports A and B, 4 m apart with a 1 m length of beam overhanging the right-hand support B. The beam carries a uniformly distributed load w N/m from A to the right-hand end and a uniformly distributed load nw N/m on that part of the beam to the left of A. If a point of contra-flexure occurs at a point 0·5 m to the left of B, find the value of n and the other point of contra-flexure. Also find the maximum B.M. between the points of contra-flexure. Sketch and S.F. and B.M. diagrams.   (*I. Mech. E.*)

$$\left(Ans.: \frac{7}{4}; \ 2 \text{ m from A}; \frac{9}{32}w \text{ N m at 2·75 m from A}\right)$$

20. A horizontal beam 10 m long, carries a uniformly distributed load of 30 kN/m over the whole length and a concentrated load of 30 kN at the right end. If the beam is freely supported at the left end, find the position of the second support so that the greatest B.M. on the beam shall be as small as possible. Draw diagrams of S.F. and B.M. and insert the principal values.   (*U. Lond.*)
        (*Ans.:* 7·66 m from L.H. end)

21. Fig. 2.22 shows the dimensions of, and the loading carried by, a beam ABC. The beam is encastré at A, has a hinge at B and is supported on a roller bearing at C. Sketch and dimension the shearing force and bending moment diagrams, and determine the position and magnitude of the maximum positive and negative bending moments.   (*I.C.E.*)   (*Ans.:* 67·5 kN m, 1·5 m from C; 160 kN m at A)

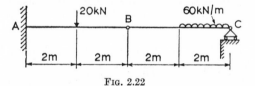

FIG. 2.22

22. The beam ABC is loaded as shown in Fig. 2.23. It is supported by a uniformly distributed reaction of w/m over AB, acting vertically upwards, and by a single concentrated reaction R at C.

Obtain the values of w and R and hence sketch the S.F. and B.M. diagrams, stating all significant values including the position and value of the maximum B.M.   (*U. Glas.*)

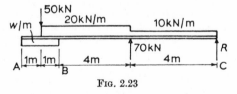

FIG. 2.23

23. A horizontal beam 3·5 m long, is freely supported at its ends and carries a vertical load of 5 kN, 1 m from the left-hand end. At a section 2 m from the left end a clockwise couple of moment 3 kN m is exerted, the axis of the couple being horizontal and perpendicular to the longitudinal axis of the beam. Draw the B.M. and S.F. diagrams and mark on them the principal dimensions.   (*I. Mech. E.*)
        (*Ans.:* 28·7 kN between A and D; 57·4 kN m at D)

24. Fig. 2.24 shows a beam ABC, 11 m in length, which is supported on a pin joint at A and rollers at B. At a point D on the beam a vertical arm DE is rigidly connected to it. Sketch diagrams of shearing force and bending moment, indicating maximum values, when the loading shown in the figure is applied.   (*I.C.E.*)

    (*Ans.:* S.F. = 21·95 kN; max. B.M. = 43·9 kN m, 2 m from L.H. end)

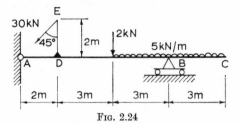

FIG. 2.24

25. A beam ABC, 9 m long, is simply supported at A and B, 6 m apart. It carries a load of 20 kN at a point 2 m from A, together with a distributed load whose intensity varies in linear fashion from zero at A and C to 30 kN/m at B.

    Draw the S.F. and B.M. diagrams, and calculate the position and magnitude of the maximum B.M.   (*U. Lond.*)   (*Ans.:* 66·67 kN m at 2·514 m from A)

26. Write down the relationship between load, S.F. and B.M. Use these to determine the position of no shear and the value of the maximum B.M. for a simply supported beam of length L m, carrying a distributed load which increases uniformly from zero at one end to q N/m at the other.   (*U. Lond.*)

    (*Ans.:* $L/\sqrt{3}$ m from end of zero load; $L^2q/9\sqrt{3}$ N m)

27. A simply supported beam with a span of 4 m carries a distributed load which varies in a linear manner from 30 kN/m run at one support to 90 kN/m run at the other support. Locate the position of the maximum bending moment and calculate the value of this maximum. Sketch the S.F. and B.M. diagrams. (*U. Lond.*)   (*Ans.:* 121 kN m at 2·16 m from lightly loaded end)

28. A horizontal beam, 4 m long, is freely supported at its two ends at the same level. A distributed load, increasing steadily from zero at both ends to a maximum of 60 kN/m at the middle, is supported by the beam. Draw the S.F. and B.M. diagrams. (*U. Lond.*)

    (*Ans.:* Max. S.F. = 60 kN at each end; max. B.M. = 80 kN m at centre)

29. Prove relations between B.M., S.F. and intensity of loading on a beam.

    A beam 8 m long is supported at the ends and carries a distributed load which varies uniformly in intensity from zero at one end to 30 kN/m at a section 2 m from the other end and over the remaining length is constant at 30 kN/m.

    Derive equations for S.F. and B.M. at any section of the beam, and sketch the S.F. and B.M. diagrams, marking on the diagrams the maximum values. (*U. Lond.*)

    (*Ans.:* 97·5 kN at heavily loaded end; 160·5 kN m at 4·58 m from lightly loaded end)

30. A horizontal beam, simply supported on a span of 4 m, carries a total load of 8 kN; the load distribution varies parabolically from zero at each end to a maximum at mid-span. Calculate the values of the B.M. at intervals of 0·5 m and draw the B.M. diagram for this loading. State the values of (*a*) the maximum B.M., and (*b*) the S.F. at the quarter span points.   (*U. Lond.*)

    (*Ans.:* 5 kN m; 2·75 kN)

CHAPTER 3

BENDING STRESSES

3.1 Pure bending. If a beam is subjected to a pure bending moment*
M, Fig. 3.1, the fibres in the upper part are extended and those in the lower
part are compressed. Tensile and compressive stresses are thereby induced in the beam which produce a moment, called the *moment of resistance*,
which is equal and opposite to the applied bending moment.

FIG. 3.1

In the theory of bending, which relates the stresses and curvature of the
beam to the applied bending moment, the following assumptions are made:

1. The beam is initially straight and the radius of curvature is large in
   comparison with the dimensions of the cross-section.
2. The material is homogeneous, elastic and obeys Hooke's Law.
3. The material has the same modulus of elasticity in tension and compression.
4. The stresses are uniform across the width and do not exceed the limit
   of proportionality.
5. The cross-section of the beam is symmetrical about the plane of
   bending.
6. A transverse section of the beam which is plane before bending remains plane after bending.
7. Every longitudinal fibre is assumed to be free to extend or contract
   without being restrained by its neighbour.

3.2 Second moment of area. If each element of an area is multiplied
by the square of its distance from an axis, the summation of these quantities
for the whole area is termed the *second moment of area* about the axis and
is denoted by I. It will be found that the stresses and curvature in a beam
for a given bending moment are proportional to the second moment of
area of the cross-section about an axis through the centroid perpendicular
to the plane of bending.

* A pure bending moment is one which is uniform along the length of the beam,
i.e. it is not accompanied by shear forces. The distortion caused by shearing action is,
however, usually very small (see Chap. 10).

The second moment of area of an element of area da, Fig. 3.2, about the axis $YY = x^2\,da$

$$\therefore \text{ total second moment about } YY = \int x^2\,da.$$

Similarly, total second moment of area about $XX = \int y^2\,da.$

The second moment of area about the axis ZZ (perpendicular to the plane of the paper) $= \int r^2\,da$. This is termed the *polar second moment of area* and is denoted by J.

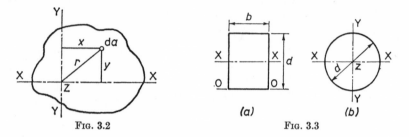

FIG. 3.2   FIG. 3.3

If the area of the plane is a, the second moment of area may be written in the form $I = ak^2$; k is termed the *radius of gyration* and is the radius at which the area would have to be imagined concentrated to give the same value of I.

Values of I for some simple cases
(*a*) Rectangle, breadth b and depth d, Fig. 3.3(*a*):

$$I_{XX} = \frac{bd^3}{12}, \qquad I_{OO} = \frac{bd^3}{3}$$

$$(k_{XX} = d/2\sqrt{3}, \qquad k_{OO} = d/\sqrt{3})$$

(*b*) Circle, diameter d, Fig. 3.3(*b*):

$$I_{XX} = I_{YY} = \frac{\pi}{64}d^4, \quad J(= I_{ZZ}) = \frac{\pi}{32}d^4$$

$$(k_{XX} = k_{YY} = d/4, \qquad k_{ZZ} = d/2\sqrt{2})$$

3.3 Theorem of parallel axes. The second moment of area of a plane about any axis is equal to the second moment about a parallel axis through the centroid, together with the product of the area and the square of the distance between the axes.

Let I_{XX} be the second moment of area of a plane about an axis XX passing through the centroid G, Fig. 3.4. It is required to find the second moment about a parallel axis OO, distance h from XX.

Second moment of area of element da about OO

$$= (y + h)^2 \, da$$
$$= (y^2 + 2yh + h^2) \, da$$
$$= y^2 \, da + 2yh \, da + h^2 \, da$$

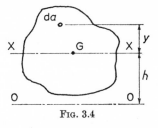

FIG. 3.4

$\therefore$ for the whole area,

$$I_{OO} = \int y^2 \, da + 2h \int y \, da + h^2 \int da$$

$$= I_{XX} + ah^2 + 2h \times \text{(total first moment of area about XX)}$$

Since XX passes through the centroid of the section, the total first moment of area about XX is zero.

Hence
$$I_{OO} = I_{XX} + ah^2 \quad . \quad . \quad . \quad . \quad (3.1)$$

3.4 Theorem of perpendicular axes. Referring to Fig. 3.2 and denoting the second moments of area of the element about the axes XX, YY and ZZ by dI_{XX}, dI_{YY} and dJ respectively, then

$$dI_{XX} + dI_{YY} = y^2 \, da + x^2 \, da = r^2 \, da = dJ$$

Therefore, for the whole area,

$$I_{XX} + I_{YY} = J \quad . \quad . \quad . \quad . \quad . \quad (3.2)$$

3.5 Equimomental system. It can be shown* that for the determination of the first and second moments of area of a triangle, its area a is equivalent to three areas, each $a/3$, imagined concentrated at the mid points of the sides. Since these areas are considered concentrated at particular points, they will have no second moment of area about their own axes.

This principle can be extended to any area which can be divided into triangles (see Examples 2 and 5).

3.6 Stress due to bending. Fig. 3.5(a) represents the cross-section of a beam, to which is applied a bending moment M, acting in a vertical plane through the centroid G. Since the section ab, Fig. 3.5(b), remains plane

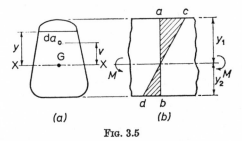

(a)   (b)

FIG. 3.5

* See *Dynamics*, Part II, by A. S. Ramsey (C.U.P.), Chap. V.

after bending, it takes up the position *cd* (shown exaggerated) and the figure *acdb* then represents the strain distribution diagram for the section, *ac* and *bd* representing the strains at the top and bottom faces respectively.

It is evident that the strain varies linearly from a maximum at the top fibres to another maximum at the bottom fibres and, in doing so, changes from tensile to compressive. The plane XX at which the strain is zero is termed the *neutral plane* and its intersection with a cross-section is termed the *neutral axis*. Thus the strain at any point, and consequently from Hooke's Law the stress, is directly proportional to the distance of that point from the neutral axis.

If the stress on a layer at a distance y from the neutral axis is σ, then the stress on an element da at a distance v from the neutral axis

$$= \frac{v}{y}\sigma$$

$$\therefore \text{ force on area } da = \frac{v}{y}\sigma\, da$$

$$\therefore \text{ moment of force about XX} = \frac{v}{y}\sigma\, da\, v$$

$$\therefore \text{ total moment of resistance} = \frac{\sigma}{y}\int v^2\, da = \frac{\sigma}{y}I$$

This is equal to the applied bending moment M,

i.e.
$$M = \frac{\sigma}{y}I$$

or
$$\frac{M}{I} = \frac{\sigma}{y} \qquad \qquad . \qquad . \qquad . \qquad . \qquad (3.3)$$

The maximum stresses induced in a section occur where y is a maximum, i.e. $\sigma_t = \frac{M}{I}y_1$ and $\sigma_c = \frac{M}{I}y_2$, where σ_t and σ_c are the maximum tensile and compressive stresses respectively.

3.7 Modulus of section. The maximum stress in a beam section is given by

$$\sigma = \frac{M}{I}y_{\max} = \frac{M}{I/y_{\max}}$$

The quantity $I/y_{\max}$ is called the *modulus of section* and is denoted by Z.

Thus
$$\sigma = \frac{M}{Z} \qquad . \qquad . \qquad . \qquad . \qquad . \qquad (3.4)$$

For a rectangular section, breadth b and depth d,

$$Z = \frac{bd^3}{12}\bigg/\frac{d}{2} = \frac{bd^2}{6}$$

For a circular section, diameter d,

$$Z = \frac{\pi}{64} d^4 \left/ \frac{d}{2} = \frac{\pi}{32} d^3 \right.$$

3.8 Position of neutral axis. In Fig. 3.6, let the total force on the section above the neutral axis be F_1 and that below this axis be F_2. Since the beam is subjected only to a bending moment, there is no resultant longitudinal force applied to the section,

$$\therefore F_1 + F_2 = 0$$

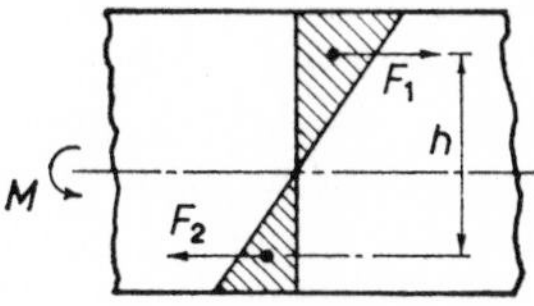

Force on element $\mathrm{d}a = \frac{v}{y} \sigma \, \mathrm{d}a$

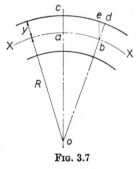

Fig. 3.6

$$\therefore \text{ total force above XX} = F_1 = \frac{\sigma}{y} \int v \, \mathrm{d}a$$

$$= \frac{\sigma}{y} \times \text{first moment about XX of area above XX}$$

Similarly,

$$F_2 = \frac{\sigma}{y} \times \text{first moment about XX of area below XX}$$

$$\therefore F_1 + F_2 = \frac{\sigma}{y} \times \text{total first moment of section about XX}$$

$$= 0$$

But σ/y cannot be zero, hence the total first moment about XX must be zero. For this condition to be satisfied, the neutral axis must pass through the centroid of the section.

The couple produced by the two equal forces F_1 and F_2 acting at a distance h apart provides the internal moment of resistance, balancing the external bending moment M.

3.9 Radius of curvature. Due to the action of the bending moment, the beam will bend; let the radius of curvature of the neutral axis at a particular section be R, Fig. 3.7. The layer formerly of length ce has become extended to cd,

$$\therefore \text{strain} = \frac{ed}{ce} = \frac{ed}{ab} = \frac{\sigma}{E} \quad (3.5)$$

From similar figures, $\dfrac{ed}{bd} = \dfrac{ab}{ob}$

i.e. $\dfrac{ed}{ab} = \dfrac{bd}{ob} = \dfrac{y}{R} \quad (3.6)$

Therefore, from equations (3.5) and (3.6),

$$\frac{\sigma}{y} = \frac{E}{R} \quad . \quad (3.7)$$

Fig. 3.7

Combining this with equation (3.3) gives the general bending formula

$$\frac{M}{I} = \frac{\sigma}{y} = \frac{E}{R} \qquad . \qquad . \qquad . \qquad . \quad (3.8)$$

3.10 Composite beams. A composite beam is one which consists of two or more materials rigidly fixed together throughout their length; examples of composite sections are shown in Fig. 3.8.

If M_1 and M_2 are the parts of the applied bending moment M carried by the two materials, then

$$M_1 + M_2 = M \qquad . \qquad . \qquad . \qquad . \quad (3.9)$$

Also the radius of curvature of the two parts is the same,

i.e. $$R_1 = R_2$$

i.e. $$\frac{E_1 I_1}{M_1} = \frac{E_2 I_2}{M_2}$$

or $$\frac{M_1}{M_2} = \frac{E_1 I_1}{E_2 I_2} . \qquad . \qquad . \qquad . \qquad . \quad (3.10)$$

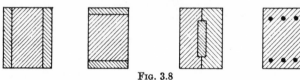

Fɪɢ. 3.8

M_1 and M_2 can be determined from equations (3.9) and (3.10) and the stresses in the two materials are then given by

$$\sigma_1 = \frac{M_1}{Z_1} \quad \text{and} \quad \sigma_2 = \frac{M_2}{Z_2}$$

Alternatively, the composite section may be replaced by an equivalent homogeneous section. Thus the section shown in Fig. 3.9(a) is equivalent to the section in Fig. 3.9(b), composed entirely of material (1) or to the section in Fig. 3.9(c), composed entirely of material (2), where $E_2/E_1 = n$.

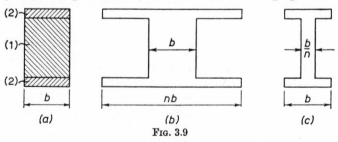

Fɪɢ. 3.9

Having obtained the value of I for the equivalent section, the stresses may then be obtained from $\sigma = \dfrac{M}{I}y$, these being the stresses which would exist in the homogeneous section. In section (*b*), the actual stresses in material (2) would be *n* times those in the equivalent section and in section (*c*), the actual stresses in material (1) would be $1/n$ times those in the equivalent section.

In the foregoing analysis, it has been assumed that the compound sections are all symmetrical about the plane of bending, otherwise twisting of the section would occur.

3.11 Combined bending and direct stresses. A combination of bending and direct stresses may occur in a variety of circumstances but in every case, the stresses due to the bending moment and direct load may be calculated separately and the results combined to give the resultant stresses. Thus $\sigma = \sigma_d \pm \sigma_b$ where σ_d and σ_b are the direct and bending stresses. The shape of the resultant stress distribution diagram will depend on whether σ_b is greater or less than σ_d.

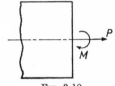

Fig. 3.10 shows a bar which is subjected to an axial load *P* and a bending moment *M* and Figs. 3.11(*a*), (*b*) and (*c*) show the possible forms of the resultant stress distribution.

Fɪɢ. 3.10

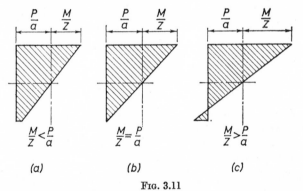

Fɪɢ. 3.11

3.12 Short column with eccentric load. A common example of combined bending and direct stresses occurs in short* columns subjected to eccentric loading. Let such a column be subjected to a load *P* which is applied at a distance *e* from the centroidal axis of the column, Fig. 3.12(*a*). The equilibrium of the column will not be affected if equal and opposite loads *P* are applied along the axis, as in Fig. 3.12(*b*). The original downward load together with the upward load along the axis constitute a moment *Pe*; thus the original load is equivalent to a direct load *P* along the axis together with a moment *Pe*.

* A long column would bend under the eccentric load and the analysis would be more complex; (see Chap. 7).

The maximum and minimum stresses in the cross-section are therefore given by

$$\sigma = \frac{P}{a} \pm \frac{Pe}{Z} . \qquad . \qquad . \qquad . \qquad . \quad (3.11)$$

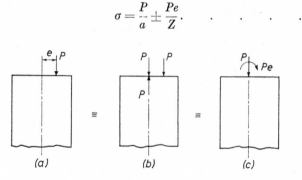

Fig. 3.12

If there is to be no tensile stress in the section (as in the case of a masonry or brick structure), the maximum eccentricity of the load is given by

$$\frac{1}{a} - \frac{e}{Z} = 0$$

For a rectangular column, of breadth b and depth d,

$$\frac{1}{bd} = \frac{e}{bd^2/6}$$

$$\therefore e = \frac{d}{6}$$

i.e. the load must lie within the middle third of the column.

For a circular column, of diameter d,

$$\frac{1}{\frac{\pi}{4}d^2} = \frac{e}{\frac{\pi}{32}d^3}$$

$$\therefore e = \frac{d}{8}$$

i.e. the load must lie within the middle quarter of the column.

3.13   Bending beyond the limit of proportionality. If a bending moment is applied to a beam sufficient to cause yielding of the material, the bending moment/angle of bending graph is of the form shown in Fig. 3.13. The onset of yield is less defined than in a simple tension or compression test as it occurs first in the outer fibres only and gradually extends towards the axis of the beam.

The stress/strain relation for a particular fibre, however, is that for simple tension and compression and for the purposes of calculation, it is assumed that, after yield, the stress at a particular point remains constant for a considerable increase in strain, giving a theoretical curve as shown in Fig. 3.14. Such a relation is approximately true for common mild steel where, after yield, the stress remains sensibly constant for a strain up to about 10 times that at the commencement of yield.

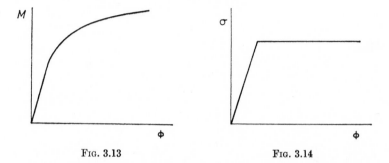

FIG. 3.13   FIG. 3.14

When yielding has commenced at the outer fibres, the stress distribution over the section is as shown in Fig. 3.15(b), the maximum stress remaining constant at the yield stress, σ_y, as M increases.

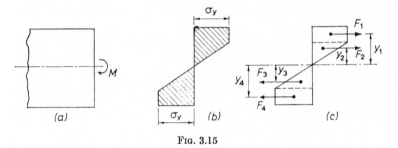

FIG. 3.15

Fig. 3.15(c) shows the forces represented by the various parts of the stress diagram.

If the beam is subjected to pure bending, there is no resultant force normal to the section, so that

$$F_1 + F_2 = F_3 + F_4 \quad . \qquad . \qquad . \qquad . \quad (3.12)$$

This condition gives the position of the neutral axis.* Having ascertained this,

$$F_1 y_1 + F_2 y_2 + F_3 y_3 + F_4 y_4 = M \quad . \qquad . \qquad . \quad (3.13)$$

* For a symmetrical section, this remains unaffected by the onset of yielding.

1. *Fig.* 3.16 *represents the cross-section of an extruded alloy member, which acts as a simply supported beam with the 60-mm wide flange at the bottom. Determine the moment of resistance of the section, if the maximum permissible stresses in tension and compression are respectively 60 and 45 MN/m².*

(I.C.E.)

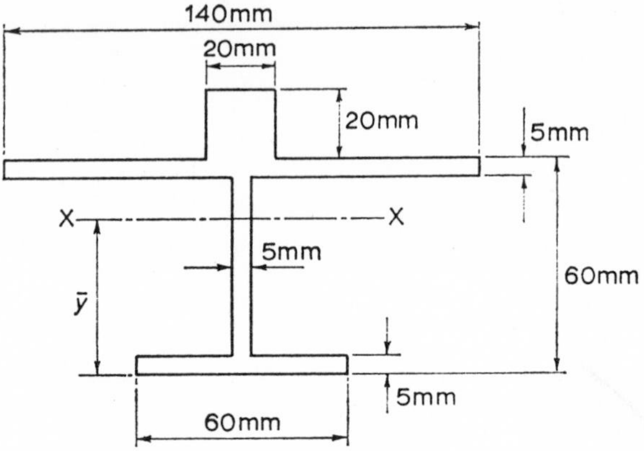

FIG. 3.16

If $\bar{y}$ is the distance of the neutral axis above the base, then, taking moments about the base,

$$20 \times 20 \times 70 + 140 \times 5 \times 57 \cdot 5 + 5 \times 50 \times 30 + 60 \times 5 \times 2 \cdot 5$$
$$= (20 \times 20 + 140 \times 5 + 5 \times 50 + 60 \times 5)\bar{y}$$
$$\therefore \bar{y} = 46 \cdot 36 \text{ mm}$$

$$\therefore I_{\mathrm{XX}} = \left(\frac{20 \times 20^3}{12} + 20 \times 20 \times 23 \cdot 64^2\right) + \left(\frac{140 \times 5^3}{12} + 140 \times 5 \times 11 \cdot 14^2\right)$$
$$+ \left(\frac{5 \times 50^3}{12} + 5 \times 50 \times 16 \cdot 36^2\right) + \left(\frac{60 \times 5^3}{12} + 60 \times 5 \times 43 \cdot 86^2\right)$$

$$= 1\ 022\ 000 \text{ mm}^4$$

For a maximum tensile stress of 60 MN/m²,

$$M = \frac{I}{y} \times \sigma = \frac{1\ 022\ 000 \times 10^{-12}}{0 \cdot 046\ 36} \times 60 \times 10^6 = 1\ 322 \text{ Nm}$$

For a maximum compressive stress of 45 MN/m²,

$$M = \frac{1\ 022\ 000 \times 10^{-12}}{0 \cdot 033\ 64} \times 45 \times 10^6 = 1\ 366 \text{ Nm}$$

$\therefore$ maximum allowable moment of resistance
$$= \underline{\underline{1 \cdot 322 \text{ kN m}}}$$

2. *A cast iron beam of the section shown in Fig.* 3.17 *is simply supported at its ends and carries a load of* 18 *kN at mid-span. Find the maximum allowable span if the stress due to bending is not to exceed* 30 *MN/m² tension. Neglect the weight of the beam.*

What will be the maximum compressive stress? (U. Lond.)

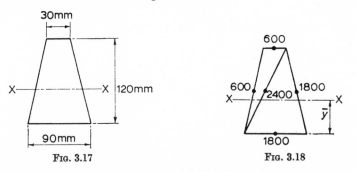

Fig. 3.17   Fig. 3.18

Dividing the section into two triangles and placing $\frac{1}{3}$ of the area of each triangle at the mid-point of its sides, the equi-momental system is as shown in Fig. 3.18 (see Art. 3.5).

Taking moments about the base,

$$600 \times 120 + 4\,800 \times 60 + 1\,800 \times 0 = 7\,200\bar{y}$$
$$\therefore \bar{y} = 50 \text{ mm}$$
$$\therefore I_{XX} = 600 \times 70^2 + 4\,800 \times 10^2 + 1\,800 \times 50^2 = 7\,920\,000 \text{ mm}^4$$
$$M_{\max} = \frac{Wl}{4} = \frac{18 \times 10^3 \times l}{4} = 4\,500l \text{ Nm, where } l \text{ is in m.}$$
$$\sigma = \frac{M}{I}y$$

i.e. $$30 \times 10^6 = \frac{4\,500l \times 0.05}{7\,920\,000 \times 10^{-12}} \text{ from which } l = \underline{1.056 \text{ m}}$$

The maximum compressive stress is given by

$$\sigma = \frac{0.07}{0.05} \times 30 = \underline{42 \text{ MN/m}^2}$$

3. *A steel tube* 40 *mm outside diameter and* 30 *mm inside diameter is used as a simply supported beam on a span of* 1 *m and it is found that the maximum safe load it can carry at mid-span is* 1.2 *kN.*

Four of these tubes are placed parallel to one another and firmly fixed together to form in effect a single beam, the centres of the tubes forming a square of 40 *mm side with one pair of centres vertically over the other pair. Find the maximum central loab which this beam can carry if the maximum stress is not to exceed that of the single tude above.* (U. Lond.)

The load $W \propto M$

$\propto Z$ for a given value of σ.

For a single tube, Fig. 3.19,

$$I_{XX} = \frac{\pi}{64}(40^4 - 30^4) \ = 85\ 900\ \text{mm}^4$$

$$\therefore Z = \frac{85\ 900}{20} \qquad = 4\ 295\ \text{mm}^3$$

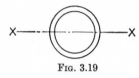

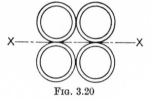

FIG. 3.19   FIG. 3.20

For four tubes, Fig. 3.20,

$$I_{XX} = 4\left\{85\ 900 + \frac{\pi}{4}\,(40^2 - 30^2) \times 20^2\right\}$$

$$= 1\ 223\ 600\ \text{mm}^4$$

$$\therefore Z = \frac{1\ 223\ 600}{40} \qquad = 30\ 950\ \text{mm}^3$$

Therefore the load which can be carried by the four tubes

$$= \frac{30\ 950}{4\ 295} \times 1{\cdot}2 \ = \underline{8{\cdot}65\ \text{kN}}$$

4. *Fig. 3.21 shows the section of a steel beam in the shape of an inverted semicircular channel with flanges. Determine the position of the neutral axis XX and the second moment of area of the section about XX.*

Calculate the moment of resistance of the beam in Nm if the maximum stress due to bending is 125 MN/m².

For a semicircular area of radius r, the distance of the centroid from the diameter is 0·424 4r.   (U. Lond.)

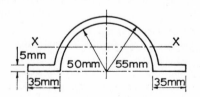

FIG. 3.21

Centroid of outer semi-circle from base $= 0.424\ 4 \times 55 = 23.35$ mm.
Centroid of inner semi-circle from base $= 0.424\ 4 \times 50 = 21.20$ mm.
Taking moments about the base,

$$60 \times 5 \times 2.5 + \frac{\pi}{2} \times 55^2 \times 23.35 - \frac{\pi}{2} \times 50^2 \times 21.20$$

$$= \left(60 \times 5 + \frac{\pi}{2} \times 55^2 - \frac{\pi}{2} \times 50^2\right)\bar{y}$$

$$\therefore \bar{y} = 25.3 \text{ mm}$$

$$I_{XX} = \left\{\frac{60 \times 5^3}{12} + 60 \times 5 \times 22.8^2\right\}$$

$$+ \left\{\frac{\pi}{8} \times 55^4 - \frac{\pi}{2} \times 55^2 \times 23.35^2 + \frac{\pi}{2} \times 55^2 \times 2.95^2\right\}^*$$

$$- \left\{\frac{\pi}{8} \times 50^4 - \frac{\pi}{2} \times 50^2 \times 21.20^2 + \frac{\pi}{2} \times 50^2 \times 4.1^2\right\}$$

$$= \underline{413\ 600 \text{ mm}^4}$$

$$M = \frac{I}{y} \times \sigma$$

$$= \frac{413\ 600 \times 10^{-12}}{0.055 - 0.025\ 3} \times 125 \times 10^6 = \underline{1\ 740 \text{ Nm}}$$

5. *Prove that the moment of resistance of a beam of square section with its diagonal in the plane of bending is increased by flattening the top and bottom corners, as shown in Fig. 3.22, and that the moment of resistance is a maximum when $y = \frac{8}{9}Y$.* (U. Lond.)

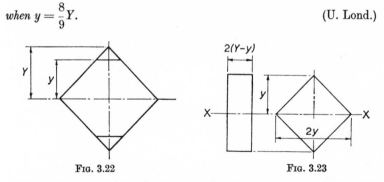

FIG. 3.22   FIG. 3.23

The section may be divided into a rectangle and a square which is being bent about its diagonal, Fig. 3.23.

* I of semi-circle about neutral axis of section $= I$ about the diameter
    − area $\times$ (distance from diameter to centroid of semi-circle)^2
    + area $\times$ (distance of centroid of semi-circle to neutral axis of section)^2

$$I_{XX} = \frac{2(Y - y) \times (2y)^3}{12} + \frac{y^{4*}}{3} = \frac{4}{3}Yy^3 - y^4$$

$$\therefore \sigma = M \times \frac{y}{\frac{4}{3}Yy^3 - y^4}$$

For σ to be a minimum, $\dfrac{\mathrm{d}\sigma}{\mathrm{d}y} = 0$

i.e. $\dfrac{4}{3}Yy^3 - y^4 = y(4Yy^2 - 4y^3)$ from which $y = \dfrac{8}{9}Y$

6. *A horizontal cantilever 3 m long is of rectangular cross-section 60 mm wide throughout its length, the depth varying uniformly from 60 mm at the free end to 180 mm at the fixed end. A load of 4 kN acts at the free end. Find the position of the most highly stressed section, and find the value of the maximum bending stress induced. Neglect the weight of the cantilever itself.* (U. Lond.)

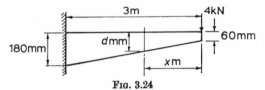

Fɪɢ. 3.24

At a section x m from the load, Fig. 3.24,
$$M = 4 \times 10^3 x \text{ Nm}$$

and $d = 60 + \dfrac{x}{3} \times 120 = 60 + 40x$ mm

$$\therefore Z = \frac{bd^2}{6} = \frac{60}{6}(60 + 40x)^2 = 4\,000(3 + 2x)^2 \text{ mm}^3$$

$$\therefore \sigma = \frac{M}{Z} = \frac{4 \times 10^3 x}{4\,000(3 + 2x)^2 \times 10^{-9}} = \frac{10^9 x}{(3 + 2x)^2} \qquad . \qquad (1)$$

For σ to be a maximum, $\dfrac{\mathrm{d}\sigma}{\mathrm{d}x} = 0$

i.e. $(3 + 2x)^2 = 4x(3 + 2x)$
from which $x = \underline{1 \cdot 5 \text{ m}}$

Substituting in equation (1),
$$\sigma_{max} = \frac{10^9 \times 1 \cdot 5}{(3 + 3)^2} \text{ N/m}^2 = \underline{41 \cdot 6 \text{ MN/m}^2}$$

* The area of each half of the square is y^2. Placing $y^2/3$ at the mid-point of each of the sloping sides and $2y^2/3$ at the mid-point of the diagonal,
$$I_{XX} = 4 \times \frac{y^2}{3} \times \left(\frac{y}{2}\right)^2 = \frac{y^4}{3},$$
the area $2y^2/3$ having no second moment about XX.

7. *A timber beam 80 mm wide by 160 mm deep is to be reinforced with two steel plates 5 mm thick. Compare the moments of resistance for the same value of the maximum bending stress in the timber when the plates are alternately:*

    (a) 80 mm wide and fixed to the top and bottom surfaces of the beam;

    (b) 160 mm deep and fixed to the vertical sides of the beam.

$$E_{\text{steel}} = 20 \times E_{\text{timber}}.$$ (U. Lond.)

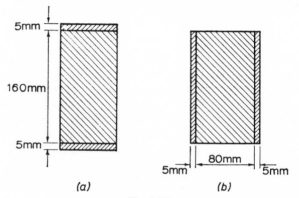

FIG. 3.25

(a)
$$I_t = \frac{80 \times 160^3}{12} = 27 \cdot 3 \times 10^6 \text{ mm}^4,$$

$$I_s = \frac{80}{12}(170^3 - 160^3) = 5 \cdot 447 \times 10^6 \text{ mm}^4$$

$$M = M_s + M_t \quad \cdot \quad \cdot \quad \cdot \quad \text{from equation (3.9)}$$

and
$$\frac{M_s}{M_t} = \frac{E_s I_s}{E_t I_t} \quad \cdot \quad \cdot \quad \cdot \quad \text{from equation (3.10)}$$

$$= 20 \times \frac{5 \cdot 447}{27 \cdot 3} \quad = 3 \cdot 98$$

$$\therefore M = 3 \cdot 98 M_t + M_t = 4 \cdot 98 M$$

(b)
$$I_t^{\cdot} = 27 \cdot 3 \times 10^6 \text{ mm}^4$$

$$I_s = \frac{10 \times 160^3}{12} \quad = 3 \cdot 413 \times 10^6 \text{ mm}^4$$

$$\frac{M_s}{M_t} = 20 \times \frac{3 \cdot 413}{2 \cdot 73} \quad = 2 \cdot 5$$

$$\therefore M = 2 \cdot 5 M_t + M_t \quad = 3 \cdot 5 M_t$$

Therefore ratio of moments of resistance in cases *(a)* and *(b)* for the same value of M_t (i.e. for the same value of σ_t) $= \dfrac{4 \cdot 98}{3 \cdot 5} = \underline{1 \cdot 425}$

8. *A compound beam is formed by joining two bars rigidly together, one of steel and the other of brass, each bar being 40 mm wide. The bars are of thickness t_1 and t_2 respectively so that the total depth is $(t_1 + t_2)$. If E for the steel is twice that for the brass, find the ratio of t_1 to t_2 so that the neutral axis of the section is at the dividing line of the two bars.*

If the total depth of the section is to be 20 mm and the stresses in the steel and brass are not to exceed 110 and 40 MN/m^2 respectively, determine the maximum moment of resistance of the beam.   (U. Lond.)

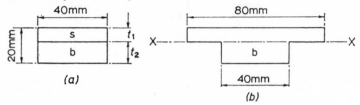

Fig. 3.26

Fig. 3.26(*a*) shows the cross-section of the composite bar and Fig. 3.26(*b*) shows the equivalent brass section.

For the neutral axis to be on the dividing line, the moments of the parts on each side of this line must be equal,

i.e.
$$80 \times t_1 \times \frac{t_1}{2} = 40 \times t_2 \times \frac{t_2}{2}$$

from which
$$\frac{t_1}{t_2} = \frac{1}{\sqrt{2}}$$

$$t_1 + t_2 = 20 \text{ mm} \quad \text{and} \quad \frac{t_1}{t_2} = \frac{1}{\sqrt{2}}$$

$$\therefore t_1 = 8{\cdot}28 \text{ mm} \quad \text{and} \quad t_2 = 11{\cdot}72 \text{ mm}$$

$$\frac{\sigma}{y} = \frac{E}{R}$$

Therefore, for a given radius of curvature, R, the stress in the material at a given distance, y, from the neutral axis is proportional to E. Hence, if the maximum permissible stress in the steel is 110 MN/m^2, the corresponding stress at the top edge of the equivalent brass section is

$$110/2 = 55 \text{ MN/m}^2.$$

Since $t_2 = \sqrt{2}t_1$, it is evident that the stress at the bottom edge will reach 40 MN/m^2 before that at the top edge reaches 55 MN/m^2, so that the moment of resistance is that which will produce the former stress.

$$I_{XX} = \frac{80 \times 8{\cdot}28^3}{3} + \frac{40 \times 11{\cdot}72^3}{3} \qquad = 36\,000 \text{ mm}^4$$

$$\therefore M = \frac{I}{y} \times \sigma = \frac{36\,630 \times 10^{-12}}{0{\cdot}011\,72} \times 40 \times 10^6 = \underline{125 \text{ N m}}$$

9. *A steel chimney is 30 m high, 1 m external diameter and 10 mm thick. It is rigidly fixed at the base. It is acted upon by a horizontal wind pressure which is taken to be of a uniform intensity of 1 kN/m² of projected area for the lower 15 m and to vary uniformly from 1 kN/m² to 2 kN/m² over the upper 15 m.*

Calculate the maximum stress in the plates at the base. Steel has a density of 7·8 Mg/m³. (U. Lond.)

The pressure distribution diagram is shown in Fig. 3.27. The total wind force can be divided into P_1, the force due to a uniform pressure of 1 kN/m² over the whole height, and P_2, the force due to the additional pressure over the upper 15 m.

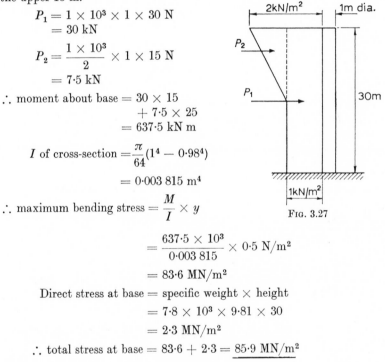

FIG. 3.27

$$P_1 = 1 \times 10^3 \times 1 \times 30 \text{ N}$$
$$= 30 \text{ kN}$$

$$P_2 = \frac{1 \times 10^3}{2} \times 1 \times 15 \text{ N}$$
$$= 7·5 \text{ kN}$$

∴ moment about base $= 30 \times 15$
$$+ 7·5 \times 25$$
$$= 637·5 \text{ kN m}$$

I of cross-section $= \dfrac{\pi}{64}(1^4 - 0·98^4)$

$$= 0·003\ 815 \text{ m}^4$$

∴ maximum bending stress $= \dfrac{M}{I} \times y$

$$= \frac{637·5 \times 10^3}{0·003\ 815} \times 0·5 \text{ N/m}^2$$

$$= 83·6 \text{ MN/m}^2$$

Direct stress at base $=$ specific weight $\times$ height

$$= 7·8 \times 10^3 \times 9·81 \times 30$$

$$= 2·3 \text{ MN/m}^2$$

∴ total stress at base $= 83·6 + 2·3 = \underline{85·9 \text{ MN/m}^2}$

10. *A short column of I-section 200 mm × 160 mm has a cross-section as shown in Fig. 3.28. A vertical load W acts through the centroid of the section together with a parallel load of W/4 acting through a point on the centre line of the web, distance 60 mm from the centroid measured towards the longer flange.*

Calculate the greatest allowable value of W if the maximum compressive stress is not to exceed 80 MN/m². What is the minimum stress in the section?

(U. Lond.)

c

Taking moments about the top edge,

$$160 \times 10 \times 5 + 180 \times 10 \times 100 + 120 \times 10 \times 195 = 4\,600y_1$$
$$\therefore y_1 = 91 \cdot 74 \text{ mm} \quad \text{and} \quad y_2 = 108 \cdot 26 \text{ mm}$$

$$I_{XX} = \left(\frac{160 \times 10^3}{12} + 160 \times 10 \times 86 \cdot 74^2\right)$$

$$+ \left(\frac{10 \times 180^3}{12} + 10 \times 180 \times 8 \cdot 26^2\right)$$

$$+ \left(\frac{120 \times 10^3}{12} + 120 \times 10 \times 103 \cdot 26^2\right)$$

$$= 29 \cdot 85 \times 10^6 \text{ mm}^4$$

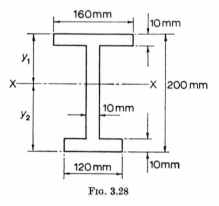

FIG. 3.28

Transferring the load $W/4$ to the axis XX, there is then a total direct load of $5W/4$, together with a bending moment about XX, of magnitude $We/4$ where e is the eccentricity of the load from XX.

$$\therefore \sigma_{\max} = \frac{5W}{4 \times 0 \cdot 004\,6} + \frac{W \times 0 \cdot 06}{4} \times \frac{0 \cdot 108\,26}{29 \cdot 85 \times 10^{-6}} = 80 \times 10^6 \text{ N/m}^2$$

from which

$$W = \underline{245 \text{ kN}}$$

Minimum stress

$$= \frac{5 \times 245 \times 10^3}{4 \times 0 \cdot 004\,6} - \frac{245 \times 10^3 \times 0 \cdot 06}{4} \times \frac{0 \cdot 086\,74}{29 \cdot 85 \times 10^{-6}} \text{ N/m}^2$$

$$= \underline{55 \cdot 92 \text{ MN/m}^2}$$

11. *A pillar 1·5 m high is of rectangular section 50 mm thick and tapers longitudinally from a width of 150 mm at the base to 50 mm at the top, as shown in Fig. 3.29. A compressive load of 100 kN acts through the centroid at the top end and parallel to the vertical edge.*

Determine the magnitude of the maximum compressive stress and the cross-section at which it will occur. (U. Lond.)

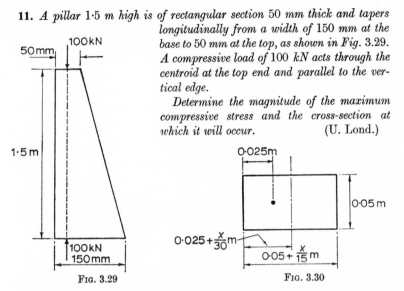

FIG. 3.29   FIG. 3.30

Fig. 3.30 shows the section of the pillar at a distance x m below the top. The width of the section is $0·05 + \dfrac{x}{1·5} \times 0·10 = 0·05 + \dfrac{x}{15}$ m so that the load has an eccentricity of $\dfrac{x}{30}$ m with respect to the centroid of the section.

$$\text{Direct stress, } \sigma_d = \frac{100 \times 10^3}{0·05\left(0·05 + \dfrac{x}{15}\right)} \text{ N/m}^2 = \frac{30}{0·75 + x} \text{ MN/m}^2$$

$$\text{Bending stress, } \sigma_b = \frac{100 \times 10^3 \times \dfrac{x}{30}}{\dfrac{0·05}{6}\left(0·05 + \dfrac{x}{15}\right)^2} \text{ N/m}^2 = \frac{90}{(0·75 + x)^2} \text{ MN/m}^2$$

$$\therefore \text{ resultant stress, } \sigma = \frac{30}{0·75 + x} + \frac{90}{(0·75 + x)^2} = \frac{22·5 + 120x}{(0·75 + x)^2} \text{ MN/m}^2$$

For σ to be a maximum,

$$\frac{d\sigma}{dx} = 0$$

from which $\qquad x = 0·375 \text{ m}$

Substituting in equation (1),

$$\sigma = \frac{67·5}{1·125^2} = \underline{53·33 \text{ MN/m}^2}$$

12. *A steel bar of circular section, 100 mm diameter, carries a longitudinal pull whose line of action is parallel with the axis of the bar. At a certain transverse section the longitudinal stresses are measured at the surface of the bar at three points A, B and C, these points being equally spaced round the section. The tensile stresses at these points are A, 90 MN/m²; B, 75 MN/m²; C, 30 MN/m².*

Determine (a) the magnitude and location of the greatest and least stresses at the section; (b) the magnitude and eccentricity of the applied pull. Make a diagram showing the stresses and their positions relative to the points A, B and C.
(U. Lond.)

It will be evident that the line of action of P lies within the sector AOB, Fig. 3.31.

At A, $\sigma = \dfrac{P}{\dfrac{\pi}{4} d^2} + \dfrac{Pe \cos \theta}{\dfrac{\pi}{32} d^3}$

$$= \dfrac{P}{\dfrac{\pi}{4} \times 0 \cdot 10^2} + \dfrac{Pe \cos \theta}{\dfrac{\pi}{32} \times 0 \cdot 10^3}$$

$$= \dfrac{400P}{\pi}\{1 + 80e \cos \theta\}$$

$$= 90 \text{ MN/m}^2 \qquad . \qquad (1)$$

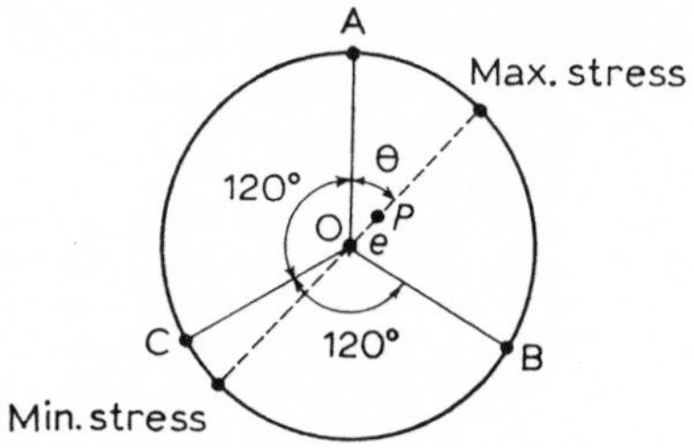

FIG. 3.31

Similarly, at B,

$$\sigma = \dfrac{400P}{\pi}\{1 + 80e \cos(120 - \theta)\}$$

$$= \dfrac{400P}{\pi}\left\{1 + 80e\left(-\tfrac{1}{2}\cos\theta + \dfrac{\sqrt{3}}{2}\sin\theta\right)\right\} = 75 \text{ MN/m}^2 \qquad (2)$$

At C, $\sigma = \dfrac{400P}{\pi}\{1 + 80e \cos(120 + \theta)\}$

$$= \dfrac{400P}{\pi}\left\{1 + 80e\left(-\tfrac{1}{2}\cos\theta - \dfrac{\sqrt{3}}{2}\sin\theta\right)\right\} = 30 \text{ MN/m}^2 \qquad (3)$$

These equations simplify to

$$1 + 80e \cos \theta = \dfrac{9\pi}{40P} \qquad . \qquad . \qquad . \qquad . \qquad (4)$$

$$1 + 40e(-\cos\theta + \sqrt{3}\sin\theta) = \dfrac{7 \cdot 5\pi}{40P} \qquad . \qquad . \qquad . \qquad (5)$$

$$1 + 40e(-\cos\theta - \sqrt{3}\sin\theta) = \dfrac{3\pi}{40P} \qquad . \qquad . \qquad . \qquad (6)$$

From equations (5) and (6),

$$2 - 80e \cos \theta = \frac{10 \cdot 5\pi}{40P} \qquad . \qquad . \qquad . \qquad (7)$$

$\therefore$ from equations (4) and (7), $\qquad P = \dfrac{19 \cdot 5\pi}{120} \qquad = \underline{0 \cdot 51 \text{ MN}}$

From equations (5) and (6),

$$80\sqrt{3}e \sin \theta = \frac{4 \cdot 5\pi}{40P} \qquad = 0 \cdot 693 \qquad . \qquad . \qquad . \qquad (8)$$

and from equation (4),

$$80e \cos \theta = \frac{9\pi}{40P} - 1 \qquad = 0 \cdot 386 \qquad . \qquad . \qquad . \qquad (9)$$

$$\therefore \tan \theta = \frac{0 \cdot 693}{0 \cdot 386\sqrt{3}} = 1 \cdot 035$$

$$\therefore \theta = \underline{46°}$$

From equations (8) or (9), $e = \overline{0 \cdot 006\ 95}$ m or 6·95 mm

$$\sigma_{\max} = \frac{400P}{\pi}(1 + 80e), \qquad \text{when } \theta = 0$$

$$= \frac{400 \times 0 \cdot 51}{\pi}(1 + 80 \times 0 \cdot 006\ 95) = 101 \text{ MN/m}^2$$

$$\sigma_{\min} = \frac{400P}{\pi}(1 - 80e), \qquad \text{when } \theta = 180°$$

$$= \frac{400 \times 0 \cdot 51}{\pi}(1 - 80 \times 0 \cdot 006\ 95) = \underline{28 \cdot 9 \text{ MN/m}^2}$$

13. *A steel bar of rectangular section* 80 *mm* × 40 *mm is used as a simply supported beam on a span of* 1·4 *m and loaded at mid-span. If the yield stress is* 300 *MN/m² and the long edges of the section are vertical, find the load when yielding first occurs.*

Assuming that a further increase in load causes yielding to spread in towards the neutral axis with the stress in the yielded part remaining constant at 300 *MN/m², determine the load required to cause yielding for a depth of* 10 *mm at the top and bottom of the section at mid-span, and find the length of beam over which yielding at the top and bottom faces will have occurred.*

(U. Lond.)

$$M_{\max} = \frac{Wl}{4}, \qquad \text{Fig. 3.32}$$

$$\therefore \sigma_{\max} = \frac{M_{\max}}{Z} = \frac{Wl}{4} \times \frac{6}{bd^2}$$

i.e. $\qquad 300 \times 10^6 = \dfrac{W \times 1 \cdot 4 \times 6}{4 \times 0 \cdot 04 \times 0 \cdot 08^2}$

$$\therefore W = \underline{36 \cdot 57 \text{ kN}}$$

After yielding, resisting moment

$$= 2\{F_1 \times 0.035 + F_2 \times 0.02\}, \quad \text{Fig. 3.33}$$

i.e. $\dfrac{W \times 1.4}{4} = 2\{(300 \times 10^6 \times 0.01 \times 0.04) \times 0.035$
$$+ (150 \times 10^6 \times 0.03 \times 0.04) \times 0.02\}$$

$$\therefore W = \underline{44.6 \text{ kN}}$$

If yielding ceases at x m from the centre

$$M = \frac{44.6 \times 10^3}{2}(0.7 - x) = 300 \times 10^6 \times \frac{0.04 \times 0.08^2}{6}$$

$$\therefore x = 0.126 \text{ m}$$

$\therefore$ length over which yielding occurs $= 2x = \underline{0.252 \text{ m}}$

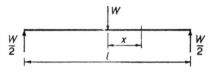

FIG. 3.32

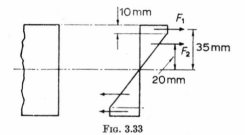

FIG. 3.33

14. *Fig. 3.34(a) shows the section of a beam which is subjected to a bending moment of such magnitude that yielding occurs at the lower part of the web over a depth of 50 mm. The yield stress of 300 MN/m² may be assumed constant over the yielded area, while over the remainder of the section the stress is proportional to the distance from the neutral axis.*

Determine: (a) the position of the neutral axis N A; (b) the stress at the top of the section; (c) the moment of resistance of the section. (U. Lond.)

The stress distribution diagram is shown in Fig. 3.34(b).

If the neutral axis after yielding is at a depth h mm below the top, then

$$\frac{\sigma}{h} = \frac{300}{150 - h}$$

$$\therefore \sigma = \frac{300h}{150 - h} \text{ MN/m}^2. \qquad . \qquad . \qquad . \qquad (1)$$

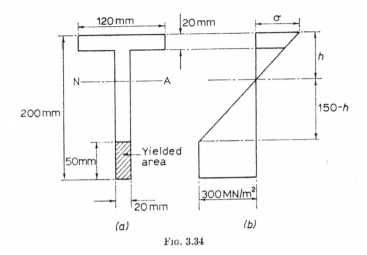

FIG. 3.34

Stress at underside of flange $= \dfrac{h - 20}{h}\sigma$

Therefore, equating forces above and below the neutral axis,

$$\dfrac{\sigma + \dfrac{h - 20}{h}\sigma}{2} \times 120 \times 20 + \dfrac{h - 20}{h}\dfrac{\sigma}{2} \times (h - 20) \times 20$$

$$= 300 \times 50 \times 20 + \dfrac{300}{2} \times (150 - h) \times 20$$

from which $\sigma = \dfrac{300(250h - h^2)}{h^2 + 200h - 2\,000}$.   .   .   .   .   (2)

Therefore, from equations (1) and (2),

$$h = \underline{65 \cdot 8 \text{ mm}} \text{ and } \sigma = \underline{234 \cdot 5 \text{ MN/m}^2}$$

$$\text{Stress at underside of flange} = \dfrac{65 \cdot 8 - 20}{65 \cdot 8} \times 234 \cdot 5$$

$$= 163 \cdot 3 \text{ MN/m}^2$$

Assuming that the force on the flange acts through its geometric centre, moment about N A

$$= \dfrac{(234 \cdot 5 + 163 \cdot 3) \times 10^6}{2} \times 0 \cdot 12 \times 0 \cdot 02 \times (0 \cdot 065\,8 - 0 \cdot 01)$$

$$= 26\,650 \text{ N m}$$

Moment about N A of force on web above N A

$$= \frac{163 \cdot 3 \times 10^6}{2} \times (0 \cdot 065\ 8 - 0 \cdot 02) \times 0 \cdot 02 \times \tfrac{2}{3}(0 \cdot 065\ 8 - 0 \cdot 02)$$

$$= 2\ 285\ \text{N m}$$

Moment about N A of force on web below N A

$$= \frac{300 \times 10^6}{2} \times (0 \cdot 15 - 0 \cdot 065\ 8) \times 0 \cdot 02 \times \tfrac{2}{3}(0 \cdot 15 - 0 \cdot 065\ 8)$$

$$= 14\ 170\ \text{N m}$$

Moment about N A of force on plastic part of web

$$= 300 \times 10^6 \times 0 \cdot 05 \times 0 \cdot 02 \times (0 \cdot 175 - 0 \cdot 068\ 5)$$

$$= 31\ 950\ \text{N m}$$

$\therefore$ total moment of resistance

$$= 75\ 055\ \text{N m} \quad \text{or} \quad \underline{75 \cdot 055\ \text{kN m}}$$

15. An I-section girder, 240 mm deep, has a web 20 mm thick. The top flange is 120 mm by 20 mm and the bottom flange is 160 mm by 20 mm. If the girder is simply supported at its ends, find the maximum span which can be used if the total distributed load per m run is 6 kN/m, and the maximum stress is limited to 70 MN/m².   (*U. Lond.*)   (*Ans.:* 7·67 m)

16. The cross-section of an I-beam has dimensions as follows: overall depth 240 mm, top flange 80 mm wide by 20 mm thick, bottom flange 160 mm wide by 20 mm thick, web 10 mm thick. The girder is simply supported over a span of 5 m and carries two concentrated loads each of 20 kN at points 1 m from the ends. Calculate the maximum bending stress due to this loading.   (*U. Lond.*)

                                            (*Ans.:* 48·4 MN/m²)

17. A tank 1·5 m × 1·5 m × 1·0 m in depth is supported symmetrically by a pair of steel cantilevers 1·5 m long, which it completely covers. If the cantilevers are of *T*-section 100 mm × 100 mm × 10 mm and the maximum tensile stress is not to exceed 100 MN/m², determine the maximum safe depth of oil of density 0·9 Mg/m³ to which the tank may be filled. Neglect the weight of the tank. What would then be the maximum compressive stress in the cantilevers?   (*U. Lond*).

                                 (*Ans.:* 0·842 5 m; 248 MN/m²)

18. A steel beam is in section an inverted channel; outside dimensions 220 mm wide, 80 mm deep, thickness of web 10 mm, thickness of vertical flanges 12 mm. The beam is simply supported over a span of 3 m and carries two equal concentrated loads at points distant 0·5 m from each support. Find the value of each of these loads if the maximum tensile stress is not to exceed 100 MN/m².   (*U. Lond.*)

                                            (*Ans.:* 7·725 kN)

19. A compound girder is a 260 mm × 100 mm steel joist, $I_{max} = 168 \times 10^{-6}\text{m}^4$ with a 180 mm × 20 mm steel plate riveted to each flange of the beam. Neglect the effects of the rivets and calculate the moment of resistance of the girder for a working stress of 120 MN/m².   (*U. Lond.*)   (*Ans.:* 247·4 kN m)

20. The T-section of a beam has the following dimensions: width of flange, 100 mm, overall depth, 80 mm, thickness of stem and flange, 10 mm.

Determine the maximum stress in the beam when a bending moment of 200 N m is acting in the plane of symmetry of the section.

Also, determine a new width for the flange required to give maximum stresses in compression and tension in the ratio of 2 to 1. (*U. Lond.*)
(*Ans.:* 12·5 MN/m²; 59 mm, assuming flange in tension and web in compression)

21. A horizontal cantilever, 1·2 m long, has a T-shaped cross-section, as shown in Fig. 3.35, and carries a uniformly distributed load along the full length of the top flange. Calculate the greatest intensity of the load which can be carried if the maximum tensile and compressive stresses are not to exceed 30 MN/m² and 90 MN/m² respectively. (*I.C.E.*)   (*Ans.:* 3·94 N/m)

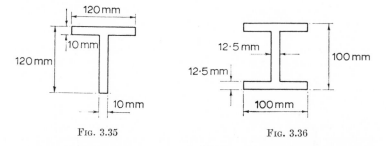

FIG. 3.35   FIG. 3.36

22. A steel I-beam of the section shown in Fig. 3.36 rests on two supports in a steel store. Determine the maximum length of beam which can be supported in this way without yielding occurring and the position of the supports. The yield stress is 240 MN/m² and the density of steel is 7·8 Mg/m³. (*I. Mech. E.*)
(*Ans.:* 66·9 m (support points at 0·207 *l* from ends))

23. A cast-iron beam has a section as shown in Fig. 3.37, being symmetrical about the axis YY. Determine the position of the neutral axis of the section, XX, and the second moment of area about XX.

If, when subjected to a bending moment in the plane YY, the tensile stress at the bottom edge is 25 MN/m², find (*a*) the value of the bending moment and (*b*) the stress at the top edge.
(*Ans.:* 141·6 mm; 484 × 10⁻⁶m⁴; 85·45 kN m; 31·5 MN/m²)

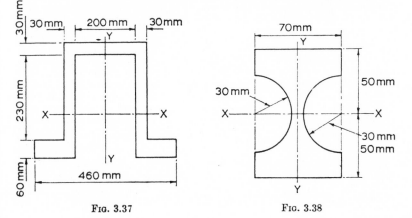

FIG. 3.37   FIG. 3.38

24. Fig. 3.38 shows the section of a beam. What is the ratio of its moment of resistance to bending in the plane YY to that for bending in the plane XX if the maximum stress due to bending is the same in both cases?

For a semi-circle of radius r the centroid is a distance of $\dfrac{4r}{3\pi}$ from the centre.

(*U. Lond.*)   (*Ans.:* 2·85)

25. A wooden beam is 80 mm wide and 120 mm deep with a semicircular groove of 25 mm radius planed out in the centre of each side. Calculate the maximum stress in the section when simply supported on a span of 2 m and loaded with a concentrated load of 400 N at a distance of 0·7 m from one end and a uniformly distributed load of 750 N/m run over the whole span. (*U. Lond.*)
(*Ans.:* 2·825 MN/m²)

26. A cantilever specimen for a fatigue-testing machine is of circular cross-section throughout its length, but in a length of 75 mm the diameter decreases from 10 mm at the fixed end to 6·25 mm at the free end. Calculate the maximum stress due to bending when a static load of 300 N is applied at the free end in a direction perpendicular to the length of the specimen. (*U. Lond.*)
(*Ans.:* 231·5 MN/m² at 62·5 mm from load)

27. A vertical flagstaff, standing 9 m above the ground, is of square section throughout, the dimensions being 150 mm by 150 mm at the ground, tapering uniformly to 75 mm by 75 mm at the top. A horizontal pull of 300 N is applied at the top, the direction of loading being along a diagonal of the section. Calculate the maximum stress due to bending. (*U. Lond.*)
(*Ans.:* 8·05 MN/m² at 4·5 m from top)

28. A timber beam 150 mm wide and 300 mm deep is to be reinforced by two steel plates 10 mm thick firmly attached to its sides and symmetrically placed about the horizontal centre line of the beam section. If the beam is to carry a central concentrated load of 52·5 kN on a span of 3 m, and the maximum stress in the timber is not to exceed 8·5 MN/m², find the minimum depth of the steel plates required, assuming the beam to be simply supported at the ends.
E for steel = 20 × E for timber. (*U. Lond.*)
(*Ans.:* 220 mm)

29. A flitched beam is made of two timber joists each 120 mm wide by 300 mm deep, with a steel plate 20 mm thick and 300 mm deep firmly fixed between them. Calculate the moment of resistance of the combined beam if the maximum stress in the timber is limited to 7·5 MN/m². Also find the maximum uniformly distributed load which the beam can carry on a simply supported span of 5 m. E_{steel} = 200 GN/m²; E_{timber} = 10 GN/m². (*U. Lond.*)
(*Ans.:* 72 kN m; 23·04 kN/m)

30. A wooden beam 25 mm wide by 50 mm deep is reinforced by two similar steel plates, each 25 mm wide, one being secured to the upper face of the beam and one to the lower face. Calculate the necessary thickness of the plates in order that the beam can resist a bending moment of 600 N m in the vertical plane without the maximum stress in the wood exceeding 5·5 MN/m². E_{steel} = 200 GN/m²; E_{wood} = 20 GN/m². (*U. Lond.*)   (*Ans.:* 6·22 mm)

31. A steel tube of 50 mm outside diameter fits very accurately over a brass rod of 25 mm diameter. Determine the moment of resistance to bending of the assembly, assuming that the maximum stresses for steel and brass should not exceed 150 and 120 MN/m² respectively. E_{steel} = 200 GN/m²; E_{brass} = 100 GN/m².
(*U. Lond.*)   (*Ans.:* 1·786 kN m)

32. Two bars of rectangular cross-section, one brass and one steel, each 30 mm wide by 10 mm deep are placed together to form a beam 30 mm wide by 20 mm deep. The beam is placed horizontally on two supports 0·75 m apart and a vertical central load is applied. Determine the maximum load if the bars are, (i) separate and can bend independently, (ii) firmly secured together throughout their length. The maximum permissible stresses in brass and steel are 70 MN/m² and 105 MN/m² respectively; $E_B = 85$ GN/m² and $E_S = 200$ GN/m². (*I.C.E.*)

(*Ans.:* 373·3 N; 825 N)

33. A timber beam, 240 mm deep by 100 mm wide, has a steel plate 10 mm thick and 100 mm wide bolted firmly to its lower edge. The beam is freely supported on a span of 4 m and is loaded uniformly. Find the load it will carry when the maximum compressive stress in the timber is 8·5 MN/m² and calculate the maximum stress in the steel under this load. The ratio of the elastic moduli of steel and timber is 18. (*U. Lond.*)   (*Ans.:* 6·77 kN/m; 67·5 MN/m²)

34. A timber beam 200 mm wide by 300 mm deep is reinforced with two rectangular steel plates each 250 mm deep by 10 mm thick. The steel plates are bolted on each side of the beam with the bottom edges of the plates flush with the underside of the beam. Determine the position of the neutral axis and find the moment of resistance of the composite beam when the limits of bending stresses in the steel and timber are 85 and 5·5 MN/m² respectively. Modular ratio = 20. (*U. Lond.*)   (*Ans.:* 134·4 mm from bottom of beam; 31·4 kN m)

35. A tie-bar of rectangular cross-section is required to take a tensile load of 250 kN. The depth of the section is to be three times the width and the maximum allowable tensile stress is 100 MN/m². If the allowable offset of the pull (from the centroid of the section) is $\frac{1}{15}$ of the width, measured in the horizontal plane at the middle of the depth, find the dimensions of the cross-section. Find also the minimum tensile stress. (*U. Lond.*)

(*Ans.:* 102·6 mm × 34·2 mm; 42·85 MN/m²)

36. A tie-bar 75 mm wide and 25 mm thick sustains an axial load of 100 kN. What depth of metal may safely be removed from one of the narrow sides in order that the maximum stress over the reduced width may not exceed 100 MN/m²? (*U. Lond.*)   (*Ans.:* 12·05 mm)

37. A short vertical column consists of a channel section 150 mm wide by 100 mm deep and of uniform thickness 25 mm. A bracket attached to the 150 mm face of the column carries a vertical load whose line of action is offset 75 mm from the face and on the centre-line of the section. Find the maximum value of this load if the tensile stress induced in the section is not to exceed 30 MN/m² and find the corresponding compressive stress. (*U. Lond.*)

(*Ans.:* 32·45 kN; 24·9 MN/m²)

38. A short hollow pier, 1·2 m square outside and 0·75 m square inside, supports a vertical point load of 120 kN located on a diagonal and 0·69 m from the vertical axis of the pier. Neglecting the self-weight of the pier, calculate the normal stresses at the four outside corners on a horizontal section of the pier. (*U. Lond.*)

(*Ans.:* 616·8 kN/m² (comp); 136·8 kN/m² (comp); 343·2 kN/m² (tensile))

39. The dimensions of a T-section are: flange 130 mm, overall depth 80 mm, thickness throughout 10 mm. The T is used as a tension member with the line of pull parallel to its length, 45 mm from the base and on the centre line of the leg. Calculate the maximum tension if the stress is limited to 100 MN/m². (*U. Lond.*)

(*Ans.:* 77·8 kN)

40. A bar of T section, 80 mm × 80 mm × 10 mm, is subjected to a tensile load, the axis of which passes through the middle of the depth of the section. Find the value of this load if the stress in the material is limited to 100 MN/m². Show by means of a diagram the variation of stress across the section. (*U. Lond.*)

(*Ans.:* 59 kN)

41. A short cast-iron column is of hollow section of uniform thickness, the external diameter being 200 mm and the internal diameter 125 mm. A vertical compressive load acts at an eccentricity of 50 mm from the axis of the column. If the maximum permitted stresses are 80 MN/m² in compression and 16 MN/m² in tension, calculate the greatest allowable load.

Assuming this load acting, plot a diagram of normal stress across the section of the column. (*U. Lond.*)   (*Ans.:* 627·5 kN)

42. A short hollow column of circular section, 200 mm outside diameter and 25 mm thick, carries an axial loading of 400 kN together with a parallel offset load W at an eccentricity of 125 mm. Calculate the maximum value of W if there is to be no tensile stress in the column.

Under these conditions, what is the maximum compressive stress? (*U. Lond.*)

(*Ans.:* 181·8 kN; 84·6 MN/m²)

43. A short hollow C.I. column of square section 200 mm × 200 mm externally and 150 mm × 150 mm internally sustains a compressive load of 1·4 MN, whose line of action passes through the centre of the external section. If the inner section is symmetrical about one centre of the outer section but is displaced to one side owing to the movement of the core during casting, find the maximum permissible amount of such a displacement if the maximum stress is not to exceed 100 MN/m². (*U. Lond.*)   (*Ans.:* 8·68 mm)

44. A brick chimney weighs 2·9 MN and the section at the base is a regular octagon, 3 m across the flats, the thickness of the brickwork being 0·675 m.

Calculate the moment of resistance of the base section if, with the resultant wind load acting normal to a plane face, there is no resultant tension across the section. (*U. Lond.*)   (*Ans.:* 1·495 MN m)

45. A 30 m high brick chimney is 2·3 m outside diameter at the top and tapers uniformly to 3·3 m outside diameter at the bottom. The chimney weighs 2·2 MN and is 0·675 m thick at the base. If a uniform horizontal wind pressure of 1 kN/m² acts on the projected area of the chimney, determine the maximum and minimum normal stresses on the base. (*U. Lond.*)   (*Ans.:* 778 kN/m²; 12 kN/m²)

46. A rectangular steel beam 60 mm deep by 30 mm wide is supported on knife-edges 2 m apart and loaded with two equal point loads at one-third of the span from each end. Find the load at which yielding just begins, the yield point of the material in simple tension being 300 MN/m².

If the loads are increased to 25 per cent above this value, estimate how far the yielding penetrates towards the neutral axis, assuming that the maximum stress remains constant and that the yield point in compression is the same as that in tension. (*U. Lond.*)   (*Ans.:* 8·10 kN; 8·89 mm)

47. A rectangular steel beam AB, 20 mm wide by 10 mm deep, is placed symmetrically on two knife-edges C and D, 0·5 m apart, and loaded by applying equal weights at the ends A and B. The steel follows a linear stress/strain law ($E = 200$ GN/m²) up to a yield stress of 300 MN/m²; at this constant stress considerable plastic deformation occurs. It may be assumed that the properties of the steel are the same in tension and compression.

Calculate the bending moment on the central part of the beam CD when yielding commences and the deflection at the centre relative to the supports. If the loads are increased until yielding penetrates half-way to the neutral axis, calculate the new value of the bending moment and the corresponding deflection. (*U. Lond.*)

(*Ans.:* 100 N m; 9·375 mm; 137·5 N m; 18·75 mm)

48. Two plates of mild steel, each of cross-section 40 mm by 3 mm, and one plate of alloy steel 40 mm by 6 mm are placed side by side and fastened rigidly together to form a symmetrical composite sandwich bar 40 mm by 12 mm. The mild steel has a definite yield point at 240 MN/m² in both tension and compression; the alloy steel is elastic up to 800 MN/m² and E is the same for both steels. The bar is tested as a beam of span 0·6 m with the 40 mm dimension as the depth, a concentrated load being applied at the centre of the span.

Find the central load at which the mild steel will just commence to yield and also the load at which the maximum bending stress in the alloy steel will reach 480 MN/m². It may be assumed that the mild steel follows a linear stress/strain law up to the yield point, at which considerable yielding occurs. (*U. Lond.*)

(*Ans.:* 5·12 kN; 8·63 kN)

49. A steel bar of T-section as shown in Fig. 3.39 is used as a simply supported beam on a span of 2 m to carry a point load at mid-span. A load of 9 kN is just sufficient to cause yielding to commence at the bottom of the vertical leg of the section at mid-span. Estimate the load which would be required to cause yielding to commence at the top of the section. State any assumptions made in deriving the answer.

Before yielding occurs, $h = 19·74$ mm and $I_{XX} = 1·003 \times 10^{-6}$ m⁴. (*U. Lond.*)

(*Ans.:* 14·9 kN)

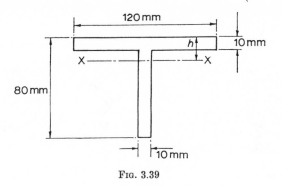

FIG. 3.39

CHAPTER 4

TORSION

4.1 Stress due to twisting. If a shaft is subjected to a pure torque, i.e. not accompanied by bending or axial thrust, every cross-section is in a state of pure shear. The shearing stress induced in the shaft produces a moment of resistance, equal and opposite to the applied torque.

In the theory of twisting, which relates the shear stress and angle of twist to the applied torque, it is assumed that:

1. The material is homogeneous, elastic and obeys Hooke's Law, i.e. the shear stress at any point is proportional to the shear strain at that point.
2. Stresses do not exceed the limit of proportionality.
3. Radial lines remain radial after twisting.
4. Plane cross-sections remain plane after twisting.*

From the third assumption, it follows that the strain (and hence the stress) is directly proportional to the radius. Thus, if the shear stress at the surface of the shaft is τ, then the stress on an element da at a distance x from the axis, Fig. 4.1

$$= \frac{x}{r}\tau$$

$\therefore$ shear force on element $= \dfrac{x}{r}\tau\, da$

$\therefore$ moment of force about $O = \dfrac{x}{r}\tau\, da\, x$

$\therefore$ total moment of resistance $= \dfrac{\tau}{r}\displaystyle\int x^2\, da$

$$= \frac{\tau}{r}J$$

Fɪɢ. 4.1

This is equal to the applied torque, T,

i.e. $\qquad T = \dfrac{\tau}{r}J \qquad\qquad$ or $\qquad\qquad \dfrac{T}{J} = \dfrac{\tau}{r}$ . . (4.1)

This formula gives the shear stress at the surface in terms of T and J but the stress at any other radius can be readily obtained since it is proportional to the radius at that point.

* For non-circular shafts, the assumption that plane sections remain plane after twisting is not justified and this theory ceases to apply.

4.2   Modulus of section. The maximum shear stress in a shaft is given
by

$$\tau = \frac{T}{J}r = \frac{T}{J/r}$$

The quantity $\dfrac{J}{r}$ is called the *modulus of section* and is denoted by Z.

Thus $\qquad\qquad\qquad\qquad \tau = \dfrac{T}{Z}$ . . . . (4.2)

For a solid shaft, $\qquad Z = \dfrac{\pi d^4/32}{d/2} = \dfrac{\pi}{16}d^3$ . . . . (4.3)

For a hollow shaft $\qquad Z = \dfrac{\pi(D^4 - d^4)/32}{D/2}$

where D and d are the outer and inner diameters respectively

$$= \frac{\pi}{16}\left(\frac{D^4 - d^4}{D}\right) \qquad . \qquad . \qquad . \qquad . \quad (4.4)$$

It should be noted that Z for a hollow shaft is *NOT* $\dfrac{\pi}{16}(D^3 - d^3)$.

4.3   Angle of twist. Due to the shear strain in the shaft, the longitudinal
line AB, Fig. 4.2, will move to the position AC, the end A being considered

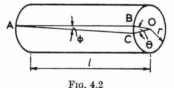

FIG. 4.2

fixed. The angle BAC is the shear strain, ϕ (see Art. 1.3), and the angle
BOC is the angle of twist, θ.

$$BC = l\phi = r\theta$$

$$\therefore \phi = \frac{r}{l}\theta = \frac{\tau}{G}$$

$$\therefore \frac{\tau}{r} = \frac{G\theta}{l} \quad . \qquad . \qquad . \qquad . \qquad . \quad (4.5)$$

Combining this with equation (4.1) gives the general twisting formula

$$\frac{T}{J} = \frac{\tau}{r} = \frac{G\theta^*}{l} \qquad . \qquad . \qquad . \qquad (4.6)$$

4.4 Strain energy. If a torque T is gradually applied to a shaft and produces an angle of twist θ, then the work done, or strain energy, is the average torque multiplied by the angle through which it acts,

i.e. $\qquad\qquad\qquad U = \tfrac{1}{2}T\theta$

But $\qquad\qquad\qquad T = \frac{\tau}{r}J \quad \text{and} \quad \theta = \frac{\tau l}{Gr}$

$$\therefore U = \frac{1}{2}\left(\frac{\tau}{r}J\right)\left(\frac{\tau l}{Gr}\right) = \frac{\tau^2}{2G} \cdot \frac{Jl}{r^2}$$

For a solid shaft, $\quad J = \frac{\pi}{32}d^4 \quad \text{and} \quad r = \frac{d}{2}$

$$\therefore U = \frac{\tau^2}{2G} \cdot \frac{\pi d^4 l/32}{d^2/4}$$

$$= \frac{\tau^2}{2G} \cdot \frac{\pi}{8}d^2 l = \frac{\tau^2}{4G} \times \text{volume} \quad . \qquad . \qquad . \quad (4.7)$$

For a hollow shaft, $\quad J = \frac{\pi}{32}(D^4 - d^4) \quad \text{and} \quad r = \frac{D}{2}$

$$\therefore U = \frac{\tau^2}{2G} \cdot \frac{\pi(D^4 - d^4)l/32}{D^2/4}$$

$$= \frac{\tau^2}{2G} \cdot \frac{\pi}{8} \frac{(D^2 - d^2)(D^2 + d^2)}{D^2}l$$

$$= \frac{\tau^2}{4G} \times \text{volume} \times \left(1 + \frac{d^2}{D^2}\right) \qquad . \qquad . \quad (4.8)$$

As $d \to 0$, $U \to \frac{\tau^2}{4G} \times$ volume, as in equation (4.7).

As $d \to D$, $U \to \frac{\tau^2}{2G} \times$ volume, as in equation (1.21), the shear stress becoming uniform as the tube thickness decreases.

---

* Comparing this equation with $\frac{M}{I} = \frac{\sigma}{y} = \frac{E}{R}$, equation (3.8), it may be considered that the two formulae are not completely analogous owing to the discrepancy in the last term. However, in the corresponding case of a beam subjected to a uniform bending moment the beam bends in the arc of a circle, Fig. 4.3, and if the change of slope between the ends is ϕ,

then $\qquad\qquad l = R\phi \quad \text{or} \quad \frac{1}{R} = \frac{\phi}{l}$

Thus, in this case $\qquad \frac{M}{I} = \frac{\sigma}{y} = \frac{E\phi}{l}$

Fig. 4.3

Equations (4.7) and (4.8) give the *mean* strain energy per unit volume of the shaft in terms of the *maximum* stress. The actual strain energy per unit volume at a particular point is $\dfrac{\tau^2}{2G}$ where τ is the shear stress at that point.

4.5   Composite shafts. A composite shaft is one which consists of two or more materials rigidly fixed together so that they share the applied torque.

If T_1 and T_2 are the parts of the applied torque T carried by the two materials, Fig. 4.4, then

$$T_1 + T_2 = T \qquad . \qquad . \qquad . \qquad (4.9)$$

Also the angle of twist of the two parts is the same,

i.e. $\qquad\qquad\qquad\qquad \theta_1 = \theta_2$

i.e. $\qquad\qquad\qquad\qquad \dfrac{T_1}{G_1 J_1} = \dfrac{T_2}{G_2 J_2}$

or $\qquad\qquad\qquad \dfrac{T_1}{T_2} = \dfrac{G_1 J_1}{G_2 J_2} \quad . \quad . \quad . \quad (4.10)$

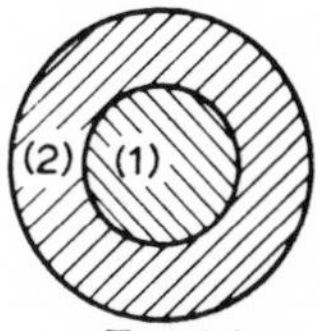

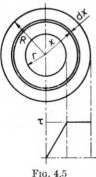

FIG. 4.4

T_1 and T_2 can be determined from equations (4.9) and (4.10) and the stresses in the two materials are then given by

$$\tau_1 = \frac{T_1}{Z_1} \quad \text{and} \quad \tau_2 = \frac{T_2}{Z_2}$$

4.6   Twisting beyond the limit of proportionality. When a torque is applied to a shaft sufficient to cause yielding in the material, the relation between the shear stress and the angle of twist is assumed to be similar to that between the direct stress and angle of bending for an overstrained beam (Art. 3.13). Thus the stress is proportional to the radius up to the limit of proportionality, after which it remains constant over the remainder of the shaft section.

Consider a shaft section of radius R, Fig. 4.5, which is subjected to a torque sufficient to cause yielding to a radius r; let the stress at the limit of proportionality be τ.

Then, for the elastic part,

$$T = \tau Z = \tau \times \frac{\pi}{2} r^3$$

For the plastic part, the torque on an elementary ring, of radius x and thickness $\mathrm{d}x$ is

$$\tau \times 2\pi\, x\, \mathrm{d}x \times x$$

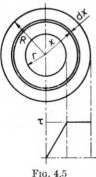

FIG. 4.5

$$\therefore \text{ total torque on plastic part} = \int_r^R \tau \times 2\pi x^2 \, dx$$

$$= \tau \times \tfrac{2}{3}\pi(R^3 - r^3) \quad . \quad (4.11)$$

The total torque carried by the shaft is then the sum of the torques carried by the elastic and plastic parts.

1. *A shaft 50 mm in diameter and 0·75 m long has a concentric hole drilled for a portion of its length. Find the maximum length and diameter of the hole so that when the shaft is subjected to a torque of 1·67 kN m, the maximum shearing stress will not exceed 75 MN/m² and the total angle of twist will not be greater than* $1\tfrac{1}{2}°$. $G = 80 \ GN/m^2$. (U. Lond.)

$$T = \tau Z = \tau \times \frac{\pi}{16}\left(\frac{D^4 - d^4}{D}\right) \quad . \quad \begin{array}{l}\text{from equations (4.2)}\\ \text{and (4.4)}\end{array}$$

$$\therefore 1·67 \times 10^3 = 75 \times 10^6 \times \frac{\pi}{16}\left(\frac{0·05^4 - d^4}{0·05}\right)$$

from which $\qquad d = 0·027\ 7$ m $\quad$ or $\quad$ <u>27·7 mm</u>

Let l be the length of the hole.

Then $\qquad \dfrac{T}{J} = \dfrac{G\theta}{l}$ . . . . . from equation (4.6)

$$\therefore \theta = \frac{Tl}{GJ}$$

i.e. $\qquad 1\tfrac{1}{2} \times \dfrac{\pi}{180} = \dfrac{1·67 \times 10^3}{80 \times 10^9}\left\{\dfrac{0·75 - l}{\dfrac{\pi}{32} \times 0·05^4} + \dfrac{l}{\dfrac{\pi}{32}(0·05^4 - 0·027\ 7^4)}\right\}$

from which $\qquad l = $ <u>0·19 m</u>

2. *A hollow marine propeller shaft turning at 110 rev/min is required to propel a vessel at 47 km/h for the expenditure of 6·4 MW, the efficiency of the propeller being 68 per cent. The diameter ratio of the shaft is to be* $\tfrac{2}{3}$ *and the direct stress due to the thrust is not to exceed 8 MN/m².*

Calculate: (a) the shaft diameters, (b) the maximum shearing stress due to the torque. (U. Lond.)

$$\text{Output power} = \frac{47 \times 10^3}{3\ 600} \times P \text{ W}$$

where P is the propulsive force in N

$$\therefore \frac{47 \times 10^3}{3\ 600} P = 0·68 \times 6·4 \times 10^6$$

$$\therefore P = 334 \text{ kN}$$

$$\therefore 334 \times 10^3 = \frac{\pi}{4}(D^2 - d^2) \times 8 \times 10^6,$$

where D and d are the outside and inside diameters respectively

$$= \frac{\pi}{4} \times \frac{5}{9} D^2 \times 8 \times 10^6 \quad \text{since } d = \tfrac{2}{3} D$$

$$\therefore D = \underline{0\cdot309\ 3\ \text{m}} \quad \text{and} \quad d = \underline{0\cdot206\ 2\ \text{m}}$$

$$T = \frac{6\cdot4 \times 10^6 \times 60}{2\pi \times 110} = 556\ 000\ \text{N m}$$

$$\therefore 556\ 000 = \tau Z = \tau \times \frac{\pi}{16}\left(\frac{D^4 - d^4}{D}\right)$$

$$= \tau \times \frac{\pi}{16} \times 0\cdot309\ 3^3(1 - [\tfrac{2}{3}]^4)$$

$$\therefore \tau = \underline{119\ \text{MN/m}^2}$$

3. *A hollow steel shaft of* 400 *mm external diameter transmits* 9 *MW at* 120 *rev/min. If the angle of twist measured over a length of* 2 *m is* 0·45° *and* G *is* 80 *GN/m*^{2}*, estimate the internal diameter of the shaft, the maximum shearing stress and the strain energy per metre length of shaft.*

Find the diameter of the solid shaft which will transmit the same power at the same maximum stress and find the ratio of the strain energy per metre length in this shaft to that in the hollow shaft. (U. Lond.)

$$T = \frac{9 \times 10^6 \times 60}{2\pi \times 120} = 717\ 500\ \text{N m}$$

$$\frac{T}{J} = \frac{G\theta}{l}$$

i.e. $$\frac{717\ 500}{\dfrac{\pi}{32}(0\cdot4^4 - d^4)} = \frac{80 \times 10^9 \times 0\cdot45 \times \dfrac{\pi}{180}}{2}$$

from which $$d = \underline{0\cdot22\ \text{m}}$$

$$T = \tau Z$$

i.e. $$717\ 500 = \tau \times \frac{\pi}{16}\left(\frac{0\cdot40^4 - 0\cdot22^4}{0\cdot40}\right) = \tau \times \frac{\pi}{16} \times 0\cdot058\ 1$$

$$\therefore \tau = \underline{62\cdot9\ \text{MN/m}^2}$$

Strain energy per metre length

$$= \tfrac{1}{2}T\theta$$

$$= \tfrac{1}{2} \times 717\ 500 \times \frac{0\cdot45}{2} \times \frac{\pi}{180} = \underline{1\ 410\ \text{J}}$$

For the solid shaft to transmit the same power (i.e. the same torque) at the same maximum stress, it must have the same modulus of section,

i.e. $$d = \sqrt[3]{0 \cdot 058\ 1} = 0 \cdot 387\ 3 \text{ m}$$

$$\text{Twist per metre length} = \frac{717\ 500}{80 \times 10^9 \times \dfrac{\pi}{32} \times 0 \cdot 387\ 3^4} = 0 \cdot 004\ 515 \text{ rad}$$

$$\therefore \text{ ratio of strain energies} = \frac{0 \cdot 004\ 515}{\dfrac{0 \cdot 45}{2} \times \dfrac{\pi}{180}} = \underline{1 \cdot 15}$$

4. *A shaft tapers uniformly from a radius* $(r + a)$ *at one end to a radius* $(r - a)$ *at the other end. If the shaft is under an axial torque T and* $a = 0 \cdot 1r$, *determine the percentage error in the angle of twist for a given length when the twist is calculated on the assumption of a constant radius* r. (U. Lond.)

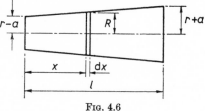

FIG. 4.6

Let the length of the shaft be l and let the radius at a distance x from the small end be R, Fig. 4.6.

Then
$$R = (r - a) + \frac{x}{l} \times 2a$$

$$= r\left(0 \cdot 9 + \frac{0 \cdot 2x}{l}\right) \quad \text{since } a = 0 \cdot 1r$$

Angle of twist of an element of length dx

$$= \frac{T\,dx}{GJ} = \frac{T\,dx}{G \times \dfrac{\pi}{2}\,r^4 \left(0 \cdot 9 + \dfrac{0 \cdot 2x}{l}\right)^4}$$

$\therefore$ total angle of twist of shaft

$$= \frac{2Tl^4}{G\pi r^4}\int_0 \frac{dx}{(0 \cdot 9l + 0 \cdot 2x)^4}$$

$$= \frac{10Tl^4}{G\pi r^4}\left[\frac{-1}{3(0 \cdot 9l + 0 \cdot 2x)^3}\right]_0^l = 2 \cdot 068\,\frac{Tl}{G\pi r^4}$$

For a uniform shaft of radius r,

$$\theta = \frac{Tl}{G \times \dfrac{\pi}{2}\,r^4} = 2\frac{Tl}{G\pi r^4}$$

$$\therefore \text{ error} = \frac{2 \cdot 068 - 2}{2 \cdot 068} \times 100 = \underline{3 \cdot 30 \text{ per cent}}$$

5. *A horizontal shaft, securely fixed at each end, has a free length of* 10 *m. Viewed from one end of the shaft, axial couples of* 30 *kN m clockwise and* 40 *kN m counterclockwise act on the shaft at distances of* 4 *and* 7 *m respectively from the viewed end. Determine the end fixing couples in magnitude and direction and find the diameter of the solid shaft for a maximum shearing stress of* 60 *MN/m².*

Draw a diagram to show how a line, originally parallel to the axis and on the outer surface of the shaft, will appear after the application of the couples and find the position along the shaft where the shaft suffers no angular twist.

(U. Lond.)

The arrangement is shown in Fig. 4.7. Let the fixing torque at A be T, assumed clockwise.

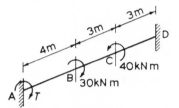

Fig. 4.7

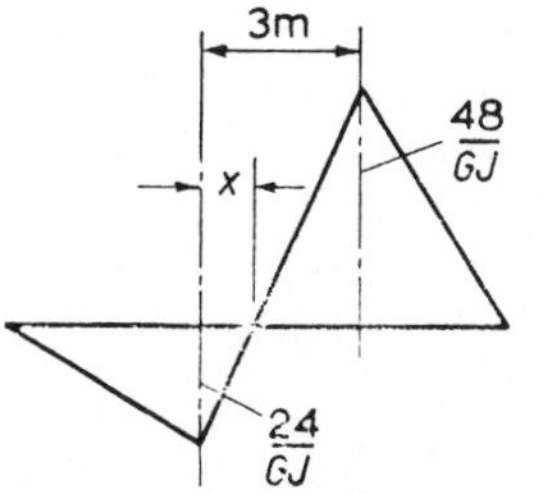

Fig. 4.8

Then   torque on AB $= T$ kN m
                torque on BC $= T + 30$ kN m
and   torque on CD $= T + 30 - 40$ kN m $= T - 10$ kN m

$$\theta_{ab} = \frac{T \times 4}{GJ}, \quad \theta_{bc} = \frac{(T + 30) \times 3}{GJ} \quad \text{and} \quad \theta_{cd} = \frac{(T - 10) \times 3}{GJ}$$

Since there is no relative twist between A and D,

$$4T + 3(T + 30) + 3(T - 10) = 0$$

$$\therefore T = -6 \text{ kN m (i.e. anticlockwise)}$$

Torque on CD $= -6 - 10 = -16$ kN m, anticlockwise looking from A. Hence the fixing torque at D is clockwise, of magnitude 16 kN m.

The maximum torque occurs in BC and is $-6 + 30 = 24$ kN m.

$$T = \tau Z$$

i.e. $$24 \times 10^3 = 60 \times 10^6 \times \frac{\pi}{16} d^3$$

$$\therefore d = \underline{0 \cdot 127 \text{ m}}$$

Twist at B $= \dfrac{6 \times 4}{GJ} = \dfrac{24}{GJ}$ and   twist at C $= \dfrac{16 \times 3}{GJ} = \dfrac{48}{GJ}$

Fig. 4.8 shows the variation in twist along the length of the shaft. From similar triangles,

$$\frac{x}{24} = \frac{3 - x}{48} \qquad \therefore x = \underline{1 \text{ m}}$$

6. *A bronze liner of 60 mm outside diameter is fitted over and firmly attached to a steel shaft of 40 mm diameter. The working shearing stresses are 60 and 38 MN/m² for the steel and bronze respectively. Calculate the power which can be transmitted by the compound shaft at 500 rev/min. $G_{steel} = 80\ GN/m²$; $G_{bronze} = 44\ GN/m²$.* (U. Lond.)

From equation (4.10),

$$\frac{T_s}{T_b} = \frac{G_s J_s}{G_b J_b}$$

$$= \frac{80}{44} \times \frac{0\cdot04^4}{0\cdot06^4 - 0\cdot04^4} = 0\cdot447\ 5\ . \qquad . \qquad . \quad (1)$$

$$T_s = \tau_s Z_s = \tau_s \times \frac{\pi}{16} \times 0\cdot04^3\ . \qquad . \qquad . \quad (2)$$

$$T_b = \tau_b Z_b = \tau_b \times \frac{\pi}{16} \times \frac{0\cdot06^4 - 0\cdot04^4}{0\cdot06} \qquad . \qquad . \quad (3)$$

$$\therefore \frac{T_s}{T_b} = \frac{\tau_s}{\tau_b} \times \frac{24}{65} = 0\cdot447\ 5 \qquad . \qquad \text{from equation (1)}$$

$$\therefore \frac{\tau_s}{\tau_b} = 1\cdot212$$

It is therefore evident that the bronze will reach its limiting stress of 38 MN/m² before the steel reaches its limiting stress of 60 MN/m².

The maximum stress in the bronze is therefore 38 MN/m² and the maximum stress in the steel is $38 \times 1\cdot212 = 46\cdot1$ MN/m².

Therefore $\qquad\qquad\qquad T_s = 580$ N m $\qquad\qquad$ from equation (2)

and $\qquad\qquad\qquad\quad T_b = 1\ 293$ N m $\qquad\qquad$ from equation (3)

$$\therefore T = 1\ 873 \text{ N m}$$

$$\therefore \text{power} = 1\ 873 \times 2\pi \times \frac{500}{60} \text{ W}$$

$$= \underline{98 \text{ kW}}$$

7. *A shaft having a diameter of 90 mm is turned down to 87 mm diameter for part of its length. If a torque is applied to the shaft of sufficient magnitude just to produce yielding at the surface of the shaft in the unturned part, determine the depth of yielding which would occur in the turned part. Find also the ratio of the angle of twist per unit length in the turned part to that in the unturned part of the shaft. State any assumptions made.* (U. Lond.)

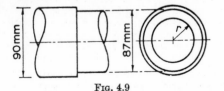

FIG. 4.9

Let τ be the maximum stress in the elastic part of the shaft and the uniform stress in the plastic part.

Then torque applied to 90 mm diameter shaft $= \tau Z = \tau \times \dfrac{\pi}{16} \times 90^3$

For the 87 mm diameter shaft, let r be the outer radius of the elastic part, Fig. 4.9.

Then torque carried by elastic part

$$= \tau Z = \tau \times \frac{\pi}{2} r^3$$

and torque carried by plastic part

$$= \tau \times \tfrac{2}{3}\pi(R^3 - r^3) \qquad \text{from equation (4.11)}$$
$$= \tau \times \tfrac{2}{3}\pi(43.5^3 - r^3)$$

Equating torques on the two parts of the shaft,

$$\tau \times \frac{\pi}{16} \times 90^3 = \tau \times \frac{\pi}{2} r^3 + \tau \times \tfrac{2}{3}\pi(43.5^3 - r^3)$$

from which $\qquad\qquad r = 38.2$ mm

i.e. $\qquad$ depth of yield $= 43.5 - 38.2 = \underline{5.3 \text{ mm}}$

For the elastic parts of the shaft, $\qquad \dfrac{\tau}{r} = \dfrac{G\theta}{l}$

$$\therefore \theta \propto \frac{1}{r}$$

$$\therefore \frac{\text{twist per unit length in turned part}}{\text{twist per unit length in unturned part}} = \frac{4.5}{3.82} = \underline{1.18}$$

8. A hollow shaft is 50 mm outside diameter and 30 mm internal diameter. An applied torque of 1·6 kN m is found to produce an angular twist of 0·4°, measured on a length of 0·2 m of the shaft. Calculate the value of the modulus of rigidity. Calculate also the maximum power which could be transmitted by the shaft at 2 000 rev/min if the maximum allowable shearing stress is 65 MN/m². (*U. Lond.*)
(*Ans.:* 86 GN/m²; 292 kW)

9. A hollow shaft of diameter ratio 3 : 5 is required to transmit 600 kW at 110 rev/min, the maximum torque being 12 per cent greater than the mean. The shearing stress is not to exceed 60 MN/m² and the twist in a length of 3 m is not to exceed 1°. Calculate the minimum external diameter of the shaft satisfying these conditions. $G = 80$ GN/m². (*U. Lond.*) (*Ans.:* 195·5 mm)

10. A hollow shaft is to have an internal diameter of 0·6 × the external diameter and is required to transmit 1 500 kW at a speed of 2 500 rev/min. It is to be fitted with a flanged coupling having 8 bolts on a circle of diameter twice that of the shaft. Assuming allowable shearing stresses in shaft and bolts of 70 MN/m² and 55 MN/m² respectively, determine the necessary diameters. (*U. Lond.*) (*Ans.:* 78·2 mm; 46·9 mm; 14·54 mm)

11. A flange coupling is required for a shaft transmitting 220 kW at 240 rev/min. The bolts are 16 mm diameter and are to be arranged on a circle of 250 mm diameter; the working shearing stress in the bolts must not exceed 60 MN/m². Determine the number of bolts required and the actual stress realised.

Briefly describe and explain how the power transmitted by the shaft may be measured. (*U. Lond.*) (*Ans.:* 6; 59·4 MN/m²)

12. A hollow shaft, subjected to a pure torque, attains a maximum shearing stress τ. Given that the strain energy stored per unit volume is $\tau^2/3G$, calculate the ratio of the shaft diameters.

Determine the actual diameters for such a shaft required to transmit 3 700 kW at 110 rev/min with uniform torque when the energy stored is 20 kJ/m³ of material. $G = 80$ GN/m². (*U. Lond.*) (*Ans.:* $\sqrt{3}$: 1; 298·2 mm; 172 mm)

13. A hollow shaft having the external diameter twice the internal diameter, subjected to a pure torque, attains a maximum shear stress τ. Show that the strain energy stored per unit volume of the shaft is $5\tau^2/16G$.

Such a shaft is required to transmit 4 500 kW at 110 rev/min with uniform torque, the maximum stress not exceeding 70 MN/m². Calculate the shaft diameters and the energy stored per m³ when transmitting this power. $G = 83$ GN/m². (*U. Lond.*) (*Ans.:* 312 mm; 156 mm; 18·44 kJ/m³)

14. A steel shaft ABCD has a total length of 1·3 m, made up as follows: AB = 0·3 m, BC = 0·4 m and CD = 0·6 m. AB is hollow, its outside diameter being 100 mm and its inside diameter d mm. BC and CD are solid, having diameters of 100 mm and 88 mm respectively. If equal opposite torques are applied to the ends of the shaft, find, to the nearest 1 mm, the maximum permissible value of d for the maximum shearing stress in AB not to exceed that in CD. If the torque applied to the shaft is 9 kN m, what is the total angle of twist? $G = 82$ GN/m². (*U. Lond.*) (*Ans.:* 75 mm; 1·148°)

15. A steel shaft ABCD having a total length of 1·5 m is made of three lengths AB, BC and CD, each 0·5 m long. AB and BC are solid, having diameters of 60 mm and 70 mm respectively, and CD is hollow having outside and inside diameters of 70 mm and 45 mm respectively. When an axial torque of 2 kN m is transmitted from one end of the shaft to the other, the total angle of twist from A to D is 1·2°. Determine: (*a*) the maximum shearing stress in the shaft and state where it occurs, (*b*) the angle of twist for each of the three lengths AB, BC and CD, (*c*) the modulus of rigidity of the material. (*U. Lond.*)

(*Ans.:* 49·4 MN/m² in AB; 0·548°; 0·296°; 0·356°; 82·2 GN/m²)

16. A shaft runs at 300 rev/min and transmits power from a pulley A at one end to two pulleys, B and C, which each drive a machine in a workshop. The distance between pulleys A and B is 3 m and that between B and C is 2·4 m (i.e. the total length of the shaft is 5·4 m). The shaft has a diameter of 50 mm between A and B and a diameter of 40 mm between B and C. If the maximum permissible shear stress in the shaft is 80 MN/m², calculate the maximum power which may be supplied from each of the pulleys B and C, assuming that both machines would be in operation at the same time. Also calculate the total angle of twist of one end of the shaft relative to the other when running on full load. $G = 80$ GN/m². (*U. Lond.*) (*Ans.:* 30·1 kW; 31·6 kW; 13·75°)

17. A cylindrical steel shaft, 450 mm long and 50 mm external diameter, has one end rigidly fixed and the other end free. A central hole, 150 mm long and 25 mm diameter, is drilled axially into the free end of the shaft. An axial twisting moment of 2·5 kN m is applied to the free end and another of 1·25 kN m in the same direction to a point 100 mm from the end. Find the maximum shearing stress in the shaft and the total angle of twist in radians. $G = 75$ GN/m². (*U. Lond.*) (*Ans.:* 163 MN/m²; 1·985°)

18. Part of a steel tube 24 mm external diameter and 6 mm thick is enlarged to an external diameter of 36 mm. Find the diameter of the bore of the enlarged section so that when the tube is twisted the maximum shearing stresses in both sections of the tube are equal. If the total length of tube is 1 m, find the length of each section when the total angle of twist is 4° and the maximum shearing stress is 75 MN/m². $G = 80$ GN/m². ($U. Lond.$)

(*Ans.:* 33·2 mm; 0·688 m; 0·312 m)

19. A solid cylindrical shaft, 50 mm diameter and 1·5 m long, is passed through the centre of a hollow cylindrical shaft of the same material, 1·5 m long, 55 mm and 75 mm inner and outer diameters. The ends of the two shafts are rigidly joined, with the shafts concentric. The composite shaft so formed is used to transmit 375 kW at a speed of 600 rev/min. Find the maximum and minimum stress in the two shafts. ($U. Lond.$)

(*Ans.:* 79·3 MN/m²; 58·1 MN/m²; 52·9 MN/m²)

20. A solid alloy shaft of 50 mm diameter is to be coupled in series with a hollow steel shaft of the same external diameter. Find the internal diameter of the steel shaft if the angle of twist per unit length is to be 75 per cent of that of the alloy shaft.

Determine the speed at which the shafts are to be driven to transmit 200 kW if the limits of shearing stress are to be 55 and 80 MN/m² in the alloy and steel respectively. $G_{steel} = 2·2 \times G_{alloy}$. ($U. Lond.$)

(*Ans.:* 39·6 mm; 1605 rev/min)

21. A hollow steel shaft 0·6 m long is firmly connected to a hollow duralumin shaft which is 0·9 m long and a torque is transmitted from one extreme end to the other. The outside and inside diameters of the shafts are: steel, 65 mm and 40 mm; duralumin, d mm and 65 mm. Find the outside diameter of the duralumin shaft if the maximum shearing stress in the shafts are: steel, 90 MN/m²; duralumin, 60 MN/m². If the connection is made by fitting the steel shaft into the duralumin shaft for a length of 150 mm and securely joining the shafts over this length, find the total angle of twist in the overall length of 1·35 m. $G_{steel} = 78$ GN/m², $G_{duralumin} = 26$ GN/m². ($U. Lond.$) (*Ans.:* 71·1 mm; 3·9°)

22. A composite shaft consists of a steel rod 80 mm diameter surrounded by a closely fitting tube of brass firmly fixed to it. Find the outside diameter of the tube so that when a torque is applied to the composite shaft, it will be equally shared by the two materials. If the torque is 16 kN m, calculate the maximum shearing stress in each material and the angle of twist on a length of 3·5 m. $G_{steel} = 80$ GN/m²; $G_{brass} = 40$ GN/m², ($U. Lond.$)

(*Ans.:* 105·3 mm; 79·6 MN/m²; 52·3 MN/m²)

23. A round steel rod is surrounded by a close-fitting tube of duralumin, the two being secured fastened together to form a composite shaft. Find the diameter of the steel rod and the outside diameter of the duralumin tube so that the maximum shearing stresses in the two materials do not exceed 90 and 60 MN/m² respectively when the composite shaft is subjected to a torque of 0·7 kN m. Also calculate the angle of twist on a length of 1·2 m. $G_{duralumin} = 26$ GN/m²; $G_{steel} = 78$ GN/m². ($U. Lond.$) (*Ans.:* 18·76 mm; 37·52 mm; 8·46°)

24. A steel bar 19 mm diameter is encased in a closely fitting brass tube of 32 mm external diameter, securely fixed together at the ends. The compound bar is subjected to a torque of 520 N m and the angle of twist measured on a gauge length of 250 mm is found to be 1·8°. If G for the steel is assumed to be 80 GN/m², calculate G for the brass.

Find also the maximum shearing stresses in the two materials and the proportions of the total strain energy taken up by each part. (*U. Lond.*)

(*Ans.:* 34·6 GN/m²; 95·5 MN/m²; 69·5 MN/m²; 0·248 : 0·752)

25. A steel shaft 90 mm diameter is solid for a certain distance from one end but hollow for the remainder of its length with an inside diameter of 38 mm. If a pure torque is transmitted from one end of the shaft to the other of such a magnitude that yielding just occurs at the surface of the solid part of the shaft, find the depth of yielding in the hollow part of the shaft and the ratio of the angles of twist per unit length for the two parts of the shaft.

State any assumptions made in arriving at the results. (*U. Lond.*)

(*Ans.:* 1·5 mm; 1·034 5 : 1)

26. A hollow shaft 50 mm outside diameter and 25 mm bore is made of steel with a yield stress in shear of 150 MN/m² and a modulus of rigidity of 83 GN/m². Calculate the torque and the angle of twist when the material first yields, if the shaft has a length of 2 m.

On the assumption that the yield stress, after initial yield, then remains constant for a considerable increase of strain, calculate the depth of penetration of plastic yield for an increase of torque of 10 per cent above that at initial yield. Determine also the angle of twist of the shaft at the increased torque. (*U. Lond.*)

(*Ans.:* 3·45 kN m; 8·29°; 2·83 mm; 9·35°)

27. A hollow steel shaft having outside and inside diameters of 32 mm and 18 mm respectively is subjected to a gradually increasing axial torque. The yield stress is reached at the surface when the torque is 1 kN m, the angle of twist per m length then being 7·3°. Find the magnitude of the yield stress.

If the torque is increased to 1·1 kN m, calculate (*a*) the depth to which yielding will have penetrated, (*b*) the angle of twist per m length. State any assumptions made and prove any special formula used. (*U. Lond.*)

(*Ans.:* 172·7 MN/m²; 1·8 mm; 8·22°)

CHAPTER 5

DEFLECTION OF BEAMS

5.1 Integration method. From Art. 3.9

$$\frac{M}{I} = \frac{E}{R}$$

If x and y are the horizontal and vertical co-ordinates of a point on the beam,

$$\frac{1}{R} = \frac{\dfrac{d^2y}{dx^2}}{\left\{1 + \left(\dfrac{dy}{dx}\right)^2\right\}^{3/2}} \qquad \text{where } R \text{ is the radius of curvature.}$$

In any practical case of bending of beams, the slope $\dfrac{dy}{dx}$ is very small and so $\left(\dfrac{dy}{dx}\right)^2$ is negligible in comparison with 1.

Thus
$$\frac{1}{R} \simeq \frac{d^2y}{dx^2}$$

so that
$$\frac{M}{I} = E\frac{d^2y}{dx^2}$$

or
$$EI\frac{d^2y}{dx^2} = M \quad . \qquad . \qquad . \qquad . \qquad . \quad (5.1)$$

If the bending moment M can be expressed as a function of x, successive integration will give expressions for $EI\dfrac{dy}{dx}$ and EIy. The constants of integration may be determined from the end-fixing conditions.

If the cross-section of the beam is varying, so that I is a function of x, then equation (5.1) must be expressed in the form $E\dfrac{d^2y}{dx^2} = \dfrac{M}{I}$, the function $\dfrac{M}{I}$ then being integrated.

Since $F = \dfrac{dM}{dx}$ and $w = \dfrac{dF}{dx}$, from Art. 2.3, it follows that

$$EI\frac{d^3y}{dx^3} = F \qquad . \qquad . \qquad . \qquad . \quad (5.2)$$

and
$$EI\frac{d^4y}{dx^4} = w \qquad . \qquad . \qquad . \qquad . \quad (5.3)$$

In cases of distributed loads which vary in a mathematical manner, it may be difficult to obtain an expression for M in terms of x. In such cases, it may be simpler to start from equation (5.3) and integrate four times to obtain the deflection equation (see Ex. 7).

Beam deflections are inversely proportional to EI, which is termed the *flexural rigidity* of the beam.

5.2   Standard cases of beam deflections.

Case (a)—cantilever with concentrated end load, Fig. 5.1.

Taking the origin at the fixed end,

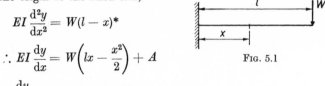

$$EI \frac{\mathrm{d}^2y}{\mathrm{d}x^2} = W(l - x)^*$$

$$\therefore EI \frac{\mathrm{d}y}{\mathrm{d}x} = W\left(lx - \frac{x^2}{2}\right) + A$$

Fig. 5.1

When $x = 0$, $\frac{\mathrm{d}y}{\mathrm{d}x} = 0$, so that $A = 0$,

$$\therefore EIy = W\left(\frac{lx^2}{2} - \frac{x^3}{6}\right) + B$$

When $x = 0$, $y = 0$, so that $B = 0$.

The maximum slope and deflection occur at the free end, where $x = l$,

i.e. $$\left(\frac{\mathrm{d}y}{\mathrm{d}x}\right)_{\max} = \frac{Wl^2}{2EI} \quad . \qquad . \qquad . \qquad . \quad (5.4)$$

and $$y_{\max} = \frac{Wl^3}{3EI} \quad . \qquad . \qquad . \qquad . \quad (5.5)$$

Case (b)—cantilever with uniformly distributed load, Fig. 5.2.

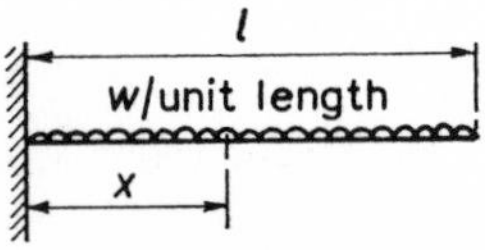

$$EI \frac{\mathrm{d}^2y}{\mathrm{d}x^2} = w(l - x) \times \frac{(l - x)}{2}$$

$$= \frac{w}{2}(l^2 - 2lx + x^2)$$

$$\therefore EI \frac{\mathrm{d}y}{\mathrm{d}x} = \frac{w}{2}\left(l^2x - lx^2 + \frac{x^3}{3}\right) + A$$

Fig. 5.2

When $x = 0$, $\frac{\mathrm{d}y}{\mathrm{d}x} = 0$, so that $A = 0$,

$$\therefore EIy = \frac{w}{2}\left(\frac{l^2x^2}{2} - \frac{lx^3}{3} + \frac{x^4}{12}\right) + B$$

When $x = 0$, $y = 0$, so that $B = 0$.

* Positive, to agree with the sign convention of Art. 2.1.

The maximum slope and deflection occur at the free end, where $x = l$,

i.e.
$$\left(\frac{dy}{dx}\right)_{max} = \frac{wl^3}{6EI} \qquad . \qquad . \qquad . \qquad . \qquad (5.6)$$

and
$$y_{max} = \frac{wl^4}{8EI} \qquad . \qquad . \qquad . \qquad (5.7)$$

Case (c)—cantilever with end couple, Fig. 5.3.

$$EI\frac{d^2y}{dx^2} = M$$

$$\therefore EI\frac{dy}{dx} = Mx + A$$

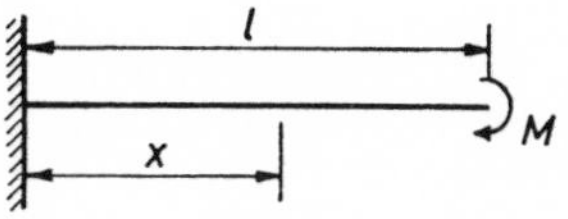

When $x = 0$, $\frac{dy}{dx} = 0$, so that $A = 0$,

Fig. 5.3

$$\therefore EIy = M\frac{x^2}{2} + B$$

When $x = 0$, $y = 0$, so that $B = 0$.

The maximum slope and deflection occur at the free end, where $x = l$,

i.e.
$$\left(\frac{dy}{dx}\right)_{max} = \frac{Ml}{EI} \qquad . \qquad . \qquad . \qquad . \qquad (5.8)$$

and
$$y_{max} = \frac{Ml^2}{2EI} \qquad . \qquad . \qquad . \qquad (5.9)$$

Case (d)—simply supported beam with central concentrated load, Fig. 5.4.

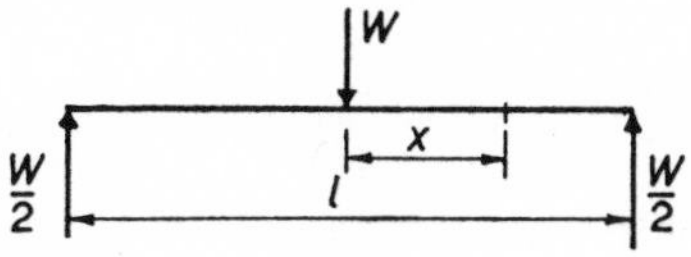

Fig. 5.4

Taking the origin at the centre,

$$EI\frac{d^2y}{dx^2} = -\frac{W}{2}\left(\frac{l}{2} - x\right)^*$$

$$\therefore EI\frac{dy}{dx} = -\frac{W}{2}\left(\frac{lx}{2} - \frac{x^2}{2}\right) + A$$

When $x = 0$, $\frac{dy}{dx} = 0$, so that $A = 0$,

$$\therefore EIy = -\frac{W}{2}\left(\frac{lx^2}{4} - \frac{x^3}{6}\right) + B$$

* The B.M. in this case is negative, since the beam is bending convex downwards.

When $x = \dfrac{l}{2}$, $y = 0$, so that $B = \dfrac{W}{2} \cdot \dfrac{l^3}{24}$,

$$\therefore EIy = -\frac{W}{2}\left(\frac{lx^2}{4} - \frac{x^3}{6} - \frac{l^3}{24}\right)$$

The maximum slope occurs at the ends, where $x = \dfrac{l}{2}$,

i.e.
$$\left(\frac{\mathrm{d}y}{\mathrm{d}x}\right)_{\max} = -\frac{Wl^2}{16EI} \qquad . \qquad . \qquad . \qquad (5.10)$$

The maximum deflection occurs at the centre, where $x = 0$,

i.e.
$$y_{\max} = \frac{Wl^3}{48EI} \qquad . \qquad . \qquad . \qquad (5.11)$$

Case (e)—simply supported beam with uniformly distributed load, Fig. 5.5.

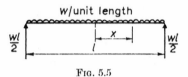

Fig. 5.5

$$EI\frac{\mathrm{d}^2 y}{\mathrm{d}x^2} = -\frac{wl}{2}\left(\frac{l}{2} - x\right) + w\left(\frac{l}{2} - x\right)\cdot\frac{\left(\frac{l}{2} - x\right)}{2}$$

$$= -\frac{w}{2}\left(\frac{l^2}{4} - x^2\right)$$

$$\therefore EI\frac{\mathrm{d}y}{\mathrm{d}x} = -\frac{w}{2}\left(\frac{l^2 x}{4} - \frac{x^3}{3}\right) + A$$

When $x = 0$, $\dfrac{\mathrm{d}y}{\mathrm{d}x} = 0$, so that $A = 0$,

$$\therefore EIy = -\frac{w}{2}\left(\frac{l^2 x^2}{8} - \frac{x^4}{12}\right) + B$$

When $x = \dfrac{l}{2}$, $y = 0$, so that $B = \dfrac{w}{2} \cdot \dfrac{5l^4}{192}$,

$$\therefore EIy = -\frac{w}{2}\left(\frac{l^2 x^2}{8} - \frac{x^4}{12} - \frac{5l^4}{192}\right)$$

The maximum slope occurs at the ends, where $x = \dfrac{l}{2}$,

i.e.
$$\left(\frac{\mathrm{d}y}{\mathrm{d}x}\right)_{\max} = -\frac{wl^3}{24EI} \qquad . \qquad . \qquad . \qquad (5.12)$$

The maximum deflection occurs at the centre, where $x = 0$,

i.e.
$$y_{\max} = \frac{5wl^4}{384EI}$$
. . . . (5.13)

NOTES. (1) With the sign convention adopted for bending moment, deflections are positive downwards and slopes are positive downwards moving away from the origin.

(2) The same results for slope and deflection may be obtained with other choices of origin for x but a fixed end or axis of symmetry usually provides the most convenient origin.

(3) Slope and deflection formulae for simply supported beams may be deduced from the cantilever formulae. Thus the central deflection for a simply supported beam of span l carrying a uniformly distributed load w per unit length is the same as the end deflection of a cantilever of length $l/2$ carrying a downward uniformly distributed load w per unit length and an upward concentrated load $wl/2$ at the free end, as shown in Fig. 5.6, i.e. central deflection for simply supported beam

$$= \frac{\frac{wl}{2}\left(\frac{l}{2}\right)^3}{3EI} - \frac{w\left(\frac{l}{2}\right)^4}{8EI} .$$
   from equations (5.5) and (5.7)

$$= \frac{5}{384} \frac{wl^4}{EI}$$

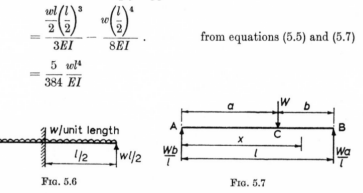

FIG. 5.6   FIG. 5.7

5.3 Single concentrated load not at centre—Macaulay's method.

Let the distances of the load W from the ends A and B be a and b respectively, Fig. 5.7. The reactions at A and B are then $\frac{Wb}{l}$ and $\frac{Wa}{l}$ respectively.

Consider first the part AC. Taking the origin at A,

$$EI \frac{d^2y}{dx^2} = -\frac{Wb}{l} x$$
. . . . . (5.14)

$$\therefore EI \frac{dy}{dx} = -\frac{Wb}{l} \frac{x^2}{2} + A_1$$
. . . . (5.15)

and
$$EIy = -\frac{Wb}{l} \frac{x^3}{6} + A_1 x + B_1 .$$
. . . (5.16)

When $x = 0$, $y = 0$, so that $B_1 = 0$.

The point at which the slope is zero is unknown and the condition that $y = 0$ when $x = l$ cannot be used since the equations do not apply beyond the point C. Thus the constant A_1 must remain unknown for the present.

Now consider the part CB, keeping the point A as origin.

$$EI\,\frac{d^2y}{dx^2} = -\frac{Wb}{l}\,x + W[x-a] \qquad . \qquad . \qquad . \qquad (5.17)$$

$$\therefore\ EI\,\frac{dy}{dx} = -\frac{Wb}{l}\,\frac{x^2}{2} + W\left[\frac{x^2}{2} - ax\right] + A_2\,. \qquad . \qquad (5.18)$$

and

$$EIy = -\frac{Wb}{l}\,\frac{x^3}{6} + W\left[\frac{x^3}{6} - a\,\frac{x^2}{2}\right] + A_2x + B_2 \qquad . \qquad (5.19)$$

When $x = l$, $y = 0$, so that $B_2 = \dfrac{Wal^2}{3} - A_2 l$.

For similar reasons to those given above, the constant A_2 cannot be determined at this stage.

Equating the slopes at C as given by equations (5.15) and (5.18) when $x = a$,

$$-\frac{Wb}{l}\,\frac{a^2}{2} + A_1 = -\frac{Wb}{l}\,\frac{a^2}{2} + W\left[\frac{a^2}{2} - a^2\right] + A_2$$

Equating the deflections at C as given by equations (5.16) and (5.19) when $x = a$,

$$-\frac{Wb}{l}\,\frac{a^3}{6} + A_1a = -\frac{Wb}{l}\,\frac{a^3}{6} + W\left[\frac{a^3}{6} - \frac{a^3}{2}\right] + A_2a + \left(\frac{Wal^2}{3} - A_2 l\right)$$

A_1 and A_2 may be determined from these equations and hence the slope and deflection obtained at any point, using equations (5.15) and (5.16) for $x < a$ and equations (5.18) and (5.19) for $x > a$.

For two concentrated loads, three sets of equations are required for the three ranges of the beam, leading to six constants of integration. Two of these are obtained from the conditions that $y = 0$ at $x = 0$ and $x = l$, and the remaining four are determined by equating slopes and deflections under the loads.

This method becomes cumbersome and it should be noted that the constants of integration are different in each range of the beam.

Referring to equation (5.17), this could just as legitimately be integrated as follows:

$$EI\,\frac{dy}{dx} = -\frac{Wb}{l}\,\frac{x^2}{2} + \frac{W}{2}[x-a]^2 + A_2' \qquad . \qquad . \qquad (5.20)$$

and

$$EIy = -\frac{Wb}{l}\,\frac{x^3}{6} + \frac{W}{6}[x-a]^3 + A_2'x + B_2'. \qquad . \qquad (5.21)$$

The constant A_2' will not be the same as A_2 previously obtained $\left(A_2 = A_2' + \dfrac{a^2}{2}\right)$ and B_2' will not be the same as B_2 $\left(B_2 = B_2' - \dfrac{a^3}{6}\right)$.

If the slopes at C are now equated, using equations (5.15) and (5.20) when $x = a$,

$$-\frac{Wb}{l}\frac{a^2}{2} + A_1 = -\frac{Wb}{l}\frac{a^2}{2} + \frac{W}{2}[a - a]^2 + A_2'$$

$$\therefore A_1 = A_2' \,(= A)$$

Similarly, equating deflections at C, using equations (5.16) and (5.21) when $x = a$,

$$-\frac{Wb}{l}\frac{a^3}{6} + Aa + B_1 = -\frac{Wb}{l}\frac{a^3}{6} + \frac{W}{6}[a - a]^3 + Aa + B_2'$$

$$\therefore B_1 = B_2' \,(= B)$$

Thus, by this method of integration, the constants of integration for each range of the beam are the same and there is the further advantage that equations (5.17), (5.20) and (5.21) are identical with equations (5.14), (5.15) and (5.16), except for the additional term involving $[x - a]$, which only comes in when $x > a$, i.e. when $[x - a]$ is positive. Thus equations (5.17), (5.20) and (5.21) may be regarded as applying to the whole beam provided that, for any value of x which makes $[x - a]$ negative, this term is ignored.

This method is known as *Macaulay's Method* and it is conventional to use square brackets for terms such as $[x - a]$ which have to be treated in this special manner.

Proceeding with this case, the deflection equation (5.21) simplifies to

$$EIy = -\frac{Wb}{l}\frac{x^3}{6} + \frac{W}{6}[x - a]^3 + Ax + B$$

When $x = 0$, $y = 0$, so that $B = 0$ since $[x - a]$ is negative for this value of x and the term involving this is therefore ignored.

When $x = l$, $y = 0$, so that $A = \dfrac{Wab}{6l}(l + b)$.

The deflection under the load is then given by

$$EIy = -\frac{Wb}{l}\frac{a^3}{6} + \frac{Wab}{6l}(l + b)a$$

$$\therefore y = \frac{Wa^2b^{2*}}{3EIl} \qquad . \qquad . \qquad . \qquad . \qquad . \qquad (5.22)$$

---

* When $a = b = l/2$, this reduces to $\dfrac{Wl^3}{48EI}$, as in equation (5.11).

D

The maximum deflection will occur between the load point and the centre of the beam. If $a > b$, this point will correspond to $x < a$, so that, from equation (5.20),

$$-\frac{Wb}{l}\frac{x^2}{2} + \frac{Wab}{6l}(l + b) = 0$$

Writing $a = l - b$, this reduces to $x = \sqrt{\left(\frac{l^2 - b^2}{3}\right)}$

Substituting in equation (5.21),

$$EIy_{max} = -\frac{Wb}{6l}\left(\frac{l^2 - b^2}{3}\right)^{3/2} + \frac{Wab}{6l}(l + b)\sqrt{\left(\frac{l^2 - b^2}{3}\right)}$$

or $\quad\quad y_{max} = \dfrac{Wb(l^2 - b^2)^{3/2}}{9\sqrt{3}EIl}$ . . . . (5.23)

As $b \to 0$, $x \to l/\sqrt{3}$, which is approximately $l/13$ from the centre of the beam. Thus the maximum deflection is very close to the centre of the beam, even for an extremely unsymmetrical load and for most normal cases of loads on beams simply supported at the ends, the maximum deflection is virtually identical with the central deflection.

5.4 Distributed loads. If the beam shown in Fig. 5.8 carries also a uniformly distributed load w per unit length over the whole span, then the bending moment equation becomes

$$EI\frac{d^2y}{dx^2} = -Rx + W[x - a] + w\frac{x^2}{2}$$

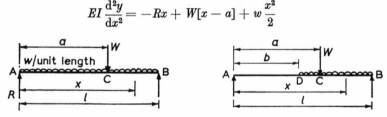

FIG. 5.8   FIG. 5.9

If the distributed load only covers the part DB, Fig. 5.9, then

$$EI\frac{d^2y}{dx^2} = -Rx + W[x - a] + \frac{w}{2}[x - b]^2$$

The last term must be treated in the same way as that for the concen- trated load, i.e. it must be integrated with respect to $[x - b]$ and must be ignored when negative.

If the distributed load does not con- tinue to the end of the beam remote from the origin, as shown in Fig. 5.10, it must be continued to the end and a compensating load added underneath.

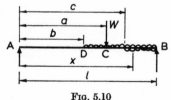

FIG. 5.10

The bending moment equation then becomes

$$EI \frac{\mathrm{d}^2y}{\mathrm{d}x^2} = -Rx + W[x - a] + \frac{w}{2}[x - b]^2 - \frac{w}{2}[x - c]^2$$

Only by this device can an expression be obtained which can apply to the whole beam under the usual Macaulay conditions. In general, any distributed load, when started, must continue to the end remote from the origin, so that the load system shown in Fig. 5.11(a) must be converted to that shown in Fig. 5.11(b) before Macaulay's Method can be applied.

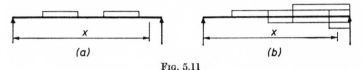

(a)   (b)

FIG. 5.11

5.5 Couple applied at a point. Taking the origin at A, Fig. 5.12, the B.M. at a point within AC is

$$-\frac{M}{l}x$$

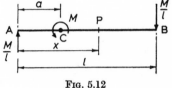

FIG. 5.12

and at a point within CB, it is

$$-\frac{M}{l}x + M,$$

the action of M being to bend the beam convex upwards if imagined held at the point P.

Thus the additional term, M, comes in only for $x > a$ and so, to correspond with the treatment necessary for loads, it must be integrated with respect to $[x - a]$. In order to proceed correctly, it is advisable to write the bending moment equation in the form

$$EI \frac{\mathrm{d}^2y}{\mathrm{d}x^2} = -\frac{M}{l}x + M[x - a]^0$$

5.6 Area-moment method. Let AB, Fig. 5.13(a), be part of a beam, which has been deflected to the position A'B' and let Fig. 5.13(b) represent the corresponding part of the B.M. diagram.

From equation (5.1),

$$EI \frac{\mathrm{d}^2y}{\mathrm{d}x^2} = M$$

∴ slope of beam at any point

$$\theta = \frac{\mathrm{d}y}{\mathrm{d}x} = \int \frac{M}{EI} \, \mathrm{d}x$$

$$= \frac{1}{EI} \int M \, \mathrm{d}x, \quad \text{if } E \text{ and } I \text{ are constants.}$$

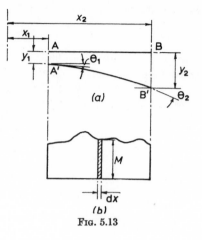

Fig. 5.13

If the slopes at A and B, distances x_1 and x_2 from an origin, are θ_1 and θ_2 respectively,

then $\theta_2 - \theta_1 = \dfrac{1}{EI} \displaystyle\int_{x_1}^{x_2} M\,\mathrm{d}x$ . . . . (5.24)

$\qquad\qquad\quad = \dfrac{1}{EI} \times$ area of B.M. diagram between points A and B.

If θ_1 is zero, then θ_2 is the actual slope of the beam at B.
Multiplying both sides of equation (5.1) by x,

$$x \frac{\mathrm{d}^2 y}{\mathrm{d}x^2} = \frac{M}{EI} x$$

Integrating by parts between the limits of x_1 and x_2,

$\left[x \dfrac{\mathrm{d}y}{\mathrm{d}x} - y \right]_{x_1}^{x_2} = \dfrac{1}{EI} \displaystyle\int_{x_1}^{x_2} Mx\,\mathrm{d}x$ . . . . . . (5.25)

$\qquad\qquad\qquad = \dfrac{1}{EI} \times$ moment of area of B.M. diagram about origin.

By a suitable choice of origin, $x \dfrac{\mathrm{d}y}{\mathrm{d}x}$ can usually be made zero at both limits and y can be made zero at one limit, leaving the value of y at the other limit to represent the required deflection.

The area–moment method is usually convenient to use only when a point of zero slope is known.

Case (a)—cantilever with concentrated end load, Fig. 5.14.

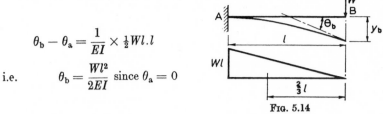

$$\theta_b - \theta_a = \frac{1}{EI} \times \tfrac{1}{2} Wl.l$$

i.e. $\qquad \theta_b = \frac{Wl^2}{2EI}$ since $\theta_a = 0$

Fig. 5.14

Taking the origin at B,

$$\left[x \frac{\mathrm{d}y}{\mathrm{d}x} - y \right]_0^l = \frac{1}{EI} \times \tfrac{1}{2} Wl.l \times \tfrac{2}{3}l$$

i.e. $\qquad (0 - 0) - (0 - y_b) = y_b = \frac{Wl^3}{3EI}$

Case (b)—cantilever with uniformly distributed load, Fig. 5.15.

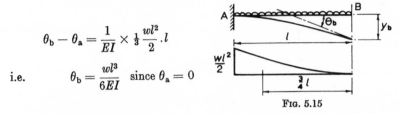

$$\theta_b - \theta_a = \frac{1}{EI} \times \tfrac{1}{3} \frac{wl^2}{2}.l$$

i.e. $\qquad \theta_b = \frac{wl^3}{6EI}$ since $\theta_a = 0$

Fig. 5.15

Taking the origin at B,

$$\left[x \frac{\mathrm{d}y}{\mathrm{d}x} - y \right]_0^l = \frac{1}{EI} \times \tfrac{1}{3} \frac{wl^2}{2}.l \times \tfrac{3}{4}l$$

i.e. $\qquad (0 - 0) - (0 - y_b) = y_b = \frac{wl^4}{8EI}$

Case (c)—cantilever with end couple, Fig. 5.16.

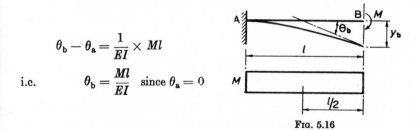

$$\theta_b - \theta_a = \frac{1}{EI} \times Ml$$

i.c. $\qquad \theta_b = \frac{Ml}{EI}$ since $\theta_a = 0$

Fig. 5.16

Taking the origin at B,

$$\left[x\frac{dy}{dx} - y\right]_0^l = \frac{1}{EI} \times Ml \times \frac{l}{2}$$

i.e. $(0 - 0) - (0 - y_b) = y_b = \dfrac{Ml^2}{2EI}$

Case (d)—simply supported beam with central concentrated load, Fig. 5.17.

$$\theta_b - \theta_c = -\frac{1}{EI} \times \frac{1}{2}\frac{Wl}{4}\cdot\frac{l}{2}^*$$

i.e. $\theta_b = -\dfrac{Wl^2}{16EI}$ since $\theta_c = 0$

Taking the origin at B and considering the part BC only,

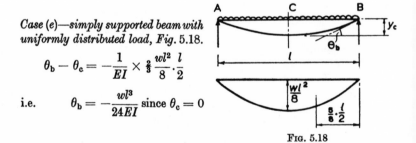

Fig. 5.17

$$\left[x\frac{dy}{dx} - y\right]_0^{l/2} = -\frac{1}{EI} \times \frac{1}{2}\frac{Wl}{4}\cdot\frac{l}{2} \times \frac{2}{3}\frac{l}{2}$$

i.e. $(0 - y_c) - (0 - 0) = -\dfrac{Wl^3}{48EI}$

i.e. $y_c = \dfrac{Wl^3}{48EI}$

Case (e)—simply supported beam with uniformly distributed load, Fig. 5.18.

$$\theta_b - \theta_c = -\frac{1}{EI} \times \frac{2}{3}\frac{wl^2}{8}\cdot\frac{l}{2}$$

i.e. $\theta_b = -\dfrac{wl^3}{24EI}$ since $\theta_c = 0$

Fig. 5.18

Taking the origin at B and considering the part BC only,

$$\left[x\frac{dy}{dx} - y\right]_0^{l/2} = -\frac{1}{EI} \times \frac{2}{3}\frac{wl^2}{8}\cdot\frac{l}{2} \times \frac{5}{8}\frac{l}{2}$$

i.e. $(0 - y_c) - (0 - 0) = -\dfrac{5}{384}\dfrac{wl^4}{EI}$

i.e. $y_c = \dfrac{5}{384}\dfrac{wl^4}{EI}$

* The area of the B.M. diagram is negative.

5.7   Maxwell's Reciprocal Rule. Let an elastic body be subjected to forces W_a and W_b at points A and B respectively, Fig. 5.19.

Let δ_{aa} be the deflection at A in the direction of W_a due to W_a*
,, δ_{ab} ,,   ,,   ,,   ,, A ,, ,,   ,,   ,, W_a ,, ,, W_b
,, δ_{bb} ,,   ,,   ,,   ,, B ,, ,,   ,,   ,, W_b ,, ,, W_b
,, δ_{ba} ,,   ,,   ,,   ,, B ,, ,,   ,,   ,, W_b ,, ,, W_a

Let W_a be applied first. Then work done $= \tfrac{1}{2}W_a\,\delta_{aa}$, assuming the load to be gradually applied.

If W_b is now applied, the additional work done $= \tfrac{1}{2}W_b\,\delta_{bb} + W_a\,\delta_{ab}$, the whole of W_a moving through the additional distance δ_{ab}.

Thus the total work done $= \tfrac{1}{2}W_a\,\delta_{aa} + \tfrac{1}{2}W_b\,\delta_{bb} + W_a\,\delta_{ab}$.

If the loads are removed and then re-applied in the reverse order (i.e. W_b is applied first), it will be seen, by analogy, that the total work done

$$= \tfrac{1}{2}W_a\,\delta_{aa} + \tfrac{1}{2}W_b\,\delta_{bb} + W_b\,\delta_{ba}.$$

Irrespective of the order in which the loads are applied, the body will assume the same strained position and hence the work done by the loads will be the same, so that

$$W_a\,\delta_{ab} = W_b\,\delta_{ba}$$

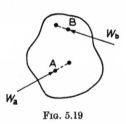

In the case where $W_a = W_b$, $\delta_{ab} = \delta_{ba}$, i.e. the deflection at A due to a load at B is the same as the deflection at B if the load is applied at A, the deflections being the movements of the points A and B in the directions shown in Fig. 5.19.

This simplified case is sometimes of use in beam deflection problems. For example, if a cantilever carries a concentrated load not at the free

FIG. 5.19

end, Fig. 5.20, the deflection at C due to the load at B is the same as the deflection at B if the load were moved to C. Similarly, the central deflection

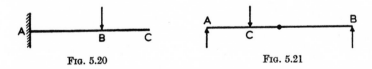

FIG. 5.20   FIG. 5.21

of a simply supported beam carrying an offset load, Fig. 5.21, is the same as the deflection at C if the load were moved to the centre, this being a standard case dealt with in Art. 5.2.

---

* The total deflections at A and B will also have components perpendicular to the lines of action of W_a and W_b respectively, but no work is done due to these movements.

5.8 Deflection due to impact. Let a mass M dropping through a height h produce a maximum instantaneous displacement y and let a load W gradually applied produce the same deflection y. Then the work done in the two cases is the same,

i.e. $$Mg(h + y) = \tfrac{1}{2}Wy$$

But $$y = kW$$

where k depends on the nature of the beam and the position of the load.

$$\therefore Mg(h + kW) = \tfrac{1}{2}kW^2 \ . \qquad . \qquad . \qquad . \ (5.26)$$

This is a quadratic from which W, the equivalent static load, can be obtained.

Then $$y = kW$$

1. *A horizontal cantilever of uniform section and of length L carries a point load W at a distance l from the fixed end. Derive expressions for the slope and deflection at the load and from these or otherwise obtain an expression for the deflection at the free end.*

A horizontal cantilever of uniform section has an effective length of 2·5 m and carries a load of 50 kN at the free end. If the 50-kN load is replaced by two equal loads, one at the free end and the other at 1·5 m from the fixed end, such that the maximum deflection is the same as in the first case, find: (a) the magnitude of the equal loads; (b) the maximum bending stress in the second case expressed as a percentage of that in the first case. (U. Lond.)

The deflected form of the beam is as shown in Fig. 5.22(*b*), the beam being straight between B and C.

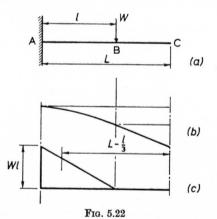

Fɪɢ. 5.22

Using the formulae derived in case (*a*), Art. 5.2,

$$\text{deflection at B} = \frac{Wl^3}{3EI} \quad \text{and} \quad \text{slope at B} = \frac{Wl^2}{2EI}$$

$$\therefore \text{ deflection at C} = \frac{Wl^3}{3EI} + \frac{Wl^2}{2EI}(L - l)$$

$$= \frac{Wl^2}{6EI}(3L - l)$$

Alternatively, using Maxwell's Reciprocal Rule, the deflection at C due to the load at B is the same as the deflection at B if the load were at C,

i.e. $$\text{deflection at C} = \frac{W}{EI}\left(\frac{Ll^2}{2} - \frac{l^3}{6}\right),$$

substituting l for x in the general deflection equation for a cantilever,

$$= \frac{Wl^2}{6EI}(3L - l)$$

Alternatively, using the area–moment method and taking the origin at C,

$$\left[x\frac{dy}{dx} - y\right]_0^L = \frac{1}{EI} \times \text{moment of area of B.M. diagram about C}$$

i.e. $$(0 - 0) - (0 - y_c) = \frac{1}{EI} \times \tfrac{1}{2}Wl.l \times \left(L - \frac{l}{3}\right)$$

i.e. $$y_c = \frac{Wl^2}{6EI}(3L - l)$$

Figs. 5.23(*a*) and (*b*) show the two cases.

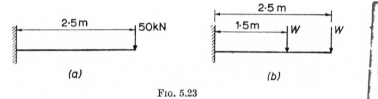

(a) (b)

Fig. 5.23

For equal end deflections,

$$\frac{50 \times 2 \cdot 5^3}{3EI} = \frac{W \times 2 \cdot 5^3}{3EI} + \frac{W \times 1 \cdot 5^2}{6EI}(3 \times 2 \cdot 5 - 1 \cdot 5)$$

from which $$W = \underline{34 \cdot 9 \text{ kN}}$$

In case (a), $$\sigma_{\max} = \frac{50 \times 2 \cdot 5}{Z} = \frac{125}{Z}$$

In case (b), $$\sigma_{\max} = \frac{34 \cdot 9 \times 2 \cdot 5 + 34 \cdot 9 \times 1 \cdot 5}{Z} = \frac{139 \cdot 6}{Z}$$

$$\therefore \frac{\text{maximum stress in case } (b)}{\text{maximum stress in case } (a)} = \frac{139 \cdot 7}{125} = 1 \cdot 117 \quad \text{or} \quad \underline{111 \cdot 7\%}$$

CRAIG LIBRARY

2. *A wooden flag-post 6 m high, is 50 mm square for the upper 3 m and 100 mm square for the lower 3 m. Find the deflection of the top due to a horizontal pull of 40 N at that point, applied in a direction parallel to one edge of the section. $E = 10 \ GN/m^2$.*

The total deflection at the top is made up of:
    (1) the deflection at B (y_1),
    (2) the slope at B, multiplied by the distance BC (y_2),
    (3) the further deflection due to bending of BC (y_3).
These deflections are shown in Fig. 5.24(c).

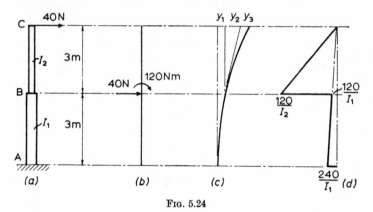

FIG. 5.24

In calculating y_1 and y_2 (but *not* y_3), it is convenient to move the load to the point B, introducing a moment of 40×3 N m to compensate for this movement. The equivalent system is as shown in Fig. 5.24(b). The slope and deflection at B due to the load and moment at this point can then be written down, using the formulae derived in case (a) and (c), Art. 5.2; y_3 represents the further deflection due to bending along BC due to the load at C.

Let the second moments of area of parts AB and BC be I_1 and I_2 respectively. Then

$$y = y_1 + y_2 + y_3$$
$$= \left\{ \frac{40 \times 3^3}{3EI_1} + \frac{120 \times 3^2}{2EI_1} \right\} + \left\{ \frac{40 \times 3^2}{2EI_1} + \frac{120 \times 3}{EI_1} \right\} \times 3 + \frac{40 \times 3^3}{3EI_2}$$
$$= \frac{360 \times 12}{10 \times 10^9} \left[\frac{7}{0 \cdot 10^4} + \frac{1}{0 \cdot 05^4} \right]$$
$$= \underline{0 \cdot 099 \ 36 \ m}$$

Alternatively, using the area–moment method and taking the origin at the top,

$$\left[x\frac{dy}{dx} - y\right]_0^6 = \frac{1}{E} \times \text{moment of area of } \frac{M}{I} \text{ diagram about top.}$$

The $\frac{M}{I}$ diagram is shown in Fig. 5.24(d).

Thus $(0 - 0) - (0 - y_c)$

$$= \frac{1}{E}\left[\frac{1}{2} \cdot \frac{120}{I_2} \cdot 3 \times \frac{2}{3} \cdot 3 + \frac{1}{2} \cdot \frac{240}{I_1} \cdot 6 \times \frac{2}{3} \cdot 6 - \frac{1}{2} \cdot \frac{120}{I_1} \cdot 3 \times \frac{2}{3} \cdot 3\right]$$

i.e. $y_c = \dfrac{360 \times 12}{10 \times 10^9}\left[\dfrac{1}{0{\cdot}05^4} + \dfrac{7}{0{\cdot}10^4}\right]$

$$= \underline{0{\cdot}099\ 36 \text{ m}}$$

3. *A horizontal cantilever 2 m long has its free end attached to a vertical tie-rod 3 m long and 300 mm² cross-sectional area, which is initially unstrained. If the second moment of area of the section of the cantilever is $6{\cdot}5 \times 10^{-6}$ m⁴, determine the load taken by the tie-rod and the deflection of the cantilever when a distributed load of 30 kN/m is placed on the outer 1 m of the cantilever. Assume E for both cantilever and tie-rod to be 200 GN/m²*

(U. Lond.)

In order to use the results obtained for standard cases, it is necessary to continue the load to the fixed end and compensate with a load underneath, as shown in Fig. 5.25.

Downward deflection at end due to load on top of beam

$$= \frac{30 \times 2^4}{8EI} = \frac{60}{EI}$$

Upward deflection at end due to load underneath beam

$$= \frac{30 \times 1^4}{8EI} + \frac{30 \times 1^3}{6EI} \times 1$$

$$= \frac{35}{4EI}$$

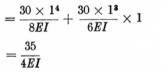

FIG. 5.25

If the tension in the tie-rod is T, then upward deflection at free end due to T

$$= \frac{T \times 2^3}{3EI} = \frac{8T}{3EI}$$

The resultant downward deflection at the free end is equal to the stretch of the tie-rod, $\dfrac{Tl}{aE}$.

Thus,
$$\frac{\left\{60 - \dfrac{35}{4} - \dfrac{8T}{3}\right\}}{E \times 6{\cdot}5 \times 10^{-6}} = \frac{T \times 3}{300 \times 10^{-6}E}$$

from which
$$T = \underline{18{\cdot}76 \text{ kN}}$$

Deflection at free end = stretch of tie-rod

$$= \frac{18{\cdot}76 \times 10^3 \times 3}{300 \times 10^{-6} \times 200 \times 10^9}$$

$$= 0{\cdot}000\ 938 \text{ m} \quad \text{or} \quad \underline{0{\cdot}938 \text{ mm}}$$

4. *Two beams AB and CD, as shown in Fig. 5.26, are of the same material and have the same cross-section. The support at B is at the same level as the fixed end A. Determine the reactions at B and D if the beam CD carries on its whole length a uniformly distributed load of 1 kN/m.* (U. Lond.)

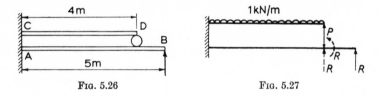

FIG. 5.26   FIG. 5.27

Let the reaction at B be R and the force in the spacer at D be P, Fig. 5.27. Then the downward deflection at B due to P must equal the upward deflection due to R, since the point B is level with A,

i.e.
$$\frac{P \times 4^3}{3EI} + \frac{P \times 4^2}{2EI} \times 1 = \frac{R \times 5^3}{3EI}$$

from which
$$P = \frac{125}{88} R \qquad . \qquad . \qquad . \qquad (1)$$

The deflection at D must be the same for the upper beam as it is for the lower beam, since the spacer is assumed rigid. For the deflection at D on the lower beam, it will be convenient to move the force R to D and introduce an anticlockwise moment $R \times 1$ to compensate,

i.e.
$$\frac{1 \times 4^4}{8EI} - \frac{P \times 4^3}{3EI} = \frac{(P - R) \times 4^3}{3EI} - \frac{R \times 4^2}{2EI}$$

from which
$$16P - 11R = 12 \qquad . \qquad . \qquad . \qquad . \qquad . \qquad (2)$$

Therefore, from equations (1) and (2),
$$P = \underline{1{\cdot}454 \text{ kN}} \quad \text{and} \quad R = \underline{1{\cdot}023 \text{ kN}}$$

5. *A vertical beam, 10 m long, is direction fixed at the lower end. The load is distributed, increasing uniformly from zero at 2 m from the top to 8 w/m at the fixed end. What horizontal force must be applied to the top if the beam must not deflect at this point?* (U. Lond.)

The load diagram is shown in Fig. 5.28. At a section distance x from the ground, the intensity of loading is $w(8 - x)/m$.

The B.M. at this section due to the distributed load is therefore

$$\tfrac{1}{2} \times w(8 - x) \times (8 - x) \times \frac{(8 - x)}{3}$$

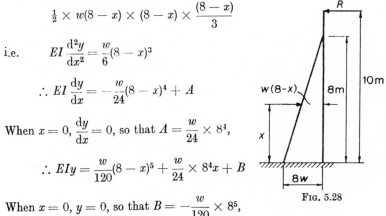

Fig. 5.28

i.e.
$$EI \frac{\mathrm{d}^2y}{\mathrm{d}x^2} = \frac{w}{6}(8 - x)^3$$

$$\therefore EI \frac{\mathrm{d}y}{\mathrm{d}x} = -\frac{w}{24}(8 - x)^4 + A$$

When $x = 0$, $\frac{\mathrm{d}y}{\mathrm{d}x} = 0$, so that $A = \frac{w}{24} \times 8^4$,

$$\therefore EIy = \frac{w}{120}(8 - x)^5 + \frac{w}{24} \times 8^4 x + B$$

When $x = 0$, $y = 0$, so that $B = -\frac{w}{120} \times 8^5$,

At $x = 8$ m,
$$\frac{\mathrm{d}y}{\mathrm{d}x} = \frac{w}{24EI} \times 8^4$$

and
$$y = \frac{1}{EI} \left\{ \frac{w}{24} \times 8^5 - \frac{w}{120} \times 8^5 \right\}$$

$$= \frac{w}{30EI} \times 8^5$$

Therefore, at the top,

$$y = \frac{w}{30EI} \times 8^5 + \frac{w}{24EI} \times 8^4 \times 2 = 1\,433 \cdot 6 \, \frac{w}{EI}$$

Equating this to the deflection produced by the horizontal force R,

$$1\,433 \cdot 6 \, \frac{w}{EI} = \frac{R \times 10^3}{3EI}$$

$$\therefore R = \underline{4 \cdot 3w}$$

6. *A cantilever of circular section tapers uniformly from a diameter D at the free end to 2D at the fixed end. It carries a single concentrated load at the free end. Calculate the diameter of a cantilever of uniform diameter which would have the same end deflection. Prove any formula used for calculating the deflection of the tapered cantilever.* (U. Lond.)

The simplest expression for the second moment of area of a typical section will be obtained by taking the point O as the origin for x, Fig. 5.29.

Then diameter of section $= \dfrac{x}{l} D$

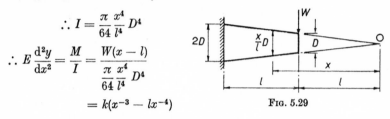

$$\therefore I = \frac{\pi}{64}\frac{x^4}{l^4}D^4$$

$$\therefore E\frac{d^2y}{dx^2} = \frac{M}{I} = \frac{W(x-l)}{\dfrac{\pi}{64}\dfrac{x^4}{l^4}D^4}$$

$$= k(x^{-3} - lx^{-4})$$

FIG. 5.29

where $\qquad k = \dfrac{64Wl^4}{\pi D^4}$

$$\therefore E\frac{dy}{dx} = k\left(-\frac{x^{-2}}{2} + \frac{lx^{-3}}{3}\right) + A$$

When $x = 2l$, $\dfrac{dy}{dx} = 0$, so that $A = \dfrac{k}{12l^2}$,

$$\therefore Ey = k\left(\frac{x^{-1}}{2} - \frac{lx^{-2}}{6} + \frac{x}{12l^2}\right) + B$$

When $x = 2l$, $y = 0$, so that $B = -\dfrac{3k}{8l}$.

When $x = l$, $\qquad y = \dfrac{k}{E}\left(\dfrac{1}{2l} - \dfrac{l}{6l^2} + \dfrac{l}{12l^2} - \dfrac{3}{8l}\right) = \dfrac{64Wl^3}{24E\pi D^4}$

Deflection at free end of cantilever of uniform diameter d

$$= \frac{Wl^3}{3E\dfrac{\pi}{64}d^4}$$

$$\therefore \frac{64Wl^3}{24E\pi D^4} = \frac{64Wl^3}{3E\pi d^4}$$

$$\therefore d = D \times \sqrt[4]{8} = \underline{1{\cdot}682D}$$

7. *The overhung crankpin of a locomotive can be considered as a cantilever of length l, and the distributed load applied to the pin by the hydrodynamic lubricating film can be assumed to be of the form k(lx − x²) per unit length; x is the distance from the built-in end and k is a constant.*

Find the expression for the deflection at the free end of the pin.

(I.Mech.E.)

The load diagram is shown in Fig. 5.30.

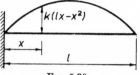

$$EI \frac{d^4y}{dx^4} = k(lx - x^2)$$

$$\therefore EI \frac{d^3y}{dx^3} = k\left(\frac{lx^2}{2} - \frac{x^3}{3}\right) + A$$

FIG. 5.30

When $x = l$, S.F. $= 0$, so that $A = -\frac{kl^3}{6}$,

$$\therefore EI \frac{d^2y}{dx^2} = k\left(\frac{lx^3}{6} - \frac{x^4}{12} - \frac{l^3x}{6}\right) + B$$

When $x = l$, B.M. $= 0$, so that $B = \frac{kl^4}{12}$,

$$\therefore EI \frac{dy}{dx} = k\left(\frac{lx^4}{24} - \frac{x^5}{60} - \frac{l^3x^2}{12} + \frac{l^4x}{12}\right) + C$$

When $x = 0$, $\frac{dy}{dx} = 0$, so that $C = 0$,

$$\therefore EIy = k\left(\frac{lx^5}{120} - \frac{x^6}{360} - \frac{l^3x^3}{36} + \frac{l^4x^2}{24}\right) + D$$

When $x = 0$, $y = 0$, so that $D = 0$.

Therefore deflection at free end $= \frac{k}{EI}\left(\frac{l^6}{120} - \frac{l^6}{360} - \frac{l^6}{36} + \frac{l^6}{24}\right) = \frac{7kl^6}{360EI}$

8. *A uniform beam AB, 8 m long, rests symmetrically on supports C and D, 4 m apart. A load of 40 kN is applied at each of the ends A and B. Neglecting the weight of the beam itself, calculate the deflection relative to the level of the supports (a) at the ends A and B, (b) at the centre of the span CD. EI = 10 MN m².*

(U. Lond.)

If the beam is imagined to be cut in half and built-in at the centre, Fig. 5.31(b), deflection of B relative to E

$$= \left[\frac{40 \times 4^3}{3EI} - \left\{\frac{40 \times 2^3}{3EI} + \frac{40 \times 2^2}{2EI} \times 2\right\}\right] \times 10^3$$

$$= \frac{586 \cdot 7 \times 10^3}{EI} \text{ m}$$

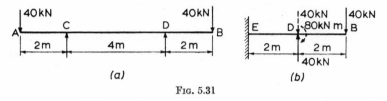

(a)   (b)

Fig. 5.31

To find the deflection of D relative to E, it is convenient to move the load from B to D, introducing a clockwise couple of $40 \times 2 = 80$ kN m to compensate. The upward and downward loads of 40 kN at D then balance each other, so that the deflection at D

$$= \frac{80 \times 10^3 \times 2^2}{2EI}$$

$$= \frac{160 \times 10^3}{EI} \text{ m}$$

Therefore, in the actual beam, deflection at centre relative to D

$$= \frac{160 \times 10^3}{10 \times 10^6} = 0.016 \text{ m}$$

Deflection of B relative to $D = \dfrac{(586.7 - 160) \times 10^3}{10 \times 10^6} = 0.042\ 67$ m

Note. The B.M. between C and D is uniform at 80 kN m. Since $\dfrac{M}{I} = \dfrac{E}{R}$, then if M, E and I are constants, R is a constant, i.e. the beam bends in the arc of a circle. Hence, from the product of intersecting chords, Fig. 5.32, the central deflection is given by

$$y(2R - y) = 2 \times 2$$

i.e. $2Ry = 4$, neglecting the term y^2 in comparison with $2Ry$

or $$y = \frac{2}{R}$$

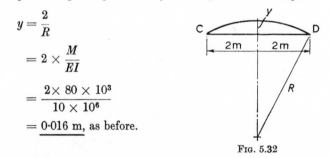

$$= 2 \times \frac{M}{EI}$$

$$= \frac{2 \times 80 \times 10^3}{10 \times 10^6}$$

$$= 0.016 \text{ m, as before.}$$

Fig. 5.32

9. *A horizontal beam which is uniformly loaded is supported at each end and at the centre. The length of the beam is 8 m, the distributed load is 12 kN/m, and the second moment of area of the cross-section of the beam is 10^{-4} m⁴. If* *the central support sinks 7 mm, determine the maximum bending moment in the beam. $E = 200 \ GN/m^2$.* (I.Mech.E.)

The downward deflection at the centre due to the uniformly distributed load exceeds the upward deflection due to the force P in the centre support by 7 mm, Fig. 5.33,

i.e. $\dfrac{5}{384} \times \dfrac{12 \times 10^3 \times 8^4}{200 \times 10^9 \times 10^{-4}} - \dfrac{P \times 8^3}{48 \times 200 \times 10^9 \times 10^{-4}} = 0 \cdot 007$

from which $P = 46 \cdot 88 \ \text{kN}$

$$R = \dfrac{12 \times 8 - 46 \cdot 88}{2} = 24 \cdot 56 \ \text{kN}$$

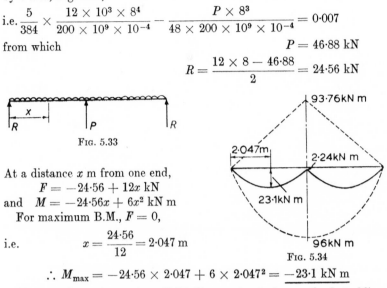

Fig. 5.33

Fig. 5.34

At a distance x m from one end,
$$F = -24 \cdot 56 + 12x \ \text{kN}$$
and $M = -24 \cdot 56x + 6x^2 \ \text{kN m}$
For maximum B.M., $F = 0$,

i.e. $x = \dfrac{24 \cdot 56}{12} = 2 \cdot 047 \ \text{m}$

$\therefore M_{\max} = -24 \cdot 56 \times 2 \cdot 047 + 6 \times 2 \cdot 047^2 = \underline{-23 \cdot 1 \ \text{kN m}}$

Fig. 5.34 shows the resultant B.M. diagram for the beam, the dotted lines representing the B.M. diagrams due to the distributed load and prop force separately.

10. *A horizontal beam, simply supported at the ends, carries a load which varies uniformly from 15 kN/m at one end to 60 kN/m at the other. Estimate the central deflection if the span is 6 m, the section 0·45 m deep and the maximum bending stress 100 MN/m². $E = 200 \ GN/m^2$.* (U. Lond.)

Dividing the load system up into a rectangle and a triangle, the loads represented by these areas are 90 and 135 kN respectively, acting at the centroids of the areas, Fig. 5.35.

$R_1 = \dfrac{90}{2} + \dfrac{135}{3}$
$= 90 \ \text{kN}$

$R_2 = \dfrac{90}{2} + \dfrac{2 \times 135}{3}$
$= 135 \ \text{kN}$

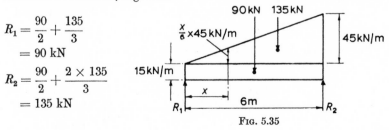

Fig. 5.35

At a section x m from R_1,

$$EI \frac{\mathrm{d}^2y}{\mathrm{d}x^2} = -90x + 15x \times \frac{x}{2} + \frac{\frac{x}{6} \times 45 \times x}{2} \times \frac{x}{3}$$

$$= -90x + 7 \cdot 5x^2 + 1 \cdot 25x^3$$

$$\therefore EI \frac{\mathrm{d}y}{\mathrm{d}x} = -45x^2 + 2 \cdot 5x^3 + 0 \cdot 312\,5x^4 + A$$

$$\therefore EIy = -15x^3 + 0 \cdot 625x^4 + 0 \cdot 062\,5x^5 + Ax + B$$

When $x = 0$, $y = 0$, so that $B = 0$.
When $x = 6$ m, $y = 0$, so that $A = 324$.
At $x = 3$ m,

$$EIy = -15 \times 3^3 + 0 \cdot 625 \times 3^4 + 0 \cdot 062\,5 \times 3^5 + 324 \times 3 = 632 \cdot 8 \text{ kN m}^3$$

For maximum B.M.,

$$EI \frac{\mathrm{d}^3y}{\mathrm{d}x^3} = 0$$

i.e. $$-90 + 15x + 3 \cdot 75x^2 = 0$$

from which $$x = 3 \cdot 293 \text{ m}$$

$$\therefore M_{\max} = -90 \times 3 \cdot 293 + 7 \cdot 5 \times 3 \cdot 293^2 + 1 \cdot 25 \times 3 \cdot 293^3$$

$$= 170 \cdot 5 \text{ kN m}$$

$$Z = \frac{M}{\sigma} = \frac{170 \cdot 5 \times 10^3}{100 \times 10^6} = 1 \cdot 705 \times 10^{-3} \text{ m}^3$$

$$\therefore I = 1 \cdot 705 \times 10^{-3} \times \frac{0 \cdot 45}{2} = 0 \cdot 384 \times 10^{-3} \text{ m}^4$$

$$\therefore \text{ central deflection} = \frac{632 \cdot 8 \times 10^3}{200 \times 10^9 \times 0 \cdot 384 \times 10^{-3}} = 0 \cdot 008\,24 \text{ m}$$
$$\text{or } \underline{8 \cdot 24 \text{ mm}}$$

NOTE. Since only the central deflection is required, this will be the same as if the load were uniform at 37·5 kN/m but the above analysis gives the deflection at any point in the beam.

11. *A horizontal beam, of uniform section and 6 m long, is simply supported at its ends. Two vertical concentrated loads of 48 kN and 40 kN act 1 m and 3 m respectively from the left hand support. Determine the position and magnitude of the maximum deflection, if $E = 200$ GN/m² and $I = 85 \times 10^{-6}$ m⁴.*
(I.C.E.)

Taking moments about R_2,
    Fig. 5.36,

$$48 \times 5 + 40 \times 3 = 6R_1$$
$$\therefore R_1 = 60 \text{ kN}$$

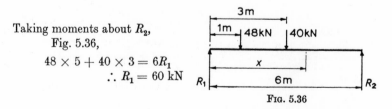

FIG. 5.36

Taking the origin at the L.H. end and using Macaulay's method,

$$EI \frac{\mathrm{d}^2 y}{\mathrm{d}x^2} = -60x + 48[x-1] + 40[x-3]$$

$$\therefore EI \frac{\mathrm{d}y}{\mathrm{d}x} = -30x^2 + 24[x-1]^2 + 20[x-3]^2 + A$$

$$\therefore EIy = -10x^3 + 8[x-1]^3 + \frac{20}{3}[x-3]^3 + Ax + B$$

When $x = 0$, $y = 0$, therefore $B = 0$ since all negative terms in square brackets are to be ignored.

When $x = 6$ m, $y = 0$, so that $A = 163 \cdot 4$.

For maximum deflection, $\frac{\mathrm{d}y}{\mathrm{d}x} = 0$

i.e. $-30x^2 + 24[x-1]^2 + 163 \cdot 4 = 0$*

from which $x = 2 \cdot 87$ m

$$\therefore EIy_{max} = -10 \times 2 \cdot 87^3 + 8 \times 1 \cdot 87^3 + 163 \cdot 4 \times 2 \cdot 87$$
$$= 284 \cdot 8 \text{ kN m}^3$$

$$\therefore y_{max} = \frac{284 \cdot 8 \times 10^3}{200 \times 10^9 \times 85 \times 10^{-6}} = 0 \cdot 016 \ 75 \text{ m}$$
$$\text{or } \underline{16 \cdot 75 \text{ mm}}$$

12. *The beam shown in Fig. 5.37 is of uniform flexural rigidity, EI. Calculate the deflection at the centre of span AB, in terms of W, L and EI.* (I.C.E.)

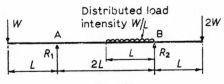

FIG. 5.37

Taking moments about R_2,

$$W \times 3L + \frac{WL}{2} = R_1 \times 2L + 2W \times L$$

$$\therefore R_1 = \frac{3}{4} W \quad \text{and} \quad R_2 = \frac{13}{4} W$$

* It is assumed that the solution for x is between 1 m and 3 m, so that the term $[x-3]$ will be negative and hence is ignored. If it is assumed that the maximum deflection occurs either to the left of the 48 kN load or to the right of the 40 kN load and the terms in square brackets are ignored or included, as appropriate, the solution for x will not lie within the assumed range, thus indicating that a false assumption has been made.

From Art. 5.3, it will be evident that the maximum deflection will occur very close to the centre of the beam.

Taking the origin at the L.H. end and using Macaulay's method, it is necessary to extend the distributed load to the R.H. end and add a compensating load underneath, as shown in Fig. 5.38.

Then

$$EI\frac{\mathrm{d}^2y}{\mathrm{d}x^2} = -\frac{3}{4}W[x-L]-\frac{13}{4}W[x-3L]+Wx+\frac{W}{2L}[x-2L]^2-\frac{W}{2L}[x-3L]^2$$

Integrating twice and inserting the conditions that $y = 0$ when $x = L$ and when $x = 3L$ gives

$$EIy = -\frac{W}{8}[x-L]^3-\frac{13}{24}W[x-3L]^3+W\frac{x^3}{6}+\frac{W}{24L}[x-2L]^4$$

$$-\frac{W}{24L}[x-3L]^4-\frac{27}{16}WL^2x+\frac{73}{48}WL^3$$

When $x = 2L$, $\quad y = -\frac{31}{48}\frac{WL^3}{EI}$ (i.e. upwards).

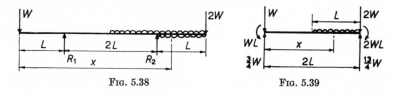

FIG. 5.38   FIG. 5.39

Alternatively, since no information is required about the overhanging ends, the given system may be reduced to the beam shown in Fig. 5.39, where the overhanging loads have been moved to the supports and the appropriate couples added.

Taking the origin at the L.H. support,

$$EI\frac{\mathrm{d}^2y}{\mathrm{d}x^2} = \frac{W}{4}x + \frac{W}{2L}[x - L]^2 + WL$$

Integrating twice and inserting the conditions that $y = 0$ when $x = 0$ and when $x = 2L$ gives

$$EIy = \frac{W}{24}x^3 + \frac{W}{24L}[x - L]^4 + \frac{WLx^2}{2} - \frac{57}{48}WL^2x$$

When $x = 2L$, $\quad y = -\frac{31}{48}\frac{WL^3}{EI}$, as before.

13. *A horizontal beam AB is freely supported at A and B, 8 m apart, and carries a uniformly distributed load of 15 kN/m run (including its own weight). A clockwise moment of 160 kN m is applied to the beam at a point C, 3 m from the left-hand support A. Calculate the reactions at A and B and sketch the bending moment diagram for the beam, stating principal values.*

Calculate the slope of the beam at C if EI = 40 MN m².   (U. Lond.)

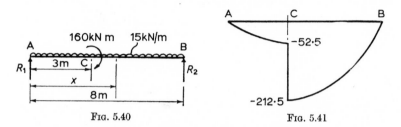

FIG. 5.40   FIG. 5.41

Taking moments about R_2, Fig. 5.40,

$$15 \times 8 \times 4 = 8R_1 + 160$$
$$\therefore R_1 = 40 \text{ kN}$$
$$\therefore R_2 = 120 - 40$$
$$= 80 \text{ kN*}$$

Taking the origin at the L.H. end and using Macaulay's method,

$$EI \frac{d^2y}{dx^2} = -40x + 7 \cdot 5x^2 - 160[x - 3]^0 \dagger$$

$$\therefore EI \frac{dy}{dx} = -20x^2 + 2 \cdot 5x^3 - 160[x - 3] + A$$

$$\therefore EIy = -\frac{20}{3} x^3 + 0 \cdot 625x^4 - 80[x - 3]^2 + Ax + B$$

When $x = 0$, $y = 0$, so that $B = 0$.
When $x = 8$ m, $y = 0$, so that $A = 356 \cdot 7$.

At C, $EI \frac{dy}{dx} = -180 + 67 \cdot 5 + 356 \cdot 7$

$$= 244 \cdot 2 \text{ kN m}^2$$

$$\therefore \frac{dy}{dx} = \frac{244 \cdot 2 \times 10^3}{40 \times 10^6}$$

$$= \underline{0 \cdot 006 \ 1 \text{ rad}}$$

* Note that the couple does not affect the sum of the reactions but only the distribution of the load on them.

† Going from left to right of the point C, there is a sudden change in *negative* moment of 160 kNm. If the origin had been taken at the R.H. end, the moment term would have been positive; this is clearly shown in the B.M. diagram, Fig. 5.41.

14. *A beam of total span L is made up of two beams, each of length L/2 joined end to end, the moment of inertia of one being twice that of the other. The beam is simply supported and carries three loads, each equal to W and spaced symmetrically along the beam, at distances L/4 apart. Obtain a formula for the central deflection.* (U. Lond.)

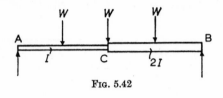

Fig. 5.42

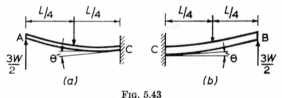

(a)   (b)

Fig. 5.43

Let the slope of the beam at the centre C, Fig. 5.42, be θ. Then the beam may be divided into two cantilevers, built-in at the point C, Figs. 5.43(a) and (b), each having a slope θ at the built-in end, downwards for the left-hand half and upwards for the right-hand half.

Then, from the formulae derived in case (a), Art. 5.2, deflection at A relative to C

$$= \frac{\frac{3W}{2}\left(\frac{L}{2}\right)^3}{3EI} - \left\{ \frac{W\left(\frac{L}{4}\right)^3}{3EI} + \frac{W\left(\frac{L}{4}\right)^2}{2EI} \cdot \frac{L}{4} \right\} - \theta \cdot \frac{L}{2}$$

$$= \frac{19}{384} \frac{WL^3}{EI} - \theta \cdot \frac{L}{2} \qquad . \qquad . \qquad . \qquad . \qquad (1)$$

Similarly, deflection at B relative to C

$$= \frac{19}{384} \frac{WL^3}{E(2I)} + \theta \cdot \frac{L}{2} \qquad . \qquad . \qquad . \qquad . \qquad (2)$$

The deflections at C relative to A and B must be equal,

hence $$\frac{19}{384} \frac{WL^3}{EI} - \theta \cdot \frac{L}{2} = \frac{19}{384} \frac{WL^3}{E(2I)} + \theta \cdot \frac{L}{2}$$

from which $$\theta \cdot \frac{L}{2} = \frac{19}{1536} \frac{WL^3}{EI}$$

Substituting in equation (1),

$$\text{central deflection} = \frac{19}{384} \frac{WL^3}{EI} - \frac{19}{1536} \frac{WL^3}{EI} = \underline{\underline{\frac{19}{512} \frac{WL^3}{EI}}}$$

15. *A 550 mm × 175 mm I-beam ($A = 0.013\ 8\ m^2$, $I = 0.000\ 655\ m^4$) is simply supported on a span of 5 m. A mass of 1 tonne drops 50 mm on to the centre of the beam. Find the maximum deflection, the bending stress induced and the equivalent static load. $E = 200\ GN/m^2$.*

If the elastic limit of the material is $250\ MN/m^2$, find the maximum distance through which the 1-tonne mass can drop without causing permanent set in the beam. (U. Lond.)

If W is the equivalent static load and y is the maximum deflection produced at the point of impact, then, equating the work done by the falling load to that done by the equivalent static load,

$$1\ 000 \times 9.81(0.05 + y) = \tfrac{1}{2}Wy$$

But
$$y = \frac{Wl^3}{48EI}$$

$$= \frac{W \times 5^3}{48 \times 200 \times 10^9 \times 0.000\ 655}$$

$$= 1.99 \times 10^{-8}W \text{ m}$$

$$\therefore 1\ 000 \times 9.81(0.05 + y) = \frac{1}{2} \times \frac{y}{1.99 \times 10^{-8}} \times y$$

from which
$$y = 0.004\ 61 \text{ m} \quad \text{or} \quad \underline{4.61 \text{ mm}}$$

$$\therefore W = \frac{0.004\ 61}{1.99 \times 10^{-8}} \text{ N} = \underline{231.5 \text{ kN}}$$

$$\sigma_{\text{max}} = \frac{M}{Z} = \frac{Wl}{4Z}$$

$$= \frac{231.5 \times 10^3 \times 5}{4 \times \dfrac{0.000\ 655}{0.275}} \text{ N/m}^2$$

$$= \underline{121.7 \text{ MN/m}^2}$$

Since the stress is proportional to the deflection, the deflection corresponding to a stress of $250\ MN/m^2$ is given by

$$0.004\ 61 \times \frac{250}{121.7} = 0.009\ 47 \text{ m}$$

$$1\ 000 \times 9.81(h + 0.009\ 47) = \frac{0.009\ 47^2}{2 \times 1.99 \times 10^{-8}},$$

where h is the height dropped

$$\therefore h = \underline{0.233 \text{ m}}$$

16. A cantilever of length L carries a load W concentrated at a distance kL from the fixed end. Derive a formula for the deflection at the free end. If the cantilever consists of a steel tube 3 m long, 120 mm outside diameter and 6 mm thick, calculate the load which, acting 1·8 m from the fixed end, will give a deflection of 2·5 mm at the free end. $E = 200$ GN/m².   (*U. Lond.*)

$$\left(Ans.:\ \frac{WL^3}{6EI}\ k^2(3 - k);\ 450\ \text{N} \right)$$

17. A horizontal cantilever of uniform section and of effective length L carries two concentrated loads, W at the free end and $2W$ at a distance a from the free end. Obtain a formula for the maximum deflection due to this loading.

If the cantilever is a steel tube of circular section, 100 mm external diameter, 6 mm thick, and $L = 1·5$ m and $a = 0·6$ m, determine the value of W to give a maximum bending stress of 120 MN/m², and calculate the maximum deflection for this loading. $E = 200$ GN/m².   (*U. Lond.*)

$$\left(Ans.:\ \frac{W}{3EI}\ \{3L^2(L - a) + a^3\};\ 1·43\ \text{kN};\ 7·1\ \text{mm} \right)$$

18. A cantilever of uniform section has a length L and carries a uniformly distributed load of w per unit length on the whole length. Derive, from first principles, expressions for the slope and deflection at the free end of the cantilever. If the load is removed for the length $L/4$ measured from the free end, what will then be the slope and deflection at the free end?   (*U. Lond.*)

$$\left(Ans.:\ \frac{wL^3}{6EI};\ \frac{wL^4}{8EI};\ \frac{9wL^3}{128EI};\ \frac{117}{2\,048}\ \frac{wL^4}{EI} \right)$$

19. A cantilever of effective length L with a concentrated load W at the free end is propped at a distance a from the fixed end to the same level as the fixed end. Find the load on the prop.

Show that there is always a real point of inflexion and find its distance from the fixed end.   (*U. Lond.*)

$$\left(Ans.:\ \frac{W}{2a}(3L - a);\ \frac{a}{3} \right)$$

20. A horizontal cantilever of length L supports a load W, uniformly distributed along its length. The cantilever is propped to the level of the fixed end at a distance $\frac{3}{4}L$ from that end. Determine the load on the prop.   (*U. Lond.*)

$$(Ans.:\ 0·593\ W)$$

21. A cantilever of effective length l carries a total load wl uniformly distributed throughout the length. If the cantilever is propped at a point $l/4$ from the free end and the level at the prop adjusted so that there is no deflection at the free end, derive a formula for the reaction at the prop and also for the deflection of the beam at the prop.

Sketch, approximately to scale, the shearing force and bending moment diagrams for the cantilever.   (*U. Lond.*)

$$\left(Ans.:\ \frac{16}{27}\ wl;\ \frac{wl^4}{6\,144EI} \right)$$

22. A horizontal cantilever of uniform section and 6 m long is maintained horizontal at one end and supported by a rigid column at a distance of 4 m from the fixed end. The beam carries a load of 80 kN midway between the fixed end and the column and a load of 15 kN at the free end. Draw to scale the bending moment and shearing force diagrams.   (*U. Lond.*)

$$(Ans.:\ \text{Prop force} = 51·25\ \text{kN})$$

23. A 225 mm × 100 mm steel joist, $I_{max} = 31.68 \times 10^{-6}$ m^4, is fixed horizontally at one end and is supported at 3 m from this fixed end by a vertical tie, 2·4 m long, 125 mm^2 sectional area, which exerts an initial upward force of 10 kN. A load of 50 kN is now applied at 1·8 m from the fixed end. Calculate the maximum stresses in the tie and beam.

For the joist, $E = 200$ GN/m^2 and for the tie, $E = 110$ GN/m^2. (*U. Lond.*)

(*Ans.:* 234 MN/m^2; 125 MN/m^2)

24. A horizontal propped cantilever of length L is securely fixed at one end and freely supported at the other and is subjected to a bending couple M in the vertical plane containing the longitudinal axis of the beam. If the couple is applied about an axis 0·75L from the fixed end of the cantilever, determine the end fixing moment and the reaction at the freely supported end.

Sketch the shape of the bending moment diagram. (*U. Lond.*)

(*Ans.:* 1·406 M/L; 0·406 M)

25. Two parallel steel cantilevers, one above the other, project horizontally from a vertical wall and their free ends are connected by frictionless pin-joints to a vertical steel tie-bar of 1·8 m effective length. Each cantilever is of I-section, 225 mm × 100 mm, second moment of area 31.68×10^{-6} m^4 and 2·4 m long, and the tie-bar is 25 mm diameter.

Assuming that the tie-bar is initially unstrained, find the proportion of the load carried by the tie-bar when a concentrated load of magnitude W is placed on the lower cantilever at its mid-point. (*U. Lond.*)　　(*Ans.:* 0·154 5 W)

26. A cantilever of uniform section is 3 m long. It is rigidly fixed at one end and is propped to the same level as the fixed end by a rigid prop 1 m from the free end. The cantilever carries a load which varies uniformly from 60 kN/m at the fixed end to zero at the free end. Calculate the load on the prop and the maximum positive and negative bending moments. (*U. Lond.*)

(*Ans.:* 35·5 kN; 19 kN m; 9·3 kN m)

27. A horizontal cantilever, 1·5 m long, tapers in section from 200 mm deep by 75 mm wide at the fixed end to 75 mm square at the extreme end. It carries an end load of 2·7 kN. Calculate the maximum stress due to bending and the deflection at the loaded end. $E = 14$ GN/m^2. (*U. Lond.*)

(*Ans.:* 8·64 MN/m^2; 9·12 mm)

28. A vertical flagpole, standing 7·5 m above the ground, is of circular cross-section throughout, but the diameter tapers from 125 mm at the base to 75 mm at the top. When a horizontal pull is applied at the top the lateral deflection there is observed to be 250 mm. Calculate the maximum stress due to bending. $E = 11$ GN/m^2. (*U. Lond.*)　　(*Ans.:* 5·69 MN/m^2)

29. A vertical column 6 m high is fixed at the base and a clockwise moment of 1·4 kN m is applied at the top of the column. A horizontal force of P N is applied to the column at a height of 3 m above the base so as to give a counter-clockwise moment.

Determine the value of P so that the horizontal deflections at the top of the column and at the point of application of P shall be equal, (*a*) when the deflections are on the same side, (*b*) when the deflections are on opposite sides of the vertical line through the foot of the column. (*U. Lond.*)　　(*Ans.:* 1·4 kN; 1·0 kN)

30. State clearly, and by reference to diagrams, the two theorems relating to the use of the bending moment diagram for a beam for the determination of the slope and deflection of the beam.

A cantilever of length L carries a point load W at the free end. The second moment of area of the section of the cantilever is as follows: for the length $L/3$ from the free end it is I, for the middle length $L/3$ it is $2I$ and for the remaining length $L/3$ it is $3I$. Determine the slope and deflection of the cantilever at the free end in terms of W, L, E and I. (*U. Lond.*)

$$\left(Ans.: \frac{25}{108}\frac{WL^2}{EI}; \frac{65}{486}\frac{WL^3}{EI}\right)$$

31. Derive a formula for the deflection under the load of a simply supported beam loaded at the centre.

A tee-bar used as a simply supported beam has a horizontal flange at the top 100 mm wide and 10 mm thick, the vertical leg is also 10 mm thick and the overall sizes are 100 mm $\times$ 60 mm. The span is 1 m and the central load causes a maximum stress in the material of 120 MN/m². Calculate the deflection if $E = 200$ GN/m². (*U. Lond.*)   (*Ans.:* 1·11 mm)

32. Derive the formula giving the maximum deflection of a beam of uniform section, uniformly loaded over its whole length, simply supported at its ends.

If such a beam is a symmetrical I-section made of steel, having $E = 200$ GN/m² and in which the maximum stress due to bending is 120 MN/m², show that the deflection may be written $\Delta = KL^2/d$, where L is the span and d the overall depth. Determine the value of the constant K when L is expressed in m and Δ and d are in mm. (*U. Lond.*)

$$\left(Ans.: \frac{5wL^4}{384EI}; 125\right)$$

33. A beam of uniform section and total length $L + 2l$ is simply supported on a span L with two equal overhanging lengths l. Derive expressions for the deflection at mid-span due to a uniformly distributed load covering (*i*) the length L between the supports, (*ii*) the two overhanging lengths.

If the beam carries a uniformly distributed load on the whole length, find the ratio l/L so that the beam at mid-span is just level with the supports. (*U. Lond.*)

$$\left(Ans.: \frac{5}{384}\frac{wL^4}{EI}; \frac{wL^2l^2}{16EI}; 0\cdot456\ 4\right)$$

34. A wooden plank is 240 mm wide and 80 mm deep. It is supported at each end of a span of 4 m. It carries concentrated loads each of 1 kN at distances of 1·2 m from each end. Assuming fundamental formulae only, calculate the deflection of the beam under the loads and at the centre of the span. Neglect the weight of the beam and assume $E = 14$ GN/m². (*U. Lond.*)

(*Ans.:* 12·65 mm; 14·75 mm)

35. A uniform section beam of length L is simply supported at its ends and carries a single concentrated load W at a distance $L/3$ from one end. Working from fundamental beam theory, derive formulae for the deflection (*a*) under the load, (*b*) at the centre, (*c*) at the point of maximum deflection. (*U. Lond.*)

$$\left(Ans.: 0\cdot016\ 46\ \frac{WL^3}{EI}; 0\cdot017\ 75\ \frac{WL^3}{EI}; 0\cdot017\ 94\ \frac{WL^3}{EI}\right)$$

36. A steel beam of uniform section has a length of 7 m and is simply supported at points 5 m apart and 1 m from the ends of the beam. The beam carries three point loads: 20 kN at the left-hand end, 40 kN at the right-hand end and 120 kN at 3 m from the left-hand end. Determine the deflection at each of the points of loading, stating in each case whether the deflection is upwards or downwards. Take $EI = 37\cdot5$ MN m². (*U. Lond.*)

(*Ans.:* $-3\cdot17$ mm; $5\cdot34$ mm; $-1\cdot88$ mm)

37. A beam, of length 8 m and $I = 0.18 \times 10^{-3}$ m^4 is simply supported at its ends, and carries two concentrated loads of 20 kN and 40 kN respectively 2 m and 6 m from the left-hand end together with a distributed load of 15 kN/m on the 4 m length of span between the concentrated loads. Calculate the deflection at the centre of the span. $E = 200$ GN/m^2. (*I.C.E.*) (*Ans.:* 28.1 mm)

38. A rolled steel joist 250 mm deep and 5 m long is simply supported at one end and at a point 3 m along the beam, both supports being at the same level. A concentrated load of 60 kN is carried at a point 1.2 m from the supported end and a concentrated load of 10 kN at the free end.

Find the greatest flange stress and the slope of the beam over each support. $I = 47.5 \times 10^{-6}$ m^4; $E = 200$ GN/m^2. (*U. Lond.*)
(*Ans.:* 92.7 MN/m^2; 0.002 58 rad; 0.001 1 rad)

39. A horizontal beam of uniform section is simply supported over a span L and carries a uniformly distributed load w per unit length over the whole span. The distributed load is to be replaced by three concentrated loads each $wL/3$, equally spaced, with the end loads each at a distance l from the nearest support. Find the values of l so that, for both types of loading, (*a*) the maximum bending moment is the same, (*b*) the maximum deflection is the same. (*U. Lond.*)
(*Ans.:* 0.125L; 0.15L)

40. A freely supported beam of span l carries a load W distant a ($<l/2$ from one end). Show that the deflection at the centre of the span is given by $\dfrac{Wa}{48EI}(3l^2 - 4a^2)$ and hence calculate by superposition of deflections, the deflection at the centre of a freely supported beam of span l carrying, uniformly distributed, a load of w per unit length over the central portion equal to one half of the span. (*U. Lond.*)
$$\left(Ans.: \ \frac{19}{2\,048} \frac{wl^4}{EI}\right)$$

41. A uniform section straight-edge of length L is loaded by its own weight only and is freely supported at two points. Find the distance between the two supports: (*a*) so that, with the supports at the same level, the two ends of the beam remain horizontal, (*b*) so that the deviation from the straight is as small as possible. (*U. Lond.*) (*Ans.:* 0.577 4L; 0.554L)

42. A 330 mm × 130 mm R.S.J. is simply supported on a span of 6 m and carries a uniformly distributed load of 24 kN/m and 3.6 m long extending from 1.8 m from the left-hand support to 0.6 m from the right-hand support. Determine the maximum stress and the maximum deflection due to bending, stating at which sections they occur. $I = 120 \times 10^{-6}$ m^4; $E = 200$ GN/m^2. (*U. Lond.*)
$$\left(Ans.: \ \begin{array}{l} 120 \text{ MN/m}^2 \text{ at } 3.24 \text{ m from L.H. end;} \\ 13.85 \text{ mm at } 3.075 \text{ m from L.H. end} \end{array}\right)$$

43. A simply supported beam of span L carries a uniformly distributed load of intensity w per unit length extending from one end over a length of $L/3$. Obtain the coefficient k in the formula, deflection $= wL^4/kEI$ for the point of maximum deflection and also for the point of mid-span. (*U. Lond.*)
(*Ans.:* 305; 311)

44. A beam 4.8 m long is supported at one end and at a point 1.2 m from the other end. It carries a uniformly distributed load of 48 kN/m over the whole length and concentrated loads, each of 60 kN, at the extreme overhanging end and at a section midway between the supports. The depth of the beam is 300 mm. Determine the section modulus in order that the stress shall not exceed 120 MN/m^2 and the deflection of the overhanging load below the supports. $E = 200$ GN/m^2. (*U. Lond.*) (*Ans.:* 0.888 × 10^{-3} m^3; 1.155 mm)

CARMARTHENSHIRE COLLEGE OF TECHNOLOGY AND ART
LLANELLI CAMPUS
LIBRARY

45. A beam of uniform section, $I = 4 \times 10^{-6}$ m⁴, is 1·8 m long and is supported horizontally at sections 0·3 m from one end and 0·6 m from the other end. It carries a uniformly distributed load of 1·5 kN/m run. Calculate the deflection at the two ends relative to the supports. $E = 200$ GN/m². (*U. Lond.*)

(*Ans.:* 0·007 594 mm; 0·064 55 mm)

46. A uniform beam of length $2L$ is propped at its middle point. It carries two equal point loads, W, symmetrically placed at a distance x on each side of the centre support. Find the value of x in terms of L, so that the reactions on the three supports are equal. Neglect the weight of the beam itself and assume that all three supports are at the same level. (*U. Lond.*)   (*Ans.:* 0·774 L)

47. A beam of uniform section and of length $2L$ is freely supported by rigid supports at its ends and by an elastic prop at the centre. If the prop deflects by an amount which is k times the load which it carries, and the beam carries a total distributed load of W, show that the load carried by the prop is $\dfrac{5W}{8(1 + 6EIk/L^3)}$.

If $L = 3$ m, $I = 6·25 \times 10^{-6}$ m⁴, $W = 45$ kN and $k = 3·96$ μm/N, find the position and value of the maximum bending moment in the beam and sketch, approximately to scale, the shearing force and bending moment diagrams. $E = 200$ GN/m². (*U. Lond.*)   (*Ans.:* 16·65 kN m at 2·107 m from one end)

48. A uniform beam, 6 m long, with a rectangular cross-section 50 mm wide by 250 mm deep, is freely supported at the ends in a horizontal position, and is also supported at the middle of its length by a vertical wire that stretches 0·45 μm/N. When the beam is unloaded there is no tension in the wire. Neglecting the weight of the beam, find the deflection at the central section and the tension in the wire when a load of 100 kN is uniformly distributed over one half of the length of the beam. $E = 200$ GN/m². (*U. Lond.*) (*Ans.:* 12·2 mm; 27·1 kN)

49. A beam for which $I = 0·002\ 5$ m⁴ is freely supported at two points A and B at the same level, 18 m apart. A third support is provided at C, midway between A and B. There is a uniformly distributed load of 8 kN/m run over the whole length. If a point load of 500 kN is applied half-way between B and C, find how much the level of C should be below that of A and B in order that there shall be no tendency for the beam to rise from its support at A. $E = 200$ GN/m². (*U. Lond.*)   (*Ans.:* 9·66 mm)

50. A horizontal steel beam, simply supported at the ends, carries a load which varies uniformly from 20 kN/m at one end to 50 kN/m at the other end over a span of 5 m. Find the magnitude of the maximum bending moment. If the depth of the beam is 0·4 m and the maximum bending stress is 100 MN/m², find the central deflection. (*U. Lond.*)   (*Ans.:* 109·6 kN m; 6·48 mm)

51. A beam of uniform section and length l is simply supported at its ends and carries a distributed load which varies uniformly from zero values at each end to a maximum intensity of w per unit length at a section $l/3$ from the right-hand end.

Show that the maximum deflection occurs at a distance of approximately 0·01 l from mid-span and find the deflection at mid-span in terms of w, l, E and I. (*U. Lond.*) $\left(Ans.: \dfrac{wl^4}{123·5\ EI}\right)$

52. A horizontal beam is simply supported at the ends and carries a uniformly distributed load of 30 kN/m between the supports placed 10 m apart. Counter-clockwise moments of 120 and 96 kN m respectively are applied to the two ends of the beam at the supports.

Draw, approximately to scale, the bending moment diagram for the be find: (a) the reactions at the supports, (b) the position and magnitude of the g bending moment. (U. Lond.)

(Ans.: 171·6 kN; 128·4 kN; 371 kN m at 5·72 m from 120 kN m couple)

53. A beam of circular section, length 1·5 m, is freely supported at the ends and carries a vertical load of 10 kN at the centre. One half of the length of the beam has a diameter of 50 mm, the other half 75 mm. What will be the deflection, due to simple bending, at the centre? Neglect the weight of the beam and the effects due to sudden change of section at the centre. $E = 200$ GN/m^2. (U. Lond.)

(Ans.: 6·87 mm)

54. A simply supported beam of span L has a second moment of area of $2I$ for the left-hand half of the span and I for the right-hand half. The beam carries a load of intensity $2w$ uniformly distributed over the left-hand half of the span and of intensity w uniformly distributed over the right-hand half. Obtain an expression for the deflection at the centre of the span. If a prop is now placed at the centre of the span to restore the beam to its original level at this point, find the force in the prop. (U. Lond.)

$$\left(Ans.: \frac{11}{768} \frac{wL^4}{EI} ; \frac{11}{12} wL \right)$$

55. A static concentrated load of 10 kN applied to a simply supported beam at mid-span, produces a deflection of 6 mm and a maximum bending stress of 25 MN/m^2. Calculate the maximum value of the momentary stress produced when a mass of 500 kg is allowed to fall through a height of 18 mm on to the beam at the middle of the span. (U. Lond.)   (Ans.: 59·6 MN/m^2)

56. A concentrated mass M is allowed to fall through a height of 12 mm to strike a simply supported steel joist at mid-span. The joist has a span of 3·6 m and for the cross-section, the depth is 240 mm and the second moment of area, $I_{xx} = 80 \times 10^{-6}$ m^4. Calculate the maximum value of M if the momentary bending stress in the joist must not exceed 120 MN/m^2. Neglect the loss of energy at impact. $E = 200$ GN/m^2. (U. Lond.)   (Ans.: 1·406 Mg)

CHAPTER 6

BUILT-IN AND CONTINUOUS BEAMS

6.1 Built-in beams. A built-in, or encastré, beam is one in which the ends are rigidly fixed in a horizontal position, usually at the same level. The walls or other constraints at the ends exert moments on the beam to hold the ends horizontal; in cases where these end fixing moments are not equal, a resultant moment is applied to the beam, which is opposed by reactions at the ends. These reactions are in addition to those required for equilibrium of the load system, so that the total reactions are different from those in a simply supported beam with similar loading.

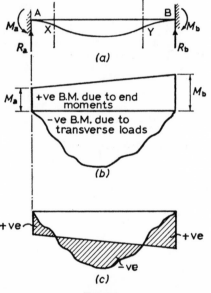

Fig. 6.1

The end fixings are assumed not to prevent a contraction of the length as the beam bends. If such contraction is prevented, the beam becomes a laterally-loaded tie-bar and is considerably stiffer than when the ends are permitted to move.

The shape of the beam will be generally as shown in Fig. 6.1(a), having points of inflexion at X and Y; at these points, the B.M. is zero.

The B.M. diagram will consist of (a) the positive B.M. due to the end fixing moments, varying linearly from M_a at one end to M_b at the other, and (*b*) the negative B.M. due to the transverse loads, calculated as if the beam were simply supported at the ends. These diagrams are shown in Fig. 6.1(*b*).

It is usual to reverse the B.M. diagram due to the end fixing moments to give the resultant B.M. diagram shown in Fig. 6.1(*c*). The base line is now sloping but the B.M. at any point remains the *vertical* height of the diagram at that point.

The S.F. diagram for the beam is similar to that for a similarly loaded simply supported beam, except for the alterations in the reactions caused by the end fixing moments.

6.2 Built-in beam with central concentrated load. Fig. 6.2(*a*) shows the loaded beam and Figs. 6.2(*b*) and (*c*) show the S.F. and B.M. diagrams respectively.

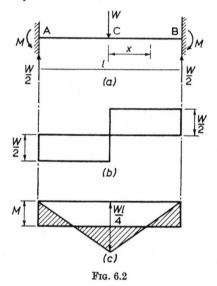

Fig. 6.2

Due to the symmetry of the loading, the reactions are each $W/2$ and the end fixing moments are equal.

Taking the origin at the centre,

$$EI \frac{\mathrm{d}^2 y}{\mathrm{d}x^2} = -\frac{W}{2}\left(\frac{l}{2} - x\right) + M$$

$$\therefore EI \frac{\mathrm{d}y}{\mathrm{d}x} = -\frac{W}{2}\left(\frac{lx}{2} - \frac{x^2}{2}\right) + Mx + A$$

When $x = 0$, $\frac{\mathrm{d}y}{\mathrm{d}x} = 0$, so that $A = 0$.

When $x = \dfrac{l}{2}$, $\dfrac{dy}{dx} = 0$, so that $M = \dfrac{Wl}{8}$,

$$\therefore EIy = -\frac{W}{2}\left(\frac{lx^2}{4} - \frac{x^3}{6}\right) + \frac{Wlx^2}{16} + B$$

When $x = \dfrac{l}{2}$, $y = 0$, so that $B = \dfrac{Wl^3}{192}$,

$$\therefore EIy = W\left(\frac{l^3}{192} - \frac{lx^2}{16} + \frac{x^3}{12}\right)$$

The maximum deflection occurs at the centre, where $x = 0$,

i.e.
$$y_{\max} = \frac{Wl^3}{192EI} \qquad . \qquad . \qquad . \qquad . \quad (6.1)$$

Alternatively, using the area moment method,

$$\theta_a - \theta_b = 0$$

$$\therefore Ml - \frac{1}{2} . \frac{Wl}{4} . l = 0$$

$$\therefore M = \frac{Wl}{8}$$

Taking the origin at C* and considering the part BC only,

$$\left[x\frac{dy}{dx} - y\right]_0^{l/2} = \frac{1}{EI} \times \frac{Ml}{2} \times \frac{l}{4} - \frac{1}{EI} \times \frac{1}{2} . \frac{Wl}{4} . \frac{l}{2} \times \frac{1}{3} . \frac{l}{2}$$

i.e. $(0 - 0) - (0 - y_c) = \dfrac{1}{EI}\left\{\dfrac{Wl^3}{64} - \dfrac{Wl^3}{96}\right\}$

i.e.
$$y_c = \frac{Wl^3}{192EI}$$

6.3 Built-in beam with uniformly distributed load. Fig. 6.3(a) shows the loaded beam and Figs. 6.3(b) and (c) show the S.F. and B.M. diagrams respectively.

Due to the symmetry of loading, the reactions are each $wl/2$ and the end fixing moments are equal.

Taking the origin at the centre,

$$EI\frac{d^2y}{dx^2} = -\frac{wl}{2}\left(\frac{l}{2} - x\right) + \frac{w}{2}\left(\frac{l}{2} - x\right)^2 + M$$

$$= -\frac{w}{2}\left(\frac{l^2}{4} - x^2\right) + M$$

$$\therefore EI\frac{dy}{dx} = -\frac{w}{2}\left(\frac{l^2x}{4} - \frac{x^3}{3}\right) + Mx + A$$

* The origin can equally well be taken at B.

When $x = 0$, $\dfrac{\mathrm{d}y}{\mathrm{d}x} = 0$, so that $A = 0$.

When $x = \dfrac{l}{2}$, $\dfrac{\mathrm{d}y}{\mathrm{d}x} = 0$, so that $M = \dfrac{wl^2}{12}$,

$$\therefore EIy = -\frac{w}{2}\left(\frac{l^2x^2}{8} - \frac{x^4}{12}\right) + \frac{wl^2x^2}{24} + B$$

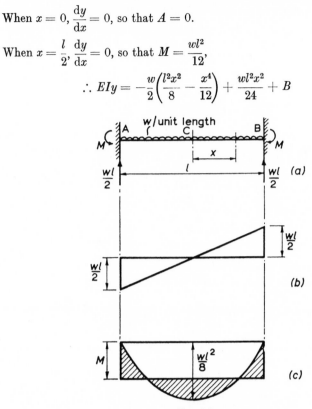

FIG. 6.3

When $x = \dfrac{l}{2}$, $y = 0$, so that $B = \dfrac{wl^4}{384}$,

$$\therefore EIy = w\left\{\frac{l^4}{384} - \frac{l^2x^2}{48} + \frac{x^4}{24}\right\}$$

The maximum deflection occurs at the centre, where $x = 0$,

i.e.
$$y_{\max} = \frac{wl^4}{384EI} \qquad . \qquad . \qquad . \qquad . \qquad (6.2)$$

Alternatively, using the area moment method,

$$\theta_a - \theta_b = 0$$

$$\therefore Ml - \frac{2}{3}\cdot\frac{wl^2}{8}\cdot l = 0$$

$$\therefore M = \frac{wl^2}{12}$$

Taking the origin at C and considering the part BC only,

$$\left[x\frac{dy}{dx} - y\right]_0^{l/2} = \frac{1}{EI} \times \frac{Ml}{2} \times \frac{l}{4} - \frac{1}{EI} \times \frac{2}{3}\cdot\frac{wl^2}{8}\cdot\frac{l}{2} \times \frac{3}{8}\cdot\frac{l}{2}$$

i.e. $(0-0) - (0-y_c) = \dfrac{1}{EI}\left\{\dfrac{wl^4}{96} - \dfrac{wl^4}{128}\right\}$

i.e.
$$y_c = \frac{wl^4}{384EI}$$

6.4 Built-in beam with concentrated load not at centre. Let the distances of the load W from the ends A and B be a and b respectively, Fig. 6.4. Since the end fixing moments will be unequal, the reactions at A and B will *not* be Wb/l and Wa/l respectively, as in a simply supported beam.

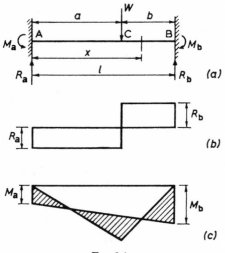

FIG. 6.4

Taking the origin at A and using Macaulay's method,

$$EI\frac{d^2y}{dx^2} = -R_a x + W[x - a] + M_a$$

$$\therefore EI\frac{dy}{dx} = -R_a\frac{x^2}{2} + \frac{W}{2}[x - a]^2 + M_a x + A. \qquad (6.3)$$

When $x = 0$, $\dfrac{dy}{dx} = 0$, so that $A = 0$, since $[x - a]$ is negative for this value of x,

$$\therefore EIy = -R_a\frac{x^3}{6} + \frac{W}{6}[x - a]^3 + M_a\frac{x^2}{2} + B$$

When $x = 0$, $y = 0$, so that $B = 0$, the term $[x - a]$ again being ignored.

When $x = l$, $\dfrac{\mathrm{d}y}{\mathrm{d}x} = 0$,

i.e. $\qquad\qquad 0 = -R_a \dfrac{l^2}{2} + \dfrac{W}{2}[l - a]^2 + M_a l$.   .   .   . (6.4)

When $x = l$, $y = 0$,

i.e. $\qquad\qquad 0 = -R_a \dfrac{l^3}{6} + \dfrac{W}{6}[l - a]^3 + M_a \dfrac{l^2}{2}$.   .   . (6.5)

From equations (6.4) and (6.5),

$$R_a = \frac{Wb^2}{l^3}(l + 2a) \quad \text{and} \quad M_a = \frac{Wab^2}{l^2}$$

and by symmetry

$$R_b = \frac{Wa^2}{l^3}(l + 2b) \quad \text{and} \quad M_b = \frac{Wa^2b*}{l^2}$$

$$\therefore EIy = -\frac{Wb^2}{l^3}(l + 2a)\frac{x^3}{6} + \frac{W}{6}[x - a]^3 + \frac{Wab^2}{l^2}\cdot\frac{x^2}{2} \quad . \quad (6.6)$$

When $x = a$, $EIy = -\dfrac{Wb^2}{l^3}(l + 2a)\dfrac{a^3}{6} + \dfrac{Wa^3b^2}{2l^2}$

$$\therefore y = \frac{Wa^3b^3\dagger}{3EIl^3} \quad . \quad . \quad . \quad . \quad . \quad . \quad . \quad (6.7)$$

The maximum deflection will occur between the load point and the centre of the beam. If $a > b$, this point will correspond with $x < a$, so that, from equation (6.3),

$$-\frac{Wb^2}{l^3}(l + 2a)\frac{x^2}{2} + \frac{Wab^2}{l^2}\,x = 0$$

from which $\qquad\qquad\qquad\qquad x = \dfrac{2al}{l + 2a}$

Substituting in equation (6.6),

$$EIy_{max} = -\frac{Wb^2}{l^3}\frac{(l + 2a)}{6}\left(\frac{2al}{l + 2a}\right)^3 + \frac{Wab^2}{2l^2}\left(\frac{2al}{l + 2a}\right)^2$$

or $\qquad\qquad y_{max} = \dfrac{2Wa^3b^2}{3EI(l + 2a)^2}$.   .   .   .   . (6.8)

* Note that the ratio $\dfrac{M_a}{M_b} = \dfrac{b}{a}$.

† When $a = b = l/2$, this reduces to $\dfrac{Wl^3}{192EI}$, as in equation (6.1).

6.5 Supports at different levels. If one end of the beam, Fig. 6.5, is at a distance h below the other end, the reactions and end fixing moments due to this may be calculated separately and superimposed on those due to the transverse loads.

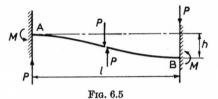

FIG. 6.5

The beam may be imagined to be cut in half and the two free ends made to coincide by the application of equal and opposite forces, P, which produce deflections at the ends of amount $h/2$.

Thus
$$\frac{h}{2} = \frac{P \times \left(\frac{l}{2}\right)^3}{3EI}$$

from which
$$P = \frac{12EIh}{l^3} \qquad . \qquad . \qquad . \qquad . \qquad (6.9)$$

The end fixing moments due to P are given by
$$M = \frac{Pl}{2} = \frac{6EIh}{l^2} \qquad . \qquad . \qquad . \qquad . \qquad (6.10)$$

The directions of the reactions and end fixing moments are shown in Fig. 6.5.

6.6 Continuous beams—three moments theorem. A beam is continuous if it is supported at more than two points. Let AB and BC, Fig. 6.6(a), be any two consecutive spans of a continuous beam and let M' be the B.M. due to the transverse loads as if each span were simply supported at the ends. Then the resultant B.M. diagram consists of the 'free' B.M. diagram due to M' (negative) and the diagram representing the effect of the end fixing moments (positive). The end fixing moments are the moments applied to a span by the adjacent spans; these will not normally be the same as those applied by the walls to a built-in beam since the continuous beam is not necessarily horizontal over the supports.

As with the built-in beams, the B.M. diagrams are usually set out to show the resultant B.M.; typical S.F. and B.M. diagrams are shown in Figs. 6.6(b) and (c).

Let A_1 and A_2 be the areas of the free B.M. diagrams for AB and BC respectively, let $\bar{x}_1$ and $\bar{x}_2$ be the distances of the centroids of these areas from A and C respectively and the second moments of area of the two spans be I_1 and I_2.

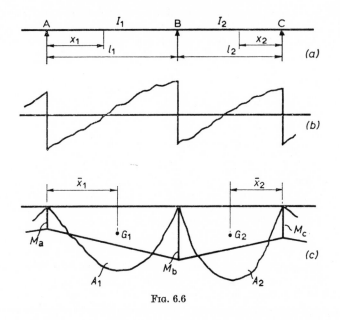

Fig. 6.6

Then $EI_1 \dfrac{\mathrm{d}^2 y}{\mathrm{d}x_1^2} = M_\mathrm{a} + \dfrac{x_1}{l_1}(M_\mathrm{b} - M_\mathrm{a}) + M_1'$ (M_1' being negative)

Multiply by x_1 and integrate from 0 to l_1. Then

$$EI_1 \left[x_1 \frac{\mathrm{d}y}{\mathrm{d}x_1} - y \right]_0^{l_1} = M_\mathrm{a} \int_0^{l_1} x_1\, \mathrm{d}x_1 + (M_\mathrm{b} - M_\mathrm{a}) \int_0^{l_1} \frac{x_1^2}{l_1}\, \mathrm{d}x_1 + \int_0^{l_1} M_1' x_1\, \mathrm{d}x_1$$

$\dfrac{\mathrm{d}y}{\mathrm{d}x_1}$ at $x_1 = l_1$ is the slope of the beam at B, looking from the end A and is denoted by θ_ba; $M_1' x_1\, \mathrm{d}x_1$ represents the moment of an element of the free B.M. diagram about A and hence $\displaystyle\int_0^{l_1} M_1 x_1\, \mathrm{d}x_1$ represents the total first moment of the free B.M. diagram for AB about A, i.e. $A_1 \bar{x}_1$.

Thus $\qquad\qquad EI_1 l_1 \theta_\mathrm{ba} = M_\mathrm{a} \dfrac{l_1^2}{2} + (M_\mathrm{b} - M_\mathrm{a})\dfrac{l_1^2}{3} + A_1 \bar{x}_1$

from which $\qquad \theta_\mathrm{ba} = \dfrac{1}{EI_1 l_1}\left\{ \dfrac{l_1^2}{6}(M_\mathrm{a} + 2M_\mathrm{b}) + A_1 \bar{x}_1 \right\}$

Similarly $\qquad \theta_\mathrm{bc} = \dfrac{1}{EI_2 l_2}\left\{ \dfrac{l_2^2}{6}(M_\mathrm{c} + 2M_\mathrm{b}) + A_2 \bar{x}_2 \right\}$

But $\theta_{bc} = -\theta_{ba}$ since the slope at B is being viewed from opposite directions, so that

$$\frac{1}{EI_1l_1}\left\{\frac{l_1^2}{6}(M_a + 2M_b) + A_1\bar{x}_1\right\} = -\frac{1}{EI_2l_2}\left\{\frac{l_2^2}{6}(M_c + 2M_b) + A_2\bar{x}_2\right\}$$

from which

$$M_a\frac{l_1}{I_1} + 2M_b\left(\frac{l_1}{I_1} + \frac{l_2}{I_2}\right) + M_c\frac{l_2}{I_2} + 6\left\{\frac{A_1\bar{x}_1}{I_1l_1} + \frac{A_2\bar{x}_2}{I_2l_2}\right\} = 0 \ . \quad (6.11)$$

This is known as *Clapeyron's Equation*.

If the beam is of uniform section, this equation reduces to

$$M_al_1 + 2M_b(l_1 + l_2) + M_cl_2 + 6\left\{\frac{A_1\bar{x}_1}{l_1} + \frac{A_2\bar{x}_2}{l_2}\right\} = 0 \quad . \quad (6.12)$$

Clapeyron's equation relates the moments at three successive supports of the beam; it is applied to each pair of consecutive spans in turn and as many equations will be obtained as there are unknown moments.

If the extreme ends of the beam are simply supported, the end moments are zero but if one or both the extreme ends are built-in, additional equations may be obtained by imagining the beam to be reflected about the wall(s), the moment at the axis of symmetry being the same as that at the wall, since the beam is horizontal at that point in each case. Thus the beam shown in Fig. 6.7(*a*) may be replaced by that in Fig. 6.7(*b*).

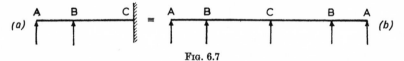

FIG. 6.7

Clapeyron's equation is first applied to spans AB and BC and then to spans BC and CB, giving two equations from which M_b and M_c may be determined, M_a being zero.

An alternative procedure is to regard the beam as being continued to X, Fig. 6.8, where CX is a virtual or imaginary span of no length and carrying no load. The equation relating M_b, M_c and M_x will be identical with that obtained for spans BC and CB above, M_x being zero.

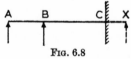

FIG. 6.8

With the sign convention adopted, A_1, A_2, etc., will be negative and the end fixing moments will be found to be positive.

After determining the fixing moments, the reactions may be obtained by taking moments about each of the supports in turn.

1. *A beam, of uniform section and 5 m long, is built-in at each end. It carries a uniformly distributed load of 10 kN/m extending for 3 m from one end and a concentrated load of 20 kN, 1 m from the other end. Sketch the bending moment diagram, inserting the principal numerical values.*

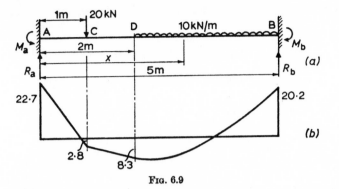

Fig. 6.9

Taking the origin at the L.H. end, Fig. 6.9(a),

$$EI\frac{d^2y}{dx^2} = -R_a x + 20[x-1] + 5[x-2]^2 + M_a \quad . \quad . \quad (1)$$

$$\therefore EI\frac{dy}{dx} = -R_a\frac{x^2}{2} + 10[x-1]^2 + \frac{5}{3}[x-2]^3 + M_a x + A$$

When $x = 0$, $\frac{dy}{dx} = 0$, $\therefore A = 0$,

$$\therefore EIy = -R_a\frac{x^3}{6} + \frac{10}{3}[x-1]^3 + \frac{5}{12}[x-2]^4 + M_a\frac{x^2}{2} + B$$

When $x = 0$, $y = 0$, $\therefore B = 0$.

When $x = 5$ m, $\frac{dy}{dx} = 0$,

$$\therefore 0 = -2\cdot5R_a + 41 + M_a \quad . \quad . \quad . \quad . \quad (2)$$

When $x = 5$ m, $y = 0$,

$$\therefore 0 = -\frac{5}{3}R_a + 19\cdot77 + M_a \quad . \quad . \quad . \quad . \quad (3)$$

Therefore, from equations (2) and (3),
$$R_a = 25\cdot5 \text{ kN} \quad \text{and} \quad M_a = 22\cdot7 \text{ kN m}$$

The B.M. diagram is shown in Fig. 6.9(b).

The points of contraflexure are obtained from equation (1). Thus, for the L.H. point $-25\cdot5x + 22\cdot7 = 0$, the terms in square brackets both being ignored since negative,

$$\therefore x = 0\cdot891 \text{ m}$$

For the R.H. point,
$$-25\cdot5x + 20[x-1] + 5[x-2]^2 + 22\cdot7 = 0$$
from which $\quad\quad x = 3\cdot95$ m

2. *A 300 mm × 125 mm I-beam is built-in at the ends of a span of 6 m and carries a uniformly distributed load of 24 kN/m throughout its length. What is the greatest bending stress in the beam?*

By how much per cent is the maximum bending stress increased if (a) the right-hand end becomes free in direction but remains supported at the same level, (b) the right-hand end remains horizontal but sinks 3 mm below the left-hand end?

I_{xx} for the beam section = 86·5 × 10⁻⁶ m⁴ and E = 200 GN/m².

(U. Lond.)

From Art. 6.3, the maximum B.M. is $\dfrac{wl^2}{12}$ and occurs at the ends,

i.e. $\qquad M_{\max} = \dfrac{24 \times 6^2}{12} = 72 \text{ kN m}$

$$\therefore \sigma_{\max} = \frac{M}{Z} = \frac{72 \times 10^3 \times 0.15}{86.5 \times 10^{-6}} \text{ N/m}^2 = \underline{124.8 \text{ MN/m}^2}$$

When the R.H. end becomes free in direction, the beam becomes a propped cantilever, Fig. 6.10. Equating downward and upward deflections at the free end,

$$\frac{wl^4}{8EI} = \frac{Pl^3}{3EI}$$

$$\therefore P = \tfrac{3}{8}wl$$

$$\therefore M_{\max} = \frac{wl^2}{2} - \tfrac{3}{8}wl \cdot l$$

$$= \frac{wl^2}{8}$$

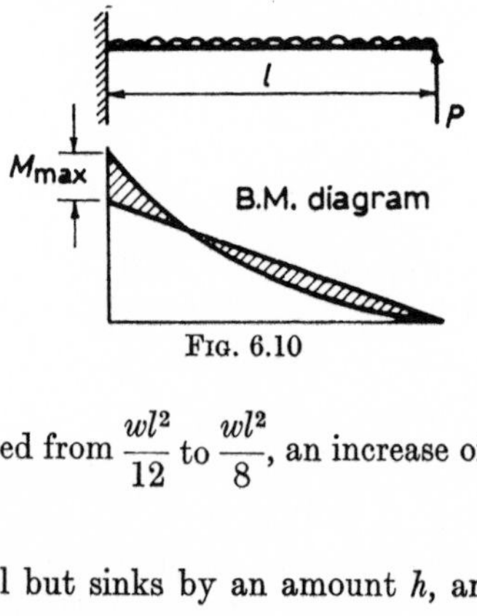

FIG. 6.10

The maximum B.M. is therefore increased from $\dfrac{wl^2}{12}$ to $\dfrac{wl^2}{8}$, an increase of $\underline{50\%}$.

When the R.H. end remains horizontal but sinks by an amount h, an additional moment $\dfrac{6EIh}{l^2}$ is induced at the L.H. end, from Art. 6.5,

i.e.

additional moment $= \dfrac{6 \times 200 \times 10^9 \times 86.5 \times 10^{-6} \times 0.003}{6^2} \text{ N m} = 8.65 \text{ kN m}$

Therefore percentage increase in maximum B.M. $= \dfrac{8.65}{72} \times 100 = \underline{\underline{12}}$

3. *A built-in beam of length l carries a distributed load which varies uniformly from zero at one end to a maximum w per unit length at the other. Find the bending moment and supporting forces at each end and the position and magnitude of the maximum deflection.*

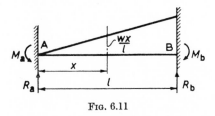

FIG. 6.11

The intensity of loading at any point distance x from A, Fig. 6.11, is $\dfrac{wx}{l}$.

$$\therefore EI \frac{\mathrm{d}^2y}{\mathrm{d}x^2} = -R_a x + \frac{1}{2} \cdot \frac{wx}{l} \cdot x \times \frac{x}{3} + M_a$$

$$= -R_a x + \frac{wx^3}{6l} + M_a \qquad . \qquad . \qquad . \qquad (1)$$

$$\therefore EI \frac{\mathrm{d}y}{\mathrm{d}x} = -R_a \frac{x^2}{2} + \frac{wx^4}{24l} + M_a x + A \qquad . \qquad . \qquad (2)$$

When $x = 0, \dfrac{\mathrm{d}y}{\mathrm{d}x} = 0, \therefore A = 0,$

$$\therefore EIy = -R_a \frac{x^3}{6} + \frac{wx^5}{120l} + M_a \frac{x^2}{2} + B \qquad . \qquad . \qquad (3)$$

When $x = 0, y = 0, \therefore B = 0.$

When $x = l, \dfrac{\mathrm{d}y}{\mathrm{d}x} = 0, \therefore 0 = -R_a \dfrac{l^2}{2} + \dfrac{wl^3}{24} + M_a l \qquad . \qquad . \qquad (4)$

When $x = l, y = 0, \therefore 0 = -R_a \dfrac{l^3}{6} + \dfrac{wl^4}{120} + M_a \dfrac{l^2}{2} \qquad . \qquad . \qquad (5)$

Therefore, from equations (4) and (5),

$$R_a = \frac{3}{20} wl \quad \text{and} \quad M_a = \frac{wl^2}{30}$$

$$R_b = \frac{wl}{2} - \frac{3}{20} wl = \frac{7}{20} wl$$

M_b is obtained from equation (1) by putting $x = l$,

i.e.
$$M_b = -\frac{3}{20} wl \cdot l + \frac{wl^2}{6} + \frac{wl^2}{30} = \frac{wl^2}{20}$$

The maximum deflection occurs when $\dfrac{dy}{dx} = 0$. Therefore, from equation (2),

$$-\frac{3}{20}\,wl\cdot\frac{x^2}{2} + \frac{wx^4}{24l} + \frac{wl^2x}{30} = 0$$

By Newton's method, or otherwise, $x = 0\cdot525l$

Substituting in equation (5) gives $y_{\text{max}} = 0\cdot001\,31\,\dfrac{wl^4}{EI}.$

4. *A beam of uniform flexural rigidity and length l is encastré at both ends. At a distance a from one end it carries a point load W and an applied moment Wl which tends further to depress the centre of the beam. Show that when $a = l/(1 + \sqrt{2})$, one of the end fixing moments is zero.* (U. Lond.)

The arrangement is shown in Fig. 6.12 and it is evident that only M_a could be made zero, since the effect of the applied moment will be to increase the moment at B due to W.

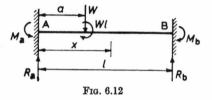

FIG. 6.12

Taking the origin at A,

$$EI\,\frac{d^2y}{dx^2} = -R_a x + W[x - a] - Wl[x - a]^0 + M_a$$

$$\therefore\ EI\,\frac{dy}{dx} = -R_a\frac{x^2}{2} + \frac{W}{2}[x - a]^2 - Wl[x - a] + M_a x + A$$

When $x = 0, \dfrac{dy}{dx} = 0, \therefore A = 0,$

$$\therefore\ EIy = -R_a\frac{x^3}{6} + \frac{W}{6}[x - a]^3 - \frac{Wl}{2}[x - a]^2 + M_a\frac{x^2}{2} + B$$

When $x = 0, y = 0, \therefore B = 0.$

When $x = l, \dfrac{dy}{dx} = 0, \therefore\ 0 = -R_a\dfrac{l^2}{2} + \dfrac{W}{2}[l-a]^2 - Wl[l-a] + M_a l$. (1)

When $x = l, y = 0, \quad \therefore\ 0 = -R_a\dfrac{l^3}{6} + \dfrac{W}{6}[l-a]^3 - \dfrac{Wl}{2}[l-a]^2 + M_a\dfrac{l^2}{2}$ (2)

Eliminating R_a between equations (1) and (2) gives

$$M_a = \frac{W}{l^2}(l - a)(l^2 - 2al - a^2)$$

For M_a to be zero, either $a = l$

or $\qquad\qquad l^2 - 2al - a^2 = 0$

from which $\qquad\qquad a = l(-1 + \sqrt{2}) \quad \text{or} \quad \dfrac{l}{1 + \sqrt{2}}$

5. *A fixed-ended beam of span 9 m carries a uniformly distributed load of 15 kN/m (including its own weight) and two equal point loads of 200 kN at the third points of the span. Assuming rigid end-fixing, find the fixing moments and the deflection at the centre. EI = 210 MN m².*

If the end-fixings are elastic, so that the slope at the ends in radians (θ) is given by θ = αM, where M is the fixing moment in N m, find the value of α so that the maximum bending moment on the beam shall be as small as possible.

(U. Lond.)

The load system is shown in Fig. 6.13(a) and Fig. 6.13(b) shows the form of the B.M. diagram. The reactions are each equal to half the load, i.e. 275 kN and the maximum ordinate of the free B.M. diagram is 785·5 kN m.

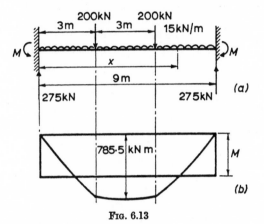

FIG. 6.13

Taking the origin at the L.H. end,

$$EI \frac{d^2y}{dx^2} = -275x + 200[x-3] + 200[x-6] + 7\cdot5x^2 + M$$

$$\therefore EI \frac{dy}{dx} = -137\cdot5x^2 + 100[x-3]^2 + 100[x-6]^2 + 2\cdot5x^3 + Mx + A \quad . \quad (1)$$

When $x = 0$, $\frac{dy}{dx} = 0$, $\therefore A = 0$.

When $x = 4\cdot5$ m, $\frac{dy}{dx} = 0$, $\therefore M = \underline{518\cdot12 \text{ kN m}}$

$$\therefore EIy = -\frac{137\cdot5}{3}x^3 + \frac{100}{3}[x-3]^3 + \frac{100}{3}[x-6]^3 + 0\cdot625x^4 + 259\cdot06x^2 + B$$

When $x = 0$, $y = 0$, $\therefore B = 0$.

When $x = 4.5$ m,

$$EIy = -\frac{137.5}{3} \times 4.5^3 + \frac{100}{3} \times 1.5^3 + 0.625 \times 4.5^4 + 259.06 \times 4.5^2$$

$$= 1\ 436.5 \text{ kN m}^3$$

$$\therefore y = \frac{1\ 436.5 \times 10^3}{210 \times 10^6} \text{ m} = \underline{6.835 \text{ mm}}$$

For the maximum B.M. to be as small as possible, the end-fixing moment M must be half the maximum ordinate of the free B.M. diagram, so that the resultant B.M. at the centre is equal to the B.M. at the ends,

i.e. $M = \dfrac{785.5}{2} = 392.75$ kN m

$$\therefore \text{ end slope} = \alpha \times 392.75 \times 10^3 \text{ rad}$$

Substituting in equation (1) when $x = 0$ gives

$$A = 210 \times 10^6 \times 392.75 \times 10^3 \alpha$$
$$= 82.5 \times 10^{12} \alpha$$

$\therefore$ when $x = 4.5$ m,

$$0 = -137.5 \times 4.5^2 + 100 \times 1.5^2 + 2.5 \times 4.5^3 + 392.75 \times 4.5 + 82.5 \times 10^{12} \alpha$$

from which $\alpha = \underline{6.84 \times 10^{-9}}$

6. *A beam of uniform section is 10 m long and is fixed horizontally at both ends. It is supported at the centre by a prop level with both ends. It carries a uniformly distributed load of 60 kN/m, extending from one fixing to the centre prop.*

Calculate (a) the reaction on the prop, (b) the bending moment at the two ends, (c) the bending moment over the prop. (U. Lond.)

Method 1

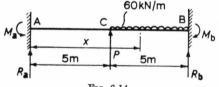

FIG. 6.14

Taking the origin at A, Fig. 6.14,

$$EI \frac{d^2y}{dx^2} = -R_a x - P[x - 5] + 30[x - 5]^2 + M_a$$

Integrating twice and inserting the conditions that the slope is zero at each end and the deflection is zero at each end and at the centre gives

$$P = 150 \text{ kN}$$
$M_a = -31.25$ kN m (i.e. opposite in direction to that shown in Fig. 6.14)
$M_b = 156.25$ kN m   and $M_c = 62.5$ kN m

Method 2

For a beam carrying a u.d.l. over the whole span, each half of the load contributes equally to the central deflection. Therefore, if the load covers only half the beam, the central deflection is

$$\frac{1}{2} \times \frac{wl^4}{384EI} . \qquad \text{from equation (6.2)}$$

Equating this to the upward deflection due to P,

$$\frac{wl^4}{768EI} = \frac{Pl^3}{192EI}$$

$$\therefore P = \frac{wl}{4} = \frac{60 \times 10}{4} = 150 \text{ kN.}$$

For a built-in beam carrying a single concentrated load W at a distance a from one end, the end fixing moment at that end is $Wa(l-a)^2/l^2$ and at the other end it is $Wa^2(l-a)/l^2$ (see Art. 6.4).

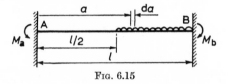

FIG. 6.15

Applying this to the u.d.l., Fig. 6.15, the moment at A due to the load on an element da at a distance a from that end is

$$\frac{w \, da}{l^2} a(l-a)^2$$

Hence the total moment at A due to the u.d.l.

$$= \int_{l/2}^{l} \frac{w \, da}{l^2} a(l-a)^2 = \frac{5}{192} wl^2$$

$$= \frac{5}{192} \times 60 \times 10^2 \quad = 156 \cdot 25 \text{ kN m.}$$

Similarly, total moment at B

$$= \int_{l/2}^{l} \frac{w \, da}{l^2} a^2(l-a) = \frac{11}{192} wl^2$$

$$= \frac{11}{192} \times 60 \times 10^2 \quad = 343 \cdot 75 \text{ kN m}$$

End fixing moments due to $P \qquad = \frac{Pl}{8} \qquad . \qquad . \qquad .$ (from Art. 6.2)

$$= \frac{150 \times 10}{8} = 187 \cdot 5 \text{ kN m,}$$

in opposite direction to those shown in Fig. 6.15.

Hence resultant moment at A $= 156{\cdot}25 - 187{\cdot}5 = -31{\cdot}25$ kN m
and   resultant moment at B $= 343{\cdot}75 - 187{\cdot}5 = 156{\cdot}25$ kN m.

Taking moments about B, Fig. 6.14,

$$60 \times \frac{5^2}{2} - 31{\cdot}25 - 10R_a - 150 \times 5 = 156{\cdot}25$$

$$\therefore R_a = -18{\cdot}75 \text{ kN (i.e. downwards)}$$

$$\therefore \text{B.M. at C} = 18{\cdot}75 \times 5 - 31{\cdot}25 = 62{\cdot}5 \text{ kN m}$$

Method 3

The beam may be treated as a continuous beam and the problem solved by the use of the three-moments theorem (Art. 6.6). Since both ends are built-in, assume a virtual span at each end, of zero length and carrying no load. These are represented by AX and BY in Fig. 6.16.

For BC, $A = -\dfrac{2}{3} \cdot \dfrac{wl^2}{8} \cdot l$

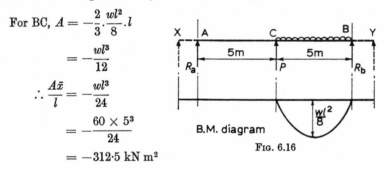

$$= -\frac{wl^3}{12}$$

$$\therefore \frac{A\bar{x}}{l} = -\frac{wl^3}{24}$$

$$= -\frac{60 \times 5^3}{24}$$

B.M. diagram

Fig. 6.16

$$= -312{\cdot}5 \text{ kN m}^2$$

Applying equation (6.12) in turn to spans XA and AC, AC and CB, and CB and BY gives

$$0 + 2M_a(0 + 5) + M_c \times 5 + 6(0 + 0) \qquad\qquad = 0 \quad . \qquad (1)$$

$$M_a \times 5 + 2M_c(5 + 5) + M_b \times 5 + 6(0 - 312{\cdot}5) = 0 \quad . \qquad (2)$$

$$M_c \times 5 + 2M_b(5 + 0) + 0 + 6(-312{\cdot}5 + 0) \qquad = 0 \quad . \qquad (3)$$

From equations (1), (2) and (3),

$$M_a = -31{\cdot}25 \text{ kN m}, M_b = 156{\cdot}25 \text{ kN m and } M_c = 62{\cdot}5 \text{ kN m}$$

Taking moments about C,

$$-31{\cdot}25 - 5R_a = 62{\cdot}5 \qquad\qquad \therefore R_a = -18{\cdot}75 \text{ kN}$$

Taking moments about B,

$$-31{\cdot}25 + 18{\cdot}75 \times 10 + 60 \times \frac{5^2}{2} - 5P = 156{\cdot}25$$

$$\therefore P = 150 \text{ kN}$$

NOTE. Readers familiar with 'moment distribution' will find that this gives the most direct solution of all.

7. *A continuous beam of uniform section 30 m long, is simply supported at A, B, C and D, all supports remaining at the same level. AB = BC = CD = 8 m. The beam overhangs 3 m at each end and carries a uniformly distributed load of 30 kN/m over its entire length. Determine the bending moments at the supports, and sketch the bending moment and shearing force diagrams for the beam.*

(U. Lond.)

The beam is shown in Fig. 6.17(*a*) and Figs. 6.17(*b*) and (*c*) show the bending moment and shearing force diagrams respectively.

The maximum ordinates of the free B.M. diagrams for spans AB, BC and CD are 240 kN m.

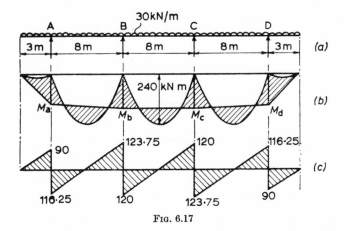

FIG. 6.17

Applying equation (6.12) to spans AB and BC,

$$M_a \times 8 + 2M_b(8 + 8) + M_c \times 8 - 6 \times 2 \times \frac{\frac{2}{3} \times 240 \times 8 \times 4}{8} = 0$$

But

$$M_a = \frac{30 \times 3^2}{2} = 135 \text{ kN m}$$

and

$$M_c = M_b$$

Hence

$$M_b = 165 \text{ kN m}$$

Taking moments about B of forces to the left of that point,

$$30 \times \frac{11^2}{2} - 8R_a = 165$$

$$\therefore R_a = 206 \cdot 25 \text{ kN}$$

$$\therefore R_b = 30 \times 15 - 206 \cdot 25 = 243 \cdot 75 \text{ kN}$$

8. *A uniform continuous beam ABCD is built-in at A and simply sup-ported at B, C and D, 4, 10 and 13 m respectively from A. All the supports are at the same level. It carries a point load of 40 kN, 3 m from A and a uniform load of 5 kN/m on BC.*

Sketch the bending moment diagram, inserting principal numerical values.

(U. Lond.)

Fig. 6.18(a) shows the arrangement of the beam and Fig. 6.18(b) shows the B.M. diagram. The maximum ordinates of the free B.M. diagrams for AB and BC are respectively 30 and 22·5 kN m. Since the end A is built-in,

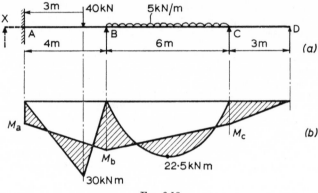

Fig. 6.18

assume an imaginary span AX is added, of zero length and carrying no load.

Applying equation (6.12) in turn to XA and AB, AB and BC, and BC and CD gives

$$0 + 2M_a(0+4) + M_b \times 4 + 6\left\{0 - \frac{\frac{1}{2}\times 3\times 30\times 2 + \frac{1}{2}\times 1\times 30\times \frac{2}{3}}{4}\right\}^* = 0$$

$$M_a \times 4 + 2M_b(4+6) + M_c \times 6$$
$$+ 6\left\{-\frac{\frac{1}{2}\times 3\times 30\times 2 + \frac{1}{2}\times 1\times 30\times 3\frac{1}{3}}{4} - \frac{\frac{2}{3}\times 6\times 22\cdot5\times 3}{6}\right\} = 0$$

$$M_b \times 6 + 2M_c(6+3) + M_d \times 3 + 6\left\{-\frac{\frac{2}{3}\times 6\times 22\cdot5\times 3}{6} + 0\right\} = 0$$

---

* Note that $\bar{x}$ must be measured from the *outer* supports of the pair of spans under consideration. For an unsymmetrical triangular diagram, it is simpler to consider the $A\bar{x}$ for the two parts of the triangle separately than to determine the position of the centroid of the complete triangle.

These equations reduce to

$$2M_a + M_b = 37 \cdot 5$$
$$2M_a + 10M_b + 3M_c = 240$$
$$M_b + 3M_c = 45 \quad \text{since } M_d = 0$$

from which $M_a = 8 \cdot 9$ kN m, $M_b = 19 \cdot 7$ kN m and $M_c = 8 \cdot 43$ kN m.

9. A horizontal I-beam, rigidly built-in at the ends, and 7·5 m long, carries a total uniformly distributed load of 100 kN as well as a central concentrated load of 40 kN. If the bending stress is limited to 75 MN/m² and the deflection must not exceed 2·5 mm, find the depth of section required. $E = 200$ GN/m². (*U. Lond.*) (*Ans.:* 594 mm)

10. A horizontal steel beam of span 6 m and of uniform section is held encastré at both ends. It carries a distributed load of 7·2 kN/m run from the centre to one end and a concentrated load of 9 kN at the centre. The depth is 0·3 m and the maximum bending stress is 120 MN/m². Calculate the central deflection. $E = 200$ GN/m². (*U. Lond.*) (*Ans.:* 7·33 mm)

11. A horizontal beam, built-in each end, has a clear span of 4·5 m, and carries loads of 50 kN at 1·5 m and 70 kN at 2·5 m from its left-hand end. Calculate the fixing moments and the position and amount of the maximum bending moment. (*U. Lond.*) (*Ans.:* 67·5 kN m; 60·5 kN m; 67·5 kN m at L.H. end)

12. A beam of uniform section, $I = 185 \times 10^{-6}$ m⁴, span 6 m, is fixed horizontally at each end. It carries a point load of 120 kN at 3·6 m from one end. Neglecting the weight of the beam itself, find (*a*) the fixing moments, proving any formula or rule you use; (*b*) the reactions; (*c*) the position and magnitude of the maximum deflection. Check the determination of the fixing moments by any method alternative to that already employed. $E = 200$ GN/m². (*U. Lond.*)

(*Ans.:* 69·12 kN m; 103·68 kN m; 42·25 kN; 77·8 kN; 3·35 mm at 0·275 m from mid-span)

13. A built-in beam of 5 m span carries a uniformly distributed load of 30 kN/m extending from one support to the centre of the span. If the moment of inertia of the section is 200×10^{-6} m⁴, calculate (*a*) the end fixing moments, (*b*) the end reactions, and (*c*) the position and magnitude of the maximum deflection. Sketch the S.F. and B.M. diagrams. $E = 200$ GN/m². (*U. Lond.*)

(*Ans.:* 19·53 kN m; 43 kN m; 14·06 kN; 60·94 kN; 3·15 mm at 2·8 m from unloaded end)

14. A 250 mm × 112·5 mm steel beam, $I = 47·6 \times 10^{-6}$ m⁴, is used as a horizontal beam with fixed ends and a clear span of 3 m. Calculate from first principles the load which can be applied at one-third span if the bending stress is limited to 120 MN/m². (*U. Lond.*) (*Ans.:* 103 kN)

15. An encastré beam of uniform flexural rigidity is subjected to the action of two vertical point loads acting as shown in Fig. 6.19. Find the value of a that will give the largest bending moment at the walls. (*U. Lond.*) (*Ans.:* 0·211 3 L)

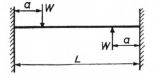

FIG. 6.19.

16. A steel joist, 400 mm × 150 mm, $I_{max} = 283 × 10^{-6}$ m⁴, 6 m long, is fixed horizontally at each end and carries loads W and $2W$ at 2 m and 4 m respectively from one end. Draw the bending moment diagram for the beam, stating the values at the principal sections. Find the maximum value of W if the bending stress must not exceed 120 MN/m². (*U. Lond.*)

(*Ans.:* End fixing moments 1·778 W and 2·222 W; 76·5 kN)

17. A horizontal tubular shaft 1 m long, having outer and inner diameters of 50 mm and 25 mm, is rigidly fixed at its ends and carries a rigid lever at the centre of its length at right angles to its axis and in the same horizontal plane. If the lever is 0·3 m long and a vertical load of 1 kN is applied at its free end, find the vertical deflection at the load. $G = 80$ GN/m²; $E = 200$ GN/m². (*U. Lond.*)

(*Ans.:* 0·579 mm [0·489 mm + 0·090 mm])

18. A beam of uniform section is position and direction fixed at both ends of a span of 7 m. At a point 4·5 m from the left-hand end a connection made to the beam exerts a vertically downwards force of 80 kN and also a clockwise couple of 60 kN m in the vertical plane of bending; in addition, the beam carries a uniformly distributed load of 8 kN/m on the whole span. Determine the fixing moments and reactions at the supports and make dimensioned sketches of the bending moment and shearing force diagrams. (*U. Lond.*)

(*Ans.:* 58·78 kN m; 118·28 kN m; 39·5 kN; 96·5 kN)

19. An encastré beam of span l carries a load wl uniformly distributed over the span. The second moment of area of the beam section is not the same throughout; for a length $l/4$ at each end the value is $2I$ and for the middle length $l/2$ it is I.

Determine the bending moment at the ends of the beam and sketch the bending moment diagram, showing on it the values at the ends and at mid-span. (*U. Lond.*)

(*Ans.:* $\frac{3}{32}wl^2$; $\frac{1}{32}wl^2$)

20. A built-in beam of uniform section and of length l carries a load which increases uniformly from zero at each end to w per unit length at the centre. Determine the end fixing moments and the central deflection.

$$\left(Ans.: \frac{5}{96}\,wl^2; \frac{7}{3\,840}\,\frac{wl^4}{EI}\right)$$

21. A beam of uniform section and span l is firmly built-in at the ends and carries a load which varies uniformly from zero intensity at the left-hand end to w per unit length at the right-hand end. Determine the fixing moments and reactions in terms of w and l and also the position and magnitude of the maximum sagging bending moment.

Make freehand sketches of the shearing force and bending moment diagrams for the beam, approximately to scale, showing on the diagrams all the calculated values. (*U. Lond.*)

$$\left(Ans.: \frac{wl^2}{30}; \frac{wl^2}{20}; \frac{3\,wl}{20}; \frac{7\,wl}{20}; 0.021\,47\,wl^2 \text{ at } 0.548\,l \text{ from R.H. end}\right)$$

22. A steel beam 0·35 m deep, $I = 376 × 10^{-6}$ m⁴ has a span of 7·2 m and is built-in at the ends. Calculate the uniformly distributed load it can carry with a maximum bending stress of 120 MN/m² if, on loading, the end fixings yield to such an extent that the fixing moments are 30% less than they would be with rigidly fixed ends. $E = 200$ GN/m². (*U. Lond.*)   (*Ans.:* 74·6 kN m)

23. A rolled steel joist, 560 mm × 180 mm ($I = 700 × 10^{-6}$ m⁴) is used as a beam of 7·2 m effective span, the ends being partially fixed. The load consists of a point load of 160 kN at the centre of the span and a uniformly distributed load (including the weight of the beam itself) of 60 kN. The rigidity of the end connections is such that the slope at the ends is $4\,M \times 10^{-8}$ where M is the end moment in N m. Calculate the value of the end moments. $E = 200$ GN/m^2. (*U. Lond.*)   (*Ans.*: 70·43 kN m)

24. A loaded horizontal beam has its ends securely built-in; the clear span is 6 m and $I = 80 \times 10^{-6}$ m^4. Later it is observed that one end has been displaced 10 mm vertically. Assuming the ends are still securely built-in, determine the alteration of the fixing moments and vertical reactions. $E = 200$ GN/m^2. (*U. Lond.*)   (*Ans.*: 26·67 kN m; 8·89 kN)

25. A continuous beam carrying a uniformly distributed load of 50 kN/m covers three spans. The end spans are each 6 m in length and the central span is 18 m. Calculate the greatest bending moment and shearing force, and the position of the points of contraflexure. (*I. Mech. E.*)
(*Ans.*: 1·145 MNm at inner supports; 450 kN at inner supports; 5·93 m from centre)

26. A continuous horizontal beam, ABC, is fixed horizontally at C and supported (to the same level) at A and B. AB = 3 m; BC = 5 m. The loading on AB consists of a vertical concentrated load of 40 kN at 1 m from B, and on BC, of a vertical concentrated load of 100 kN at 1 m from B.
Give dimensioned sketches of the bending moment and shearing force diagrams for the beam ABC. (*U. Lond.*)
(*Ans.*: $M_b = 45\cdot5$ kN m; $M_c = 25\cdot3$ kN m; $R_a = -1\cdot83$ kN; $R_b = 125\cdot87$ kN; $R_c = 15\cdot96$ kN)

27. A continuous beam 15 m long rests on three supports at the same level. One span is 6 m and carries a concentrated load of 100 kN at its centre, and the other is 9 m and carries a uniformly distributed load of 120 kN. Calculate the maximum positive and negative bending moments for each span and the reactions. Draw the B.M. and S.F. diagrams roughly to scale. (*U. Lond.*)
(*Ans.*: $+126$ and -87 kN m; $+126$ and $-79\cdot4$ kN m; 29 kN; 145 kN; 46 kN)

28. A beam AC, 22 m long, rests on supports at A, B and C at the same level. AB = 10 m; BC = 12 m. A uniformly distributed load of 16 kN/m is carried over the entire beam and, in addition, there is a 60 kN load placed mid-way between supports A and B. Calculate (*a*) the bending moments at the centre of each span and at the support B, and (*b*) the reactions at the three supports. Sketch the S.F. and B.M. diagrams for the loaded beam. (*U. Lond.*)
(*Ans.*: 200·5 kN m; 138·5 kN m; 299 kN m; 80·1 kN; 260·8 kN; 71·1 kN)

29. A continuous beam rests on four supports with the right-hand end rigidly fixed. The first span at the left-hand end is 6 m and carries 36 kN uniformly distributed. The second span is 9 m and carries 18 kN at the centre and the third span is 12 m carrying 12 kN uniformly distributed. Calculate the bending moments and reactions and draw the B.M. and S.F. diagrams to scale. (*U. Lond.*)
(*Ans.*: $M_b = 24\cdot485$ kN m; $M_c = 15\cdot05$ kN m; $M_d = 10\cdot425$ kN m; $R_a = 13\cdot92$ kN; $R_b = 32\cdot11$ kN; $R_c = 14\cdot28$ kN; $R_d = 5\cdot69$ kN)

30. An R.S.J. is used for a horizontal beam ABC, which is built-in at one end A, and carried on two unyielding supports B and C, the spans AB and BC being 6 and 9 m respectively. A uniformly distributed load of 16 kN/m (inclusive of weight of joist) is carried along the full length AC. Draw the bending moment diagram and from it determine a suitable size for the R.S.J., using an allowable stress of 120 MN/m^2. (*U. Lond.*)
(*Ans.*: $M_{max} = 124$ kN m at B; $Z = 1\cdot033 \times 10^{-3}$ m^3)

CHAPTER 7

STRUTS

7.1 Introduction. A *strut* usually refers to a compression member which is long in comparison with its cross-sectional dimensions. Such a member will fail due to buckling before the direct compressive stress reaches the yield point.

For a very long strut, where the effect of direct compression is negligible, the load which will cause buckling is given by Euler's Theory but for shorter struts, the Rankine Formula, which makes allowance for the effect of direct compression, is more appropriate.

For both theories, it is assumed that:

(*a*) the strut is initially straight,
(*b*) the load is applied axially,
(*c*) the material is homogeneous.

For such an ideal case, the strut will remain straight as the load is gradually increased until the critical load is reached when, if disturbed, it will suddenly buckle. If the load is further increased, the strut will collapse; if it is reduced, the strut will straighten again. The amount of buckling under the critical load is indeterminate; theoretically an infinite number of positions are possible, up to that in which the combined effect of buckling and direct stresses causes failure in the outer fibres of the material.

If any of the above conditions are not fulfilled, bending will take place as soon as any load is applied; see Arts. 7.5, 7.6 and 7.7.

7.2 Euler's Theory.

Case (a)—strut with both ends pinned, Fig. 7.1.

Taking the origin at the centre,

$$EI \frac{\mathrm{d}^2 y}{\mathrm{d}x^2} = -Py*$$

or

$$\frac{\mathrm{d}^2 y}{\mathrm{d}x^2} + \frac{P}{EI} y = 0$$

i.e.

$$\frac{\mathrm{d}^2 y}{\mathrm{d}x^2} + \mu^2 y = 0 \quad \text{where } \mu^2 = \frac{P}{EI}$$

The solution is

$$y = A \cos \mu x + B \sin \mu x$$

---

* If the strut is turned into the horizontal position and the deflection is downwards. y is positive and M is negative. If the deflection is upwards, y is negative and M is positive. With the opposite sign convention, the signs of y and M are reversed in each case, so that in all circumstances, M is opposite in sign to y, i.e. $M = -Py$.

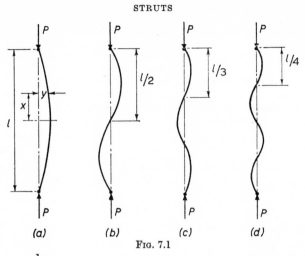

Fɪɢ. 7.1

When $x = 0$, $\dfrac{dy}{dx} = 0$, $\therefore B = 0$.

When $x = \dfrac{l}{2}$, $y = 0$, $\therefore 0 = A \cos \mu \dfrac{l}{2}$

Therefore either $A = 0$ or $\cos \mu \dfrac{l}{2} = 0$ but A cannot be zero, otherwise $y = 0$ for all values of x, i.e. no buckling has occurred,

i.e. $\qquad\qquad \cos \mu \dfrac{l}{2} = 0$

$$\therefore \mu \frac{l}{2} = \frac{\pi}{2}, \frac{3\pi}{2}, \text{etc.}$$

from which $\qquad P = \dfrac{\pi^2 EI}{l^2}$, taking the smallest solution .   . (7.1)

The shape of the deflected strut is shown in Fig. 7.1(a).

If, however, the strut is prevented from moving at the centre, the next mode of buckling will be as shown in Fig. 7.1(b)

When $x = 0$, $y = 0$, $\qquad \therefore A = 0$

When $x = \dfrac{l}{2}$, $y = 0$, $\qquad \therefore 0 = B \sin \mu \dfrac{l}{2}$

$$\therefore \sin \mu \frac{l}{2} = 0 \text{ since } B \text{ cannot also be zero,}$$

$$\therefore \mu \frac{l}{2} = \pi, 2\pi, \text{etc.}$$

from which $\qquad\qquad P = \dfrac{4\pi^2 EI}{l^2}$, taking the smallest solution.

Further modes of buckling are possible, as shown in Figs. 7.1(c) and (d), these corresponding with $\mu \dfrac{l}{2} = \dfrac{3\pi}{2}$, 2π, etc.

Case (b)—strut with one end fixed and one end free, Fig. 7.2.

Taking the origin at the base,

$$EI \frac{\mathrm{d}^2 y}{\mathrm{d}x^2} = P(a - y)^*$$

i.e. $\qquad \dfrac{\mathrm{d}^2 y}{\mathrm{d}x^2} + \mu^2 y = \mu^2 a$

The solution is

$$y = A \cos \mu x + B \sin \mu x + a$$

When $x = 0$, $y = 0$, $\therefore A = -a$

When $x = 0$, $\dfrac{\mathrm{d}y}{\mathrm{d}x} = 0$, $\therefore B = 0$

$$\therefore y = a - a \cos \mu x$$

When $x = l$, $y = a$,

$$\therefore a = a - a \cos \mu l$$
$$\therefore \cos \mu l = 0$$

since $a \neq 0$ if buckling has occurred

$$\therefore \mu l = \frac{\pi}{2}$$

from which $\qquad P = \dfrac{\pi^2 EI}{4l^2}$ . . . . (7.2)

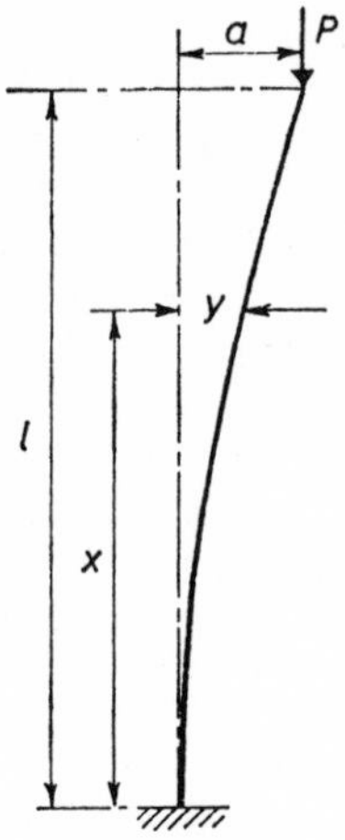

Fig. 7.2

Case (c)—strut with both ends fixed, Fig. 7.3.

Taking the origin at the centre,

$$EI \frac{\mathrm{d}^2 y}{\mathrm{d}x^2} = - Py + M$$

i.e. $\qquad \dfrac{\mathrm{d}^2 y}{\mathrm{d}x^2} + \mu^2 y = \dfrac{M}{EI}$

The solution is

$$y = A \cos \mu x + B \sin \mu x + \frac{M}{P}$$

When $\qquad x = 0$, $\dfrac{\mathrm{d}y}{\mathrm{d}x} = 0$, $\therefore B = 0$.

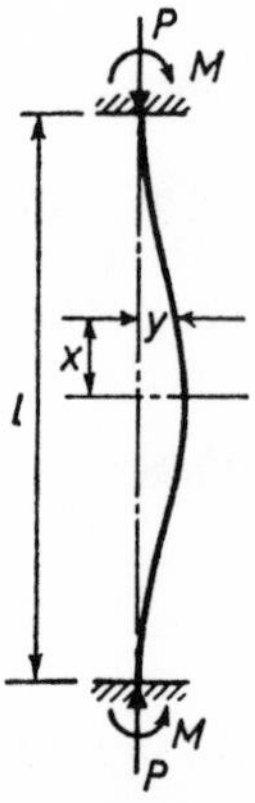

Fig. 7.3

* The B.M. in this case is opposite in effect to that in case (a), i.e. it is positive.

When $x = \dfrac{l}{2}, \dfrac{dy}{dx} = 0, \therefore 0 = -\mu A \sin \mu \dfrac{l}{2}$

$$\therefore \sin \mu \frac{l}{2} = 0$$

$$\therefore \mu \frac{l}{2} = \pi$$

from which $\qquad P = \dfrac{4\pi^2 EI}{l^2}$ . . . . (7.3)

Further modes of buckling are possible, as in case (a).

Case (d)—strut with one end fixed and one end pinned, Fig. 7.4.

In this case, there will be a horizontal reaction F at the pin to keep the top end of the strut on the vertical axis; the product $F \times l$ balances the fixing moment M at the base.

Taking the origin at the base,

$$EI \frac{d^2y}{dx^2} = -Py + F(l - x)$$

i.e. $\qquad \dfrac{d^2y}{dx^2} + \mu^2 y = \dfrac{F}{EI}(l - x)$

The solution is

$$y = A \cos \mu x + B \sin \mu x + \frac{F}{P}(l - x)$$

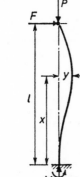

When $x = 0, y = 0, \therefore A = -\dfrac{Fl}{P}$

When $x = 0, \dfrac{dy}{dx} = 0, \therefore B = \dfrac{F}{\mu P}$

$$\therefore y = \frac{F}{P}\left\{-l \cos \mu x + \frac{\sin \mu x}{\mu} + (l - x)\right\}$$

When $x = l, y = 0$,

$$\therefore 0 = \frac{F}{P}\left\{-l \cos \mu l + \frac{\sin \mu l}{\mu}\right\}$$

$$\therefore \tan \mu l = \mu l$$

The smallest solution is $\mu l = 4{\cdot}5$ rad

Fig. 7.4

from which $\qquad P = 20{\cdot}25\dfrac{EI}{l^2} \simeq \dfrac{2\pi^2 EI}{l^2}$ . . . . (7.4)

7.3   Validity limit for Euler's Theory. For the case of a short strut, Euler's theory may give a critical load which is greater than that required to produce failure due to direct compression. The limiting case occurs when

$$P = \sigma_c a$$

where σ_c is the compressive stress at the yield point and a is the cross-sectional area.

But $$P = n\frac{\pi^2 EI}{l^2} = n\frac{\pi^2 E(ak^2)}{l^2}$$

where n is a constant depending on the end fixing conditions and k is the least radius of gyration of the cross-section.

$$\therefore \; n\frac{\pi^2 Ek^2}{l^2} = \sigma_c$$

or $$\frac{l}{k} = \sqrt{\frac{n\pi^2 E}{\sigma_c}} \qquad . \quad . \quad . \quad . \quad . \quad . \quad (7.5)$$

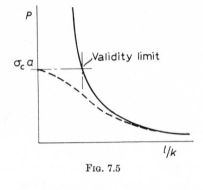

Fig. 7.5

The quantity l/k is called the *slenderness ratio* and its value at this point is called the *validity limit*. For a mild steel pin-ended strut, $n = 1$, $E = 208$ GN/m² and $\sigma_c = 325$ MN/m², so that $l/k \eqsim 80$. It would therefore be impossible to use Euler's theory for such a strut of slenderness ratio less than this value and, in fact, this theory would give an excessive value for the crippling load before this limiting case was reached.

Fig. 7.5 shows how P varies with l/k according to Euler's theory and the dotted line shows the corresponding values of P as given by Rankine's theory, where an allowance is made for the effect of direct compression.

7.4   Rankine's Theory. For a very long strut, the crippling load is given by $P = P_e$, where P_e is the load given by Euler's theory. For a very short strut, the crippling load is given by $P = P_c$, where P_c is the load at failure due to direct compression.

For a strut of intermediate length, Rankine's criterion of failure is

$$\frac{1}{P} = \frac{1}{P_c} + \frac{1}{P_e}$$

$$\therefore P = \cfrac{1}{\cfrac{1}{\sigma_c a} + \cfrac{l^2}{n\pi^2 EI}}$$

$$= \cfrac{\sigma_c a}{1 + \cfrac{\sigma_c}{n\pi^2 E}\left(\frac{l}{k}\right)^2}$$

The quantity $\sigma_c/\pi^2 E$ is a constant for a given material and is denoted by c.

Hence
$$P = \frac{\sigma_c a}{1 + \frac{c}{n}\left(\frac{l}{k}\right)^2} \qquad . \qquad . \qquad . \qquad . \quad (7.6)$$

where n has the value 1, $\frac{1}{4}$, 4 or 2·05 for the various types of end fixing considered in Art. 7.2.

Although the value of c could be calculated from $\sigma_c/\pi^2 E$, it is usually determined directly by experiment and the following are the values of σ_c and c normally used:

Material	$\sigma_c(\text{MN/m}^2)$	c
Mild steel	325	1/7500 (theoretically 1/6200)
Cast iron	550	1/1600 (theoretically 1/2040)

Due to the discrepancy between the usually accepted values of c and the theoretical values, the Rankine curve shown in Fig. 7.5 will not coincide with the Euler curve for very long struts, as it should theoretically do.

7.5 Strut with eccentric load. Fig. 7.6 shows a pin-ended strut in which the load is applied with an eccentricity e at each end. For such a case, there is no buckling load; the strut will commence to bend immediately any load is applied and the deflection at any point is directly related to the load.

Taking the origin at the centre,

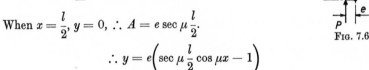

$$EI\frac{d^2y}{dx^2} = -P(y + e)$$

i.e.
$$\frac{d^2y}{dx^2} + \mu^2 y = -\mu^2 e$$

The solution is
$$y = A \cos \mu x + B \sin \mu x - e$$

When $x = 0$, $\dfrac{dy}{dx} = 0$, $\therefore B = 0$.

When $x = \dfrac{l}{2}$, $y = 0$, $\therefore A = e \sec \mu \dfrac{l}{2}$.

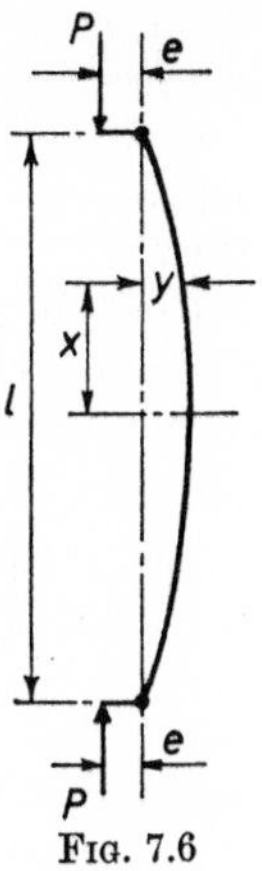

$$\therefore y = e\left(\sec \mu \frac{l}{2} \cos \mu x - 1\right)$$

$$\therefore y_{\max} = e\left(\sec \mu \frac{l}{2} - 1\right), \quad \text{when } x = 0 \quad . \qquad . \quad (7.7)$$

$$M_{\max} = P(y_{\max} + e) = Pe \sec \mu \frac{l}{2} \qquad . \qquad . \qquad . \quad (7.8)$$

and
$$\sigma_{\max} = \frac{P}{a} \pm \frac{Pe}{Z} \sec \mu \frac{l}{2} . \qquad . \qquad . \qquad . \quad (7.9)$$

FIG. 7.6

7.6 Strut with initial curvature. Fig. 7.7 shows a pin-ended strut in which the load is applied axially at the ends but the strut has initial curvature, the central deflection from the axis through the ends being h. As in the previous case, bending occurs immediately any load is applied.

Assuming that the initial curvature is relatively small, the exact shape of the curve has little effect upon the subsequent bending and since the fundamental shape of a strut which is deflected by an end thrust is a cosine curve, it is convenient to assume that the initial curvature is also of the form of a cosine curve.

Thus, taking the origin at the centre,* the equation of the initial curvature is

$$u = h \cos \frac{\pi}{l} x$$

The subsequent movement of the strut due to the force P is $y - u$, hence

$$EI \frac{d^2}{dx^2}(y - u) = -Py$$

i.e.
$$EI \frac{d^2y}{dx^2} + Py = EI \frac{d^2u}{dx^2}$$

$$= -EIh \frac{\pi^2}{l^2} \cos \frac{\pi}{l} x$$

i.e.
$$\frac{d^2y}{dx^2} + \mu^2 y = -h \frac{\pi^2}{l^2} \cos \frac{\pi}{l} x$$

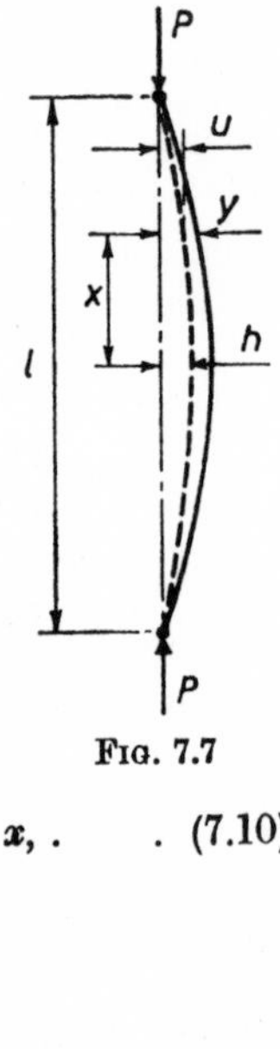

The solution is

$$y = A \cos \mu x + B \sin \mu x - \frac{h \dfrac{\pi^2}{l^2} \cos \dfrac{\pi}{l} x}{\mu^2 - \dfrac{\pi^2}{l^2}}$$

$$= A \cos \mu x + B \sin \mu x + \frac{P_e}{P_e - P} h \cos \frac{\pi}{l} x, \qquad . \qquad (7.10)$$

FIG. 7.7

where P_e is the Euler crippling load for the strut.

When $x = 0$, $\dfrac{dy}{dx} = 0$, $\therefore B = 0$.

When $x = \dfrac{l}{2}$, $y = 0$, $\therefore 0 = A \cos \mu \dfrac{l}{2}$

If $\cos \mu \dfrac{l}{2} = 0$, then $\mu \dfrac{l}{2} = \dfrac{\pi}{2}$, whence $P = \dfrac{\pi^2 EI}{l^2} = P_e$.

In this case, however, y would be infinite, from equation (7.10) and so, assuming that P is less than this value,

* If the origin is taken at one end, the curve will be a sine wave.

$$\cos \mu \frac{l}{2} \neq 0$$

so that $$A = 0$$

$$\therefore y = \frac{P_e}{P_e - P} h \cos \frac{\pi}{l} x \qquad . \qquad . \qquad . \quad (7.11)$$

i.e. due to the action of the load, the deflection at any point is increased in the ratio $P_e/(P_e - P)$.

$$y_{max} = \frac{P_e h}{P_e - P}, \quad \text{when } x = 0 \quad . \qquad . \quad (7.12)$$

$$M_{max} = \frac{PP_e h}{P_e - P} \qquad . \qquad . \qquad . \qquad . \quad (7.13)$$

and $$\sigma_{max} = \frac{P}{a} \pm \frac{PP_e}{P_e - P} \cdot \frac{h}{Z} \qquad . \qquad . \qquad . \quad (7.14)$$

If the load is applied eccentrically at each end, the total deflection at any point is the sum (or difference) of the deflections due to the eccentricity and initial curvature.

7.7 Laterally loaded struts.

Case (a)—central concentrated load, Fig. 7.8.

Taking the origin at the centre,

$$EI \frac{d^2 y}{dx^2} = -Py - \frac{W}{2}\left(\frac{l}{2} - x\right)$$

i.e. $$\frac{d^2 y}{dx^2} + \mu^2 y = -\frac{W}{2EI}\left(\frac{l}{2} - x\right)$$

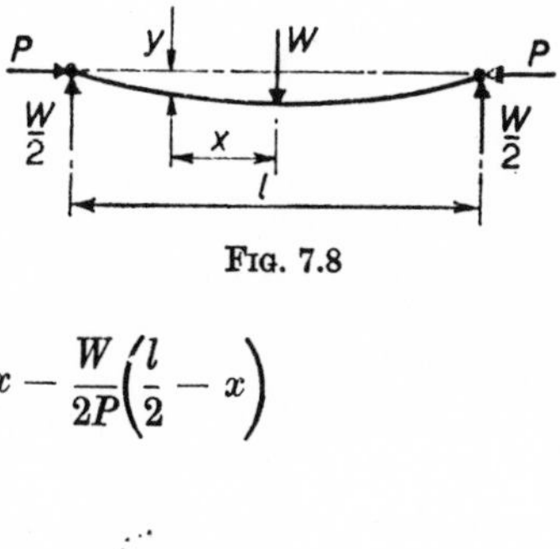

FIG. 7.8

The solution is

$$y = A \cos \mu x + B \sin \mu x - \frac{W}{2P}\left(\frac{l}{2} - x\right)$$

When $x = 0$, $\dfrac{dy}{dx} = 0$, $\therefore B = -\dfrac{W}{2\mu P}$

When $x = \dfrac{l}{2}$, $y = 0$, $\therefore A = \dfrac{W}{2\mu P} \tan \mu \dfrac{l}{2}$,

$$\therefore y = \frac{W}{2P}\left\{\frac{1}{\mu}\left(\tan \mu \frac{l}{2} \cos \mu x - \sin \mu x\right) - \left(\frac{l}{2} - x\right)\right\} \quad . \quad (7.15)$$

$$y_{max} = \frac{W}{2P}\left\{\frac{1}{\mu} \tan \mu \frac{l}{2} - \frac{l}{2}\right\} \quad \text{when } x = 0 \quad . \qquad . \quad (7.16)$$

$$M_{max} = -Py_{max} - \frac{W}{2} \cdot \frac{l}{2} = -\frac{W}{2\mu} \tan \mu \frac{l}{2} \qquad . \qquad . \quad (7.17)$$

Case (b)—uniformly distributed load, Fig. 7.9.

Taking the origin at the centre,

$$EI \frac{d^2y}{dx^2} = -Py - \frac{w}{2}\left(\frac{l^2}{4} - x^2\right)$$

i.e. $\frac{d^2y}{dx^2} + \mu^2 y = -\frac{w}{2EI}\left(\frac{l^2}{4} - x^2\right)$

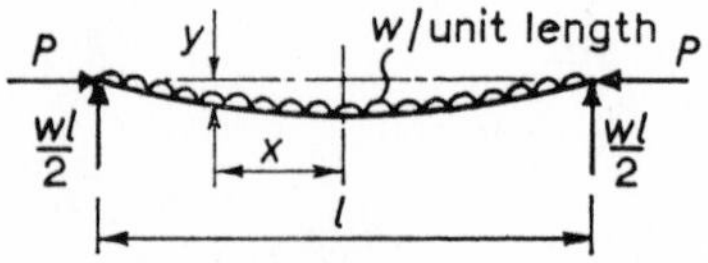

FIG. 7.9

The solution is

$$y = A \cos \mu x + B \sin \mu x - \frac{w}{2P}\left(\frac{l^2}{4} - x^2 + \frac{2}{\mu^2}\right)$$

When $x = 0$, $\frac{dy}{dx} = 0$, $\therefore B = 0$.

When $x = \frac{l}{2}$, $y = 0$, $\therefore A = \frac{w}{\mu^2 P} \sec \mu \frac{l}{2}$

$$\therefore y = \frac{w}{P}\left\{\frac{1}{\mu^2}\left(\sec \mu \frac{l}{2} \cos \mu x - 1\right) - \frac{l^2}{8} + \frac{x^2}{2}\right\} \quad . \quad (7.18)$$

$$\therefore y_{max} = \frac{w}{P}\left\{\frac{1}{\mu^2}\left(\sec \mu \frac{l}{2} - 1\right) - \frac{l^2}{8}\right\} \quad \text{when } x = 0 \quad . \quad (7.19)$$

$$\therefore M_{max} = -Py_{max} - \frac{wl^2}{8} = -\frac{w}{\mu^2}\left(\sec \mu \frac{l}{2} - 1\right) \quad . \quad (7.20)$$

7.8 Alternative method for determining bending moment. In the preceding articles, the deflection of the strut has first been obtained and the bending moment derived from this. If, however, only the bending moment is required, it is more direct to proceed with a differential equation for M.

If M' is the B.M. due to the transverse loads, then

$$M = -Py + M'$$

or $$M + Py = M'$$

Differentiating twice with respect to x,

$$\frac{d^2M}{dx^2} + P\frac{d^2y}{dx^2} = \frac{d^2M'}{dx^2}$$

But $$P\frac{d^2y}{dx^2} = \frac{P}{EI} . EI \frac{d^2y}{dx^2} = \mu^2 M$$

$$\therefore \frac{d^2M}{dx^2} + \mu^2 M = \frac{d^2M'}{dx^2} \quad . \quad . \quad . \quad . \quad . \quad (7.21)$$

If there is no transverse load or if it consists of a concentrated load, then

$$\frac{\mathrm{d}^2 M'}{\mathrm{d}x^2} = 0$$

The solution for M is then

$$M = A \cos \mu x + B \sin \mu x$$

For an eccentrically loaded strut, (Art. 7.5),

$$\frac{\mathrm{d}M}{\mathrm{d}x} = 0 \text{ when } x = 0, \therefore B = 0$$

and

$$M = Pe \text{ when } x = \frac{l}{2}, \therefore A = Pe \sec \mu \frac{l}{2}$$

so that

$$M = Pe \sec \mu \frac{l}{2} \cos \mu x$$

and

$$M_{\max} = Pe \sec \mu \frac{l}{2}$$

For a strut with a central concentrated load, (Art. 7.7(a)),

$$\frac{\mathrm{d}M}{\mathrm{d}x} = \frac{W}{2} \text{ when } x = 0, \therefore B = \frac{W}{2\mu}$$

and

$$M = 0 \text{ when } x = 0, \therefore A = -\frac{W}{2\mu} \tan \mu \frac{l}{2}$$

so that

$$M = -\frac{W}{2\mu} \left\{ \tan \mu \frac{l}{2} \cos \mu x + \sin \mu x \right\}$$

and

$$M_{\max} = -\frac{W}{2\mu} \tan \mu \frac{l}{2}$$

For a strut with a uniformly distributed load, (Art. 7.7(b)),

$$\frac{\mathrm{d}^2 M'}{\mathrm{d}x^2} = w$$

$$\therefore M = A \cos \mu x + B \sin \mu x + \frac{w}{\mu^2}$$

When $x = 0$, $\frac{\mathrm{d}M}{\mathrm{d}x} = 0$, $\therefore B = 0$.

When $x = \frac{l}{2}$, $M = 0$, $\therefore A = -\frac{w}{\mu^2} \sec \mu \frac{l}{2}$

$$\therefore M = -\frac{w}{\mu^2} \left(\sec \mu \frac{l}{2} \cos \mu x - 1 \right)$$

and

$$M_{\max} = -\frac{w}{\mu^2} \left(\sec \mu \frac{l}{2} - 1 \right)$$

7.9 Eccentrically and transversely loaded tie-bars. If the axial load is tensile instead of compressive, the term Py becomes positive instead of negative and the complementary function becomes $A \cosh \mu x + B \sinh \mu x$. The subsequent analysis is identical with that for struts and the results are similar except for the substitution of hyperbolic functions for trigonometrical functions and occasional changes of sign.

Alternatively, the results for tie-bars may be obtained from those for struts by replacing P by $-P$, from which μ changes to $i\mu$.

Thus, in the case of a tie-bar with a uniformly distributed load, equation (7.20) becomes

$$M_{\max} = -\frac{w}{(i\mu)^2}\left(\sec i\mu \frac{l}{2} - 1\right)$$

$$= \frac{w}{\mu^2}\left(\text{sech}\, \mu \frac{l}{2} - 1\right)$$

1. *A straight bar of alloy 1 m long and 12·5 mm × 5 mm in section is mounted in a strut testing machine and loaded axially till it buckles. Assuming the Euler formula for pinned-ends to apply, estimate the maximum central deflection before the material attains its yield point, at 280 MN/m². E = 75 GN/m².* (U. Lond.)

For a pin-ended strut

$$P = \frac{\pi^2 EI}{l^2} \quad . \qquad . \qquad . \qquad . \qquad \text{from equation (7.2)}$$

$$= \frac{\pi^2 \times 75 \times 10^9 \times 0.012\,5 \times 0.005^3}{1^2 \times 12} = 96.4 \text{ N}$$

$$\therefore \sigma_{\text{d}} = \frac{P}{a} = \frac{96.4}{0.012\,5 \times 0.005} \text{ N/m}^2 = 1.56 \text{ MN/m}^2$$

If the central deflection of the strut is δ,

$$M_{\max} = P \times \delta$$

$$\therefore \sigma_{\text{b}} = \frac{P \times \delta}{Z}$$

$$= \frac{96.4 \times \delta \times 6}{0.012\,5 \times 0.005^2} \text{ N/m}^2 = 1\,850\, \delta \text{ MN/m}^2$$

$$\therefore 1.56 + 1\,850\, \delta = 280$$

$$\therefore \delta = \underline{0.15 \text{ m}}$$

2. *From some tests on steel struts with ends fixed in position but free in direction, two of the results obtained were:*

Test No.	1	2
Ratio of slenderness	70	170
Average stress at failure (MN/m²)	200	69

(a) *Assuming these two values are in agreement with the Rankine formula,
find the two constants in the formula.*

(b) *If a steel bar of rectangular section 60 mm by 20 mm and of length
1·25 m is used as a strut with both ends fixed in position and direction, find
the safe load using the constants derived in (a) and employing a load factor of 4.*
(U. Lond.)

(a)
$$P = \frac{\sigma_c a}{1 + c\left(\dfrac{l}{k}\right)^2} \qquad . \qquad . \qquad \text{from equation (7.6)}$$

i.e.
$$200 = \frac{\sigma_c}{1 + c \times 70^2}$$

and
$$69 = \frac{\sigma_c}{1 + c \times 170^2}$$

from which $\quad \sigma_c = \underline{326\cdot4\ \text{MN/m}^2} \quad$ and $\quad c = \underline{\dfrac{1}{7\ 750}}$

(b) For built-in-ends $P = \dfrac{\sigma_c a}{1 + \dfrac{c}{4}\left(\dfrac{l}{k}\right)^2}$

$$k^2 = \frac{d^2}{12} = \frac{0\cdot02^2}{12} = \frac{1}{3 \times 10^4}\ \text{m}^2$$

$$\therefore P = \frac{1}{4} \times \frac{326\cdot4 \times 10^6 \times 0\cdot06 \times 0\cdot02}{1 + \dfrac{1\cdot25^2 \times 3 \times 10^4}{4 \times 7\ 750}}$$

$$= \underline{38\cdot9\ \text{kN}}$$

3. *A steel tubular strut is pin-jointed at each end and it is subjected to a
load parallel to its axis but eccentric to it. If the tube is 50 mm external diameter, 40 mm bore diameter and 2·5 m long, find the maximum permissible
load if the eccentricity is 5 mm and the maximum allowable stress is 300
MN/m². E = 200 GN/m².* (I.Mech.E.)

$$\sigma_{\text{max}} = \frac{P}{a} + \frac{Pe}{Z} \sec \mu \frac{l}{2} \qquad . \qquad . \qquad . \qquad . \qquad \text{from equation (7.9)}$$

$$a = \frac{\pi}{4}(0\cdot05^2 - 0\cdot04^2) = 7\cdot07 \times 10^{-4}\ \text{m}^2$$

$$Z = \frac{\pi}{32}\left(\frac{0\cdot05^4 - 0\cdot04^4}{0\cdot05}\right) = 7\cdot24 \times 10^{-6}\ \text{m}^3$$

$$\mu = \sqrt{\frac{P}{EI}} = \sqrt{\frac{P}{200 \times 10^9 \times \dfrac{\pi}{64}(0\cdot05^4 - 0\cdot04^4)}} = 0\cdot005\ 25\sqrt{P}\ \text{m}^{-1}$$

$I = \dfrac{bd^3}{12} \qquad I = \dfrac{\pi d^4}{64}$

$y = \dfrac{bd^2}{6} \qquad y = \dfrac{\pi d^3}{32}$

$$\therefore \ 300 \times 10^6 = P\left\{\frac{10^4}{7 \cdot 07} + \frac{0 \cdot 005 \times 10^6}{7 \cdot 24} \sec\left(0 \cdot 005\ 25\sqrt{\bar{P}} \times \frac{2 \cdot 5}{2}\right)\right\}$$

which reduces to $\quad \dfrac{434\ 800}{P} - 2 \cdot 05 - \sec 0 \cdot 006\ 56\sqrt{\bar{P}} = 0$

By use of Newton's method or by plotting,

$$P = \underline{47 \cdot 5 \text{ kN}}$$

4. *A horizontal light alloy tube 60 mm external and 50 mm internal diameter, 2·4 m long, is freely supported at its ends. It carries an axial compressive load of 20 kN, and also two vertical point loads of 1 kN at 0·8 m from each end. Find approximately the maximum stress in the tube.*

The beam may be treated as a slightly curved strut, the initial deflection being that due to the transverse loads. Neglect the weight of the tube and take E as 70 GN/m². (U. Lond.)

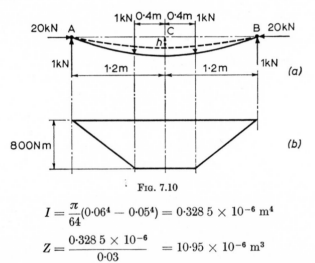

Fig. 7.10

$$I = \frac{\pi}{64}(0 \cdot 06^4 - 0 \cdot 05^4) = 0 \cdot 328\ 5 \times 10^{-6} \text{ m}^4$$

and $\qquad Z = \dfrac{0 \cdot 328\ 5 \times 10^{-6}}{0 \cdot 03} = 10 \cdot 95 \times 10^{-6} \text{ m}^3$

The strut is shown in Fig. 7.10(*a*) and Fig. 7.10(*b*) shows the B.M. diagram due to the transverse loads alone. The initial central deflection is most easily obtained by the area–moment method; taking the origin at B and considering the part BC only,

$$\left[x\frac{dy}{dx} - y\right]_0^{1 \cdot 2} = \frac{1}{EI} \times \begin{array}{l}\text{moment of area of B.M. diagram between C}\\\text{and B about B}\end{array}$$

i.e. $\quad (0 - h) - (0 - 0) = - \dfrac{\dfrac{0 \cdot 8 \times 800}{2} \times \frac{2}{3} \times 0 \cdot 8 + 0 \cdot 4 \times 800 \times 1 \cdot 0}{70 \times 10^9 \times 0 \cdot 328\ 5 \times 10^{-6}}$

$$\therefore h = 0 \cdot 021\ 35 \text{ m}$$

$$y_{\max} = \frac{P_e h}{P_e - P} \qquad . \qquad . \qquad . \qquad . \qquad \text{from equation (7.12)}$$

$$P_e = \frac{\pi^2 EI}{l^2} \qquad . \qquad . \qquad . \qquad . \qquad \text{from equation (7.2)}$$

$$= \frac{\pi^2 \times 70 \times 10^9 \times 0.328\ 5 \times 10^{-6}}{2.4^2} = 56\ 200\ \text{N}$$

$$\therefore y_{\max} = \frac{56\ 200 \times 0.021\ 35}{56\ 200 - 20\ 000} = 0.033\ 2\ \text{m}$$

$$\therefore M_{\max} = -20\ 000 \times 0.033\ 2 - 800 \qquad = -1\ 464\ \text{N m}$$

$$\therefore \sigma_{\max} = \frac{20\ 000}{\frac{\pi}{4}(0.06^2 - 0.05^2)} + \frac{1\ 464}{10.95 \times 10^{-6}}\ \text{N/m}^2 = \underline{156.6\ \text{MN/m}^2}$$

5. *A thin vertical strut of uniform cross-section and length L is rigidly fixed at the bottom, and the top end is free. At the top there is a horizontal load H and a vertical downward load W acting through the centroid of the section. Prove that the horizontal deflection at the top is*

$$\frac{H}{W}\left(\frac{\tan \mu L}{\mu} - L\right) \quad \text{where } \mu = \sqrt{\frac{W}{EI}}.$$

If the strut is 2 m long and the horizontal deflection at the top produced by a horizontal load of 100 N is 112·5 mm, find the deflection where there is, in addition, a vertical load of 180 N. Find also the maximum bending moment in the strut. (U. Lond.)

Referring to Fig. 7.11,

$$EI \frac{d^2 y}{dx^2} = W(a - y) + H(l - x)$$

i.e. $\quad \dfrac{d^2 y}{dx^2} + \mu^2 y = \mu^2 a + \dfrac{H}{EI}(l - x)$

The solution is

$$y = A \cos \mu x + B \sin \mu x + a + \frac{H}{W}(l - x)$$

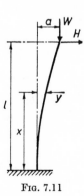

FIG. 7.11

When $x = 0, \dfrac{dy}{dx} = 0, \therefore B = \dfrac{H}{\mu W}$

When $x = 0, y = 0, \therefore A = -\left(a + \dfrac{Hl}{W}\right)$

$$\therefore y = -\left(a + \frac{Hl}{W}\right)\cos \mu x + \frac{H}{\mu W}\sin \mu x + a + \frac{H}{W}(l - x)$$

F

When $x = l$, $y = a$,

$$\therefore a = -\left(a + \frac{Hl}{W}\right)\cos \mu l + \frac{H}{\mu W}\sin \mu l + a$$

from which

$$a = \frac{H}{W}\left(\frac{\tan \mu l}{\mu} - l\right)$$

Due to H alone,

$$\text{deflection at top} = \frac{Hl^3}{3EI}$$

i.e.

$$0.112\,5 = \frac{100 \times 2^3}{3EI}$$

$$\therefore EI = 2\,370 \text{ N m}^2$$

$$\mu = \sqrt{\frac{W}{EI}} = \sqrt{\frac{180}{2\,370}} = 0.276 \text{ m}^{-1}$$

$$\therefore a = \frac{100}{180}\left(\frac{\tan\ 0.276 \times 2}{0.276} - 2\right)$$

$$= \underline{0.130\,5 \text{ m}}$$

6. *A thin vertical strut, 1 m long and initially straight, is pinned at each end and carries an axial load P. A spring of stiffness 4·5 kN/m is attached at the centre with its axis horizontal and when the strut is straight, the spring is stretched 30 mm.*

Find the central deflection when P is one quarter of the Euler crippling load and EI is 30 N m².

The strut is shown in Fig. 7.12. From equation (7.16), the central deflection under a central load W is given by

$$y_{\max} = \frac{W}{2P}\left\{\frac{1}{\mu}\tan \mu \frac{l}{2} - \frac{l}{2}\right\}$$

Denoting the central deflection by δ

$$W = S(0.03 - \delta)$$
$$= 4.5 \times 10^3(0.03 - \delta) \text{ N}$$
$$\therefore \frac{W}{2P} = \frac{4.5 \times 10^3(0.03 - \delta)}{\dfrac{2 \times \pi^2 EI}{4l^2}}$$

$$= \frac{4.5 \times 10^3(0.03 - \delta) \times 2 \times 1^2}{\pi^2 \times 30}$$

$$= 30.4(0.03 - \delta)$$

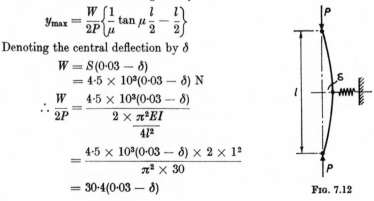

Fig. 7.12

$$\mu = \sqrt{\frac{P}{EI}} = \sqrt{\frac{\pi^2 EI}{4l^2 EI}} = \frac{\pi}{2l}$$

$$\therefore \frac{1}{\mu} \tan \mu \frac{l}{2} - \frac{l}{2} = \frac{2l}{\pi} \tan \frac{\pi}{4} - \frac{l}{2} = 0\cdot136$$

$$\therefore \delta = 30\cdot4(0\cdot03 - \delta) \times 0\cdot136 = 4\cdot13(0\cdot03 - \delta) \text{ m}$$

from which $\qquad \delta = 0\cdot024\ 15 \text{ m} \quad \text{or} \quad \underline{24\cdot15 \text{ mm}}$

7. *A uniform tie-rod of length 2a, pin-jointed at its ends, supports a uniformly distributed transverse load w per unit length, in addition to an axial pull P. Derive an expression for the maximum bending moment.*

A steel tie-bar of length 1·5 m between pin centres and diameter 25 mm carries an axial tension of 12·5 kN and, in addition, a lateral load of 450 N uniformly distributed along its length. Calculate the maximum bending moment in the tie-bar.

If the axial force becomes reversed in direction (i.e. compressive), calculate the percentage change in stress. E = 200 GN/m². (U. Lond.)

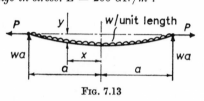

Fig. 7.13

Referring to Fig. 7.13, $M = Py - \dfrac{w}{2}(a^2 - x^2)$

or $\qquad M - Py = -\dfrac{w}{2}(a^2 - x^2)$

$$\therefore \frac{\mathrm{d}^2 M}{\mathrm{d}x^2} - P\frac{\mathrm{d}^2 y}{\mathrm{d}x^2} = w$$

or $\qquad \dfrac{\mathrm{d}^2 M}{\mathrm{d}x^2} - \mu^2 M = w$, writing $P\dfrac{\mathrm{d}^2 y}{\mathrm{d}x^2}$ as $\dfrac{P}{EI}.EI\dfrac{\mathrm{d}^2 y}{\mathrm{d}x^2}$

The solution is $M = A \cosh \mu x + B \sinh \mu x - \dfrac{w}{\mu^2}$

When $x = 0$, $\dfrac{\mathrm{d}M}{\mathrm{d}x} = 0$, $\therefore B = 0$.

When $x = a$, $M = 0$, $\therefore A = \dfrac{w}{\mu^2} \operatorname{sech} \mu a$

$$\therefore M = \frac{w}{\mu^2}(\operatorname{sech} \mu a \cosh \mu x - 1)$$

$$\therefore M_{\max} = -\frac{w}{\mu^2}(1 - \operatorname{sech} \mu a), \text{ since } \operatorname{sech} \mu a < 1$$

$$\mu^2 = \frac{P}{EI} = \frac{12 \cdot 5 \times 10^3}{200 \times 10^9 \times \dfrac{\pi}{64} \times 0 \cdot 025^4} = 3 \cdot 26 \text{ m}^{-2}$$

$$\therefore M_{\max} = -\frac{450}{1 \cdot 5 \times 3 \cdot 26}\left(1 - \text{sech } \sqrt{3 \cdot 26} \times \frac{1 \cdot 5}{2}\right)$$

$$= \underline{-47 \cdot 6 \text{ N m}}$$

When P is compressive,

$$M_{\max} = -\frac{w}{\mu^2}\left(\sec \mu \frac{l}{2} - 1\right) \qquad . \qquad . \qquad . \qquad \text{from equation (7.20)}$$

$$= -\frac{450}{1 \cdot 5 \times 3 \cdot 26}\left(\sec \sqrt{3 \cdot 26} \times \frac{1 \cdot 5}{2} - 1\right)$$

$$= -336 \cdot 5 \text{ N m}$$

$$\sigma_{\max} = \frac{P}{a} + \frac{M_{\max}}{Z}$$

For tie-bar,

$$\sigma_{\max} = \frac{12\,500}{\dfrac{\pi}{4} \times 0 \cdot 025^2} + \frac{47 \cdot 6}{\dfrac{\pi}{32} \times 0 \cdot 025^3} \text{ N/m}^2 = 56 \cdot 5 \text{ kN/m}^2$$

For strut,

$$\sigma_{\max} = \frac{12\,500}{\dfrac{\pi}{4} \times 0 \cdot 025^2} + \frac{336 \cdot 5}{\dfrac{\pi}{32} \times 0 \cdot 025^3} \text{ N/m}^2 = 245 \text{ kN/m}^2$$

percentage change of stress

$$= \frac{245 - 56 \cdot 5}{56 \cdot 5} \times 100 = \underline{333}$$

8. What are the fundamental assumptions in deriving the Euler formula for the buckling load of a strut? Calculate this buckling load for a strut of tee-section, the flange width being 100 mm, overall depth 80 mm, and with both flange and stem 10 mm thick. The strut is 3 m long and hinged at both ends. $E = 200 \text{ GN/m}^2$. (*U. Lond.*) (*Ans.:* 209 kN)

9. Derive the Euler formula for a strut hinged at both ends. State clearly what you regard as the three most important assumptions made in deriving this formula.

A straight cylindrical bar is 16 mm diameter and 1·2 m long. It is freely supported at its two ends in a horizontal position and loaded at the centre with a concentrated load of 90 N. The central deflection is found to be 5 mm.

If placed vertical and loaded along its axis, what load would cause it to buckle? What is the ratio of the maximum stresses in the two cases? (*U. Lond.*) (*Ans.:* 4·44 kN; 3·04)

10. A steel strip 0·64 m long and of rectangular section, when tested as a strut with direction-free ends, was found to buckle when the load reached 515 N. In a preliminary test the strip was arranged as a simply supported beam on a span of 0·5 m and loaded in the centre when it was found that, with the long edges of the section horizontal, the deflection per N of load was 0·11 mm. Deduce from the bending test the relevant EI for the strut, and hence calculate the Euler critical load.

Compare the experimental and calculated values for the critical load and give possible reasons to account for any disagreement. (*U. Lond.*) (*Ans.: 570 N*)

11. A flat strip of steel, 75 mm long, 12 mm wide, and 0·25 mm thick is to be used as a strut with encastré ends. Working from first principles, find the critical load. $E = 200 \text{ GN/m}^2$. (*U. Lond.*)   (*Ans.: 21·9 N*)

12. A hollow cast-iron column with fixed ends supports an axial load of 1 MN. If the column is 4·5 m long and has an external diameter of 250 mm, find the thickness of metal required.

Use the Rankine formula, taking a constant of 1/6 400 and assume a working stress of 80 MN/m². (*U. Lond.*)   (*Ans.: 28 mm*)

13. A cast-iron column 200 mm external diameter is 20 mm thick and has a length of 4·5 m. Assuming it can be treated as rigidly fixed at each end, calculate the safe load by Rankine's formula, using the following empirical constants: $\sigma_c = 550 \text{ MN/m}^2$, c (for hinged ends) = 1/1 600, factor of safety 4. (*U. Lond.*)
(*Ans.: 879 kN*)

14. Compare the crippling loads given by Euler's and Rankine's formulae for a tubular steel strut 2·25 m long, having outer and inner diameters of 38 mm and 33 mm respectively, loaded through pin-joints at both ends. Take the yield stress as 325 MN/m², the Rankine constant = 1/7 500 and $E = 200 \text{ GN/m}^2$. For what length of strut of this cross-section does the Euler formula cease to apply?
(*U. Lond.*)   (*Ans.: 17·24 kN; 17·20 kN; 0·98 m*)

15. In the experimental determination of the buckling loads for 12·5 mm diameter mild steel pin-ended struts of various lengths, two of the values obtained were: (*i*) length 0·5 m, load 9·25 kN, (*ii*) length 0·2 m, load 25 kN.

(*a*) Make the necessary calculations and then state whether either of the values conforms with the Euler formula for the critical load.

(*b*) Assuming that both values are in agreement with the Rankine formula, find the two constants for this formula. Take E as 200 GN/m². (*U. Lond.*)
(*Ans.: 301·5 MN/m²; 1/8540*)

16. Derive a formula for the maximum stress in an eccentrically loaded column. A steel tube is initially straight, has an external diameter of 40 mm, is 1·6 mm thick, 1·5 m long and carries a compressive load of 20 kN acting parallel to the axis of the tube but 2·5 mm from it. Calculate the maximum stress in the tube. $E = 200 \text{ GN/m}^2$. (*U. Lond.*)   (*Ans.: 194·4 MN/m²*)

17. A strut 3 m long is constructed of steel tube 75 mm outside diameter and 3 mm thick. The ends are pin-joined, but the end load of 50 kN is applied eccentrically through a line parallel to and 2·5 mm away from the axis of the strut, which is initially straight. Find the deflection and the maximum stress at the centre of the length. $E = 200 \text{ GN/m}^2$. (*U. Lond.*)   (*Ans.: 3·38 mm; 98·7 MN/m²*)

18. A steel tubular strut is pin joined at each end, and is subjected to a load parallel to its axis but eccentric to it. If the tube is 64 mm external diameter,

50 mm bore and 2·5 m long, find the maximum permissible eccentricity if the load is 120 kN and the maximum permissible stress is 300 MN/m². Any equations used should be proved. $E = 200$ GN/m².   (*I. Mech. E.*)

(*Ans.:* 6 mm)

19. Derive a formula for the maximum compressive stress induced in an initially straight, slender, uniform strut when loaded along an axis having an eccentricity e at both ends, which are pin-jointed.

A straight steel pin-jointed strut is 50 mm diameter and 1·25 m long. Calculate (*a*) the (Euler) crippling load when loaded along the central axis; (*b*) the eccentricity which will cause failure at 75 per cent of this load if the yield-point stress of the material is 280 MN/m². $E = 200$ GN/m².   (*U. Lond.*)

(*Ans.:* 387·5 kN; 1·166 mm)

20. A hollow circular steel strut with its end position-fixed has a length of 2·4 m, its external diameter being 100 mm and its internal diameter 87·5 mm. Before loading, the strut is bent with a maximum deviation of 4·5 mm. Assuming that the centre-line of the strut is sinusoidal, determine the maximum stress due to a central compressive end load of 10 kN. $E = 200$ GN/m².   (*U. Lond.*)

(*Ans.:* 6·55 MN/m²)

21. A steel bar 25 mm diameter and 1·8 m long is tested as a free-ended strut. Calculate the crippling load if the bar is initially straight and is centrally loaded. Find the load which will produce the yield stress of 300 MN/m² in this bar, if it is centrally loaded, but has initial curvature with an eccentricity of 9 mm at the centre of its length. $E = 200$ GN/m².   (*U. Lond.*)   (*Ans.:* 11·7 kN; 9·4 kN)

22. A long slender strut, originally straight and securely fixed at one end and free at the other end, is loaded at the free end with an eccentric load whose line of action is parallel to the original axis of the strut. Deduce an expression for the deviation of the free end from its original position.

Determine this deviation and the greatest compressive stress for a steel strut complying with the above conditions; length 3 m, circular cross-section 50 mm external diameter and 25 mm internal diameter; load 3·6 kN and original eccentricity 75 mm. $E = 200$ GN/m².   (*U. Lond.*)

(*Ans.:* $\delta = e\,(\sec \mu l - 1)$; 27·6 mm; 34·6 MN/m²)

23. A slender column is built-in at one end and an eccentric load is applied at the free end. Working from first principles find the expression for the maximum length of column such that the deflection of the free end does not exceed the eccentricity of loading.   (*I. Mech. E.*)   (*Ans.:* $\sqrt{\pi^2 EI/9P}$)

24. A vertical strut of uniform section is fixed rigidly at the base and carries a vertical load W at the top acting with an eccentricity e. In addition there is a horizontal force at the top, H, acting so as to produce bending in the same plane as W and tending to increase the deflection. Obtain a formula for the maximum bending moment.

If the column is a tube 50 mm outside diameter and 44 mm inside diameter of free length 1·5 m and if $W = 9$ kN acting with an eccentricity of 25 mm, find H to produce a maximum stress of 275 MN/m². $E = 200$ GN/m².   (*U. Lond.*)

$$\left(Ans.:\ We \sec \mu l + \frac{H}{\mu} \tan \mu l;\ 419\ \text{N}\right)$$

25. A strut of length l and flexural rigidity EI is encastred at its lower end. The upper end is elastically supported against lateral deflection so that the resisting force is k times the deflection. Show that the crippling load is given by

$$\frac{\tan al}{al} = 1 - \frac{P}{kl} \quad \text{where} \quad a^2 = \frac{P}{EI}. \qquad (U.\ Lond.)$$

26. A straight circular section strut of length L has an applied axial compressive load P. It is loaded at the centre with a load W acting at right angles to its axis. Prove that the maximum bending moment is

$$-\frac{W}{2m}\tan\frac{mL}{2} \quad \text{where} \quad m^2 = \frac{P}{EI}$$

and derive a formula for the central deflection.

If the strut is of steel 25 mm diameter and 1·5 m long with an axial load of 16 kN, calculate the value of W which will cause collapse if the yield-point stress is 280 MN/m² and $E = 200$ GN/m². (*U. Lond.*) (*Ans.*: See Art. 7.7(a); 133 N)

27. A slender strut of uniform section and of length L has pin-jointed ends and it is initially straight and vertical. It carries an axial load P and also a horizontal lateral load W applied at the middle of its length and acting in the plane in which P would cause bending to occur. Show that the maximum deflection is

$$\Delta = \frac{W}{2mP}\tan\frac{mL}{2} - \frac{WL}{4P} \quad \text{where } m^2 = \frac{P}{EI}.$$

In the case of a given strut the magnitude of P is $P_e/4$, where P_e is the Euler critical load for the strut. Find the ratio of the maximum deflection produced by P and the lateral load W acting together, to that produced by W acting alone. (*U. Lond.*) (*Ans.*: 1·328)

28. A locomotive coupling rod, 2·5 m between centres, is of symmetrical I-section: the outside dimensions are: 40 mm wide by 120 mm deep, web, 14 mm thick and flanges each 20 mm thick. Find the maximum compressive stress in the rod due to an end thrust of 150 kN and a uniform transverse load of 5 kN/m. $E = 200$ GN/m². (*U. Lond.*) (*Ans.*: 111·4 MN/m²)

29. A R.S.J. 300 mm by 125 mm and 6 m long is used as a strut with hinged ends. It carries an axial load of 300 kN together with a lateral load of 16 kN/m uniformly distributed along one flange over the entire length. Determine the maximum stress produced. $I = 86 \times 10^{-6}$ m⁴; $A = 5\cdot89 \times 10^{-3}$ m²; $E = 200$ GN/m². (*U. Lond.*) (*Ans.*: 185·6 MN/m²)

30. Derive an expression for the deflection of a laterally loaded tie-rod.

A steel tube, 50 mm outside diameter and 40 mm inside diameter, 1·8 m long, has a tensile load of 50 kN. Calculate the maximum uniform lateral load which can be carried if the maximum working stress is 120 MN/m². $E = 200$ GN/m². (*U. Lond.*)

$$\left(Ans.: \delta = \frac{w}{\mu^2 P}\operatorname{sech}\mu l \cosh\mu x - \frac{wl^2}{2P} + \frac{w}{\mu^2 P}[\text{origin at centre}]; 1\cdot29 \text{ kN/m}\right)$$

CHAPTER 8

THIN CURVED BARS

8.1 Strain energy due to bending. Fig. 8.1 shows an element of a beam subjected to a bending moment which varies from M at one end to $M + dM$ at the other. The length of the element is dx, the mean radius of curvature is R and the change of slope between the ends is $d\phi$.

Then work done in bending element

$$= \tfrac{1}{2} \times \text{mean bending moment} \times \text{angle of bending},$$

assuming that the moment is gradually applied.

This work is stored in the element as strain energy.

Thus,   strain energy $= \dfrac{M + \alpha\, dM}{2} \times d\phi$, where $0 < \alpha < 1$

i.e. $dU = \tfrac{1}{2}M\, d\phi$, to the first order of small quantities

But $d\phi = \dfrac{dx}{R} = dx\, \dfrac{M}{EI}$

$$\therefore dU = \dfrac{M^2}{2EI}\, dx$$

$\therefore$ total strain energy, $U = \displaystyle\int_0^l \dfrac{M^2}{2EI}\, dx$.   .   .   .   .   (8.1)

The appropriate expression for M in terms of x must be substituted in the above expression before the strain energy can be evaluated.

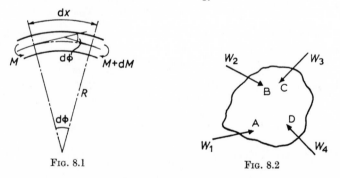

FIG. 8.1   FIG. 8.2

8.2 Castigliano's Theorem. Fig. 8.2 shows an elastic body which is subjected to forces W_1, W_2, W_3, etc. At each load point, the deflection can be resolved into components in the direction of, and perpendicular to, the line of action of the force at that point.

Let x_1 be the deflection at A in the direction of W_1,
Let x_2 be the deflection at B in the direction of W_2,
Let x_3 be the deflection at C in the direction of W_3, etc.

Then work done, $U = \frac{1}{2}W_1x_1 + \frac{1}{2}W_2x_2 + \frac{1}{2}W_3x_3 + \ldots$
or $\qquad\qquad\qquad 2U = W_1x_1 + W_2x_2 + W_3x_3 + \ldots$

Differentiating with respect to W_1, remembering that the deflection at each point is a function of all the loads,

$$2\frac{\partial U}{\partial W_1} = x_1 + W_1\frac{\partial x_1}{\partial W_1} + W_2\frac{\partial x_2}{\partial W_1} + W_3\frac{\partial x_3}{\partial W_1} + \ldots \quad . \quad (8.2)$$

Let W_1 increase gradually to $W_1 + \delta W_1$, the other forces remaining constant. Due to this change, let x_1 increase to $x_1 + \delta x_1$, x_2 to $x_2 + \delta x_2$, etc.

Then additional work done,

$$\delta U = (W_1 + \tfrac{1}{2}\delta W_1)\,\delta x_1 + W_2\,\delta x_2 + W_3\,\delta x_3 + \ldots$$

$$\therefore \frac{\delta U}{\delta W_1} = W_1\frac{\delta x_1}{\delta W_1} + \tfrac{1}{2}\delta x_1 + W_2\frac{\delta x_2}{\delta W_1} + W_3\frac{\delta x_3}{\delta W_1} + \ldots$$

Therefore, in the limit as $\delta W_1 \to 0$,

$$\frac{\partial U}{\partial W_1} = W_1\frac{\partial x_1}{\partial W_1} + W_2\frac{\partial x_2}{\partial W_1} + W_3\frac{\partial x_3}{\partial W_1} + \ldots \qquad . \qquad . \quad (8.3)$$

Subtracting (8.3) from (8.2),

$$x_1 = \frac{\partial U}{\partial W_1} \qquad . \qquad . \qquad . \qquad . \qquad . \qquad . \qquad . \quad (8.4)$$

i.e. the movement of A in the direction of W_1 is equal to the partial derivative of the *total* strain energy of the system with respect to W_1.

Similarly, $\qquad\qquad x_2 = \dfrac{\partial U}{\partial W_2}, \; x_3 = \dfrac{\partial U}{\partial W_3}$, etc.

The above theorem applies equally well to couples and to mixtures of forces and couples. The rotation at any point is the partial derivative of the total strain energy with respect to the couple at that point.

8.3 Application of Castigliano's Theorem to deflection of curved bars.

From equation (8.1), $\qquad U = \displaystyle\int_0^l \frac{M^2}{2EI}\,dx$

If it is required to find the deflection δ at a point at which there is a load P in the direction of the required deflection, then

$$\delta = \frac{\partial U}{\partial P} = \frac{1}{2EI}\int_0^l \frac{\partial}{\partial P}(M^2)\,dx, \text{ assuming } I \text{ to be constant}$$

$$= \frac{1}{2EI}\int_0^l 2M\frac{\partial M}{\partial P}\,dx = \frac{1}{EI}\int_0^l M\frac{\partial M}{\partial P}\,dx \qquad . \qquad . \qquad . \quad (8.5)$$

If there is no force P at the required point and in the required direction, such a force can be applied and when an expression for the deflection is obtained, this force is then made zero.

For the rotation in the direction of a couple C,

$$\phi = \frac{1}{EI}\int_0^l M\frac{\partial M}{\partial C}\,dx \qquad . \qquad . \qquad . \qquad . \qquad (8.6)$$

8.4   Strain energy due to twisting. There will be some strain energy in most cases due to shear forces and axial forces but this is usually negligible in comparison with that due to bending. In cases of twisting, however, the strain energy may be comparable with that due to bending. If the torque at any point is T, strain energy in an element of length dx

$$= \tfrac{1}{2}T\,d\theta = \tfrac{1}{2}T\frac{T\,dx}{GJ}$$

$$\therefore \text{ total strain energy} = \int_0^l \frac{T^2}{2GJ}\,dx . \qquad . \qquad . \qquad (8.7)$$

1. *A simply supported beam of span l carries a single concentrated load W at distances a and b respectively from the two ends A and B. Obtain an expression for the deflection under the load.*

Reaction at $A = \dfrac{Wb}{l}$,   Fig. 8.3

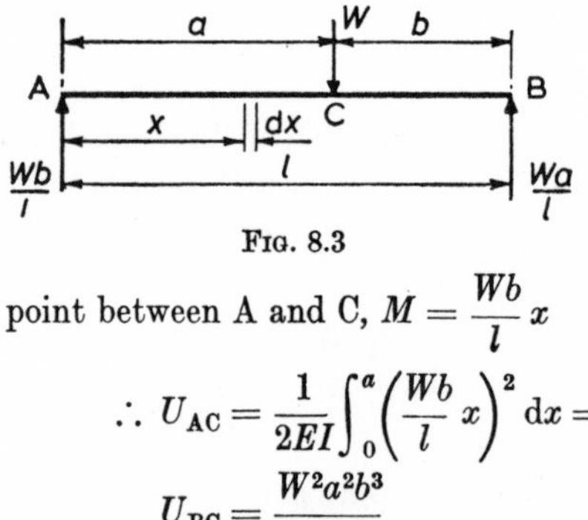

FIG. 8.3

Therefore, at any point between A and C, $M = \dfrac{Wb}{l}x$

$$\therefore U_{AC} = \frac{1}{2EI}\int_0^a \left(\frac{Wb}{l}x\right)^2 dx = \frac{W^2b^2a^3}{6EIl^2}$$

Similarly, $U_{BC} = \dfrac{W^2a^2b^3}{6EIl^2}$

$$\therefore \text{ total strain energy} = \frac{W^2a^2b^2}{6EIl^2}(a+b)$$

i.e. $\tfrac{1}{2}W\delta = \dfrac{W^2a^2b^2}{6EIl}$

$$\therefore \delta = \frac{Wa^2b^2}{3EIl}, \quad \text{as from equation (5.22)}$$

NOTES. (1) The sign of M in such an application is of no consequence, since M is squared subsequently.

(2) It is unnecessary to use Castigliano's Theorem in cases where there is only one load and the deflection is required at the load point and in the direction of the load.

2. *A steel spring, ABC, of the dimensions shown in Fig. 8.4 is firmly clamped at A. If a vertical force of 20 N is applied at C, find the vertical deflection of this point. E = 200 GN/m².*

For BC, taking the origin at C,

$$M = 20x$$

$$\therefore U_{BC} = \frac{1}{2EI}\int_0^{0.10} (20x)^2 \, dx$$

$$= \frac{0.2}{3EI} \text{ J}$$

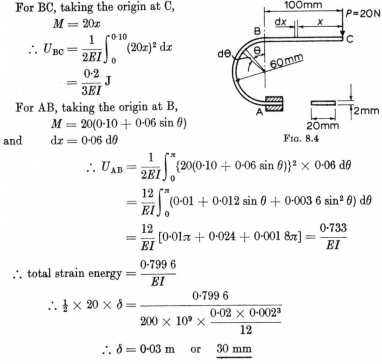

FIG. 8.4

For AB, taking the origin at B,

$$M = 20(0.10 + 0.06 \sin \theta)$$

and $$dx = 0.06 \, d\theta$$

$$\therefore U_{AB} = \frac{1}{2EI}\int_0^\pi \{20(0.10 + 0.06 \sin \theta)\}^2 \times 0.06 \, d\theta$$

$$= \frac{12}{EI}\int_0^\pi (0.01 + 0.012 \sin \theta + 0.0036 \sin^2 \theta) \, d\theta$$

$$= \frac{12}{EI}[0.01\pi + 0.024 + 0.0018\pi] = \frac{0.733}{EI}$$

$$\therefore \text{ total strain energy} = \frac{0.7996}{EI}$$

$$\therefore \frac{1}{2} \times 20 \times \delta = \frac{0.7996}{200 \times 10^9 \times \dfrac{0.02 \times 0.002^3}{12}}$$

$$\therefore \delta = 0.03 \text{ m} \quad \text{or} \quad \underline{30 \text{ mm}}$$

3. *A spring plate made of steel strip of rectangular section 20 mm × 3mm is curved to the shape shown in Fig. 8.5. Determine the deflection at the centre when P = 200 N. Neglect friction. E = 200 GN/m².* (U. Lond.)

For AB, taking the origin at A, Fig. 8.6,

$$M = \frac{P}{2} \times 0.05 \sin \theta$$

$$\therefore U_{AB} = \frac{1}{2EI}\int_0^{\pi/6} \left(\frac{0.05}{2} P \sin \theta\right)^2 \times 0.05 \, d\theta = 0.708 \times 10^{-6} \frac{P^2}{EI}$$

For BC, taking the origin at C,

$$M = \frac{P}{2} \times 0.05(1 - \sin \theta)$$

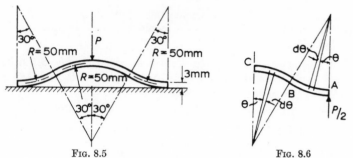

FIG. 8.5

FIG. 8.6

$$\therefore U_{BC} = \frac{1}{2EI} \int_0^{\pi/6} \left\{ \frac{0 \cdot 05}{2} P(1 - \sin \theta) \right\}^2 \times 0 \cdot 05 \, d\theta = 4 \cdot 7 \times 10^{-6} \frac{P^2}{EI}$$

$\therefore$ total strain energy

$$= 5 \cdot 408 \times 10^{-6} \frac{P^2}{EI} \times 2$$

$$\therefore \tfrac{1}{2} P\delta = \frac{10 \cdot 816 P^2}{200 \times 10^9 \times \dfrac{0 \cdot 02 \times 0 \cdot 003^3}{12}}$$

$$\therefore \delta = 0 \cdot 000 \, 481 \text{ m} \quad \text{or} \quad \underline{0 \cdot 481 \text{ mm}}$$

4. *A strip of steel of rectangular section 25 mm $\times$ 3 mm is bent to the shape of a quadrant and loaded by a force W inclined at α to the vertical, as shown in Fig. 8.7. Derive formulae for the vertical and horizontal movements at the free end B and hence find the value of α to give no horizontal movement at B.*

For the value of α found, determine the radius R to give a vertical deflection at B of 0·25 mm when W = 5 N. E = 200 GN/m². (U. Lond.)

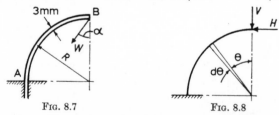

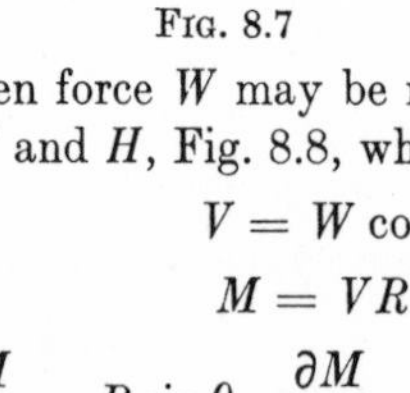

FIG. 8.7

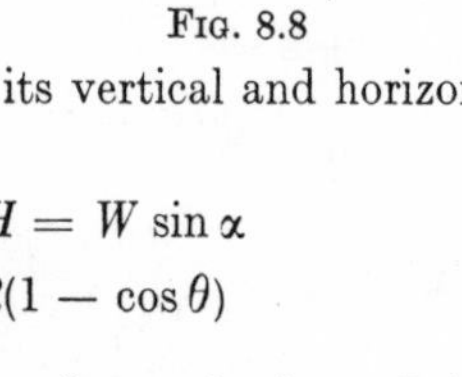

FIG. 8.8

The given force W may be replaced by its vertical and horizontal components V and H, Fig. 8.8, where

$$V = W \cos \alpha \quad \text{and} \quad H = W \sin \alpha$$

$$M = VR \sin \theta - HR(1 - \cos \theta)$$

$$\frac{\partial M}{\partial V} = R \sin \theta, \quad \frac{\partial M}{\partial H} = -R(1 - \cos \theta) \quad \text{and} \quad dx = R \, d\theta$$

Vertical deflection, $\delta_v = \dfrac{\partial U}{\partial V} = \dfrac{1}{EI} \displaystyle\int_0^l M \frac{\partial M}{\partial V} \, dx$

$$= \frac{1}{EI} \int_0^{\pi/2} \{VR\sin\theta - HR(1-\cos\theta)\} \times R\sin\theta \times R\, d\theta$$

$$= \frac{R^3}{EI} \int_0^{\pi/2} \{V\sin^2\theta - H(\sin\theta - \sin\theta\cos\theta)\}\, d\theta$$

$$= \frac{R^3}{EI} \left\{V\frac{\pi}{4} - \frac{H}{2}\right\}$$

$$= \frac{WR^3}{EI} \left\{\frac{\pi}{4}\cos\alpha - \frac{1}{2}\sin\alpha\right\}$$

Horizontal deflection, $\delta_h = \dfrac{\partial U}{\partial H} = \dfrac{1}{EI} \displaystyle\int_0^l M\dfrac{\partial M}{\partial H}\, dx$

$$= \frac{1}{EI} \int_0^{\pi/2} \{VR\sin\theta - HR(1-\cos\theta)\} \times \{-R(1-\cos\theta)\} \times R\, d\theta$$

$$= \frac{R^3}{EI} \int_0^{\pi/2} \{-V(\sin\theta - \sin\theta\cos\theta) + H(1 - 2\cos\theta + \cos^2\theta)\}\, d\theta$$

$$= \frac{R^3}{EI} \left\{-\frac{V}{2} + H\left(\frac{3\pi}{4} - 2\right)\right\}$$

$$= \frac{WR^3}{EI} \left\{-\frac{1}{2}\cos\alpha + \left(\frac{3\pi}{4} - 2\right)\sin\alpha\right\}$$

For no horizontal movement of B, $\delta_h = 0$

i.e. $\quad \frac{1}{2}\cos\alpha = \left(\dfrac{3\pi}{4} - 2\right)\sin\alpha$

from which $\quad \alpha = \underline{54°\,31'}$

When $\delta_v = 0.25$ mm, then

$$0.25 \times 10^{-3} = \frac{5R^3\left\{\dfrac{\pi}{4}\cos 54°31' - \dfrac{1}{2}\sin 54°31'\right\}}{200 \times 10^9 \times \dfrac{0.025 \times 0.003^3}{12}}$$

from which $\quad\quad R = \underline{0.226 \text{ m}}$

5. *A steel rod, 10 mm diameter, is bent into the shape shown in Fig. 8.9, one end being rigidly clamped, the other end being constrained to move in a horizontal slide. Determine the horizontal deflection of the slider when acted upon by a force of 100 N. E = 200 GN/m².* (U. Lond.)

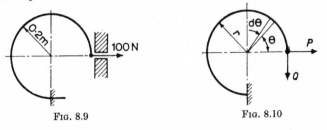

FIG. 8.9   FIG. 8.10

Denoting the applied force by P, Fig. 8.10, there will also be a reaction Q applied by the guide to constrain the free end to move in a horizontal line. This reaction has been assumed to be downwards but if this assumption is incorrect, the value of Q will be found to be negative.

Since there is no vertical movement of the free end,

$$\frac{\partial U}{\partial Q} = 0$$

i.e. $\int M \dfrac{\partial M}{\partial Q} \, dx = 0$, an equation which will determine Q.

The horizontal movement will then be given by

$$\delta = \frac{\partial U}{\partial P} = \frac{1}{EI} \int_0^l M \frac{\partial M}{\partial P} \, dx$$

Taking the origin at the free end,

$$M = Pr \sin \theta - Qr(1 - \cos \theta)$$

$$\frac{\partial M}{\partial P} = r \sin \theta, \quad \frac{\partial M}{\partial Q} = -r(1 - \cos \theta) \quad \text{and} \quad dx = r \, d\theta$$

$$\therefore \int_0^{3\pi/2} \{Pr \sin \theta - Qr(1 - \cos \theta)\} \times \{-r(1 - \cos \theta)\} \times r \, d\theta = 0$$

i.e. $P \displaystyle\int_0^{3\pi/2} (\sin \theta - \sin \theta \cos \theta) \, d\theta = Q \int_0^{3\pi/2} (1 - 2 \cos \theta + \cos^2 \theta) \, d\theta$

i.e.
$$\frac{P}{2} = Q\left(\frac{9\pi}{4} + 2\right)$$

or
$$Q = \frac{2P}{9\pi + 8}$$

$$\delta = \frac{1}{EI} \int_0^{3\pi/2} \{Pr \sin \theta - Qr(1 - \cos \theta)\} \times r \sin \theta \times r \, d\theta$$

$$= \frac{r^3}{EI} \int_0^{3\pi/2} \{P \sin^2 \theta - Q(\sin \theta - \sin \theta \cos \theta)\} \, d\theta$$

$$= \frac{r^3}{EI}\left\{P \times \frac{3\pi}{4} - \frac{Q}{2}\right\}$$

$$= \frac{Pr^3}{EI}\left\{\frac{3\pi}{4} - \frac{1}{9\pi + 8}\right\}$$

$$= \frac{100 \times 0 \cdot 2^3 \times 2 \cdot 327\,5}{200 \times 10^9 \times \dfrac{\pi}{64} \times 0 \cdot 01^4}$$

$$= 0 \cdot 019 \, \text{m} \quad \text{or} \quad \underline{19 \text{ mm}}$$

6. *The ring shown in Fig. 8.11 is made of flat steel strip* 20 *mm* × 3 *mm and is shaped in the form of a circle of mean diameter* 0·2 *m. The ends at B are cut square and not joined. A pull P is applied along the diameter CD which is at right.angles to the diameter AB. If the maximum tensile stress due to P is* 125 *MN/m², find the increase in the opening at B due to P. E* = 200 *GN/m².*

(U. Lond.)

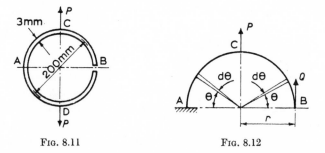

FIG. 8.11   FIG. 8.12

The increase in opening at B is twice the movement of B relative to A in the half ring shown in Fig. 8.12. Since there is no force at B in the direction of the required deflection, a force Q, of zero magnitude, must be applied there.

The required deflection is given by

$$\delta = 2\,\frac{\partial U_{AB}}{\partial Q} = \frac{2}{EI}\int M\,\frac{\partial M}{\partial Q}\,dx$$

For BC, taking the origin at B,

$$M = Qr(1 - \cos\theta), \quad \frac{\partial M}{\partial Q} = r(1 - \cos\theta) \quad \text{and} \quad dx = r\,d\theta$$

For AC, taking the origin at A,
$$M = Qr(1 + \cos\theta) + Pr\cos\theta$$

$$\frac{\partial M}{\partial Q} = r(1 + \cos\theta) \quad \text{and} \quad dx = r\,d\theta$$

$$\therefore\ \delta = \frac{2}{EI}\Bigg[\int_0^{\pi/2} Qr(1 - \cos\theta) \times r(1 - \cos\theta) \times r\,d\theta$$

$$+ \int_0^{\pi/2}\{Qr(1 + \cos\theta) + Pr\cos\theta\} \times r(1 + \cos\theta) \times r\,d\theta\Bigg]$$

$$= \frac{2Pr^3}{EI}\int_0^{\pi/2}\cos\theta(1 + \cos\theta)\,d\theta \quad . \quad . \quad . \quad . \quad \text{since } Q = 0$$

$$= \frac{2Pr^3}{EI}\Big(1 + \frac{\pi}{4}\Big)$$

The maximum stress occurs at A, where $M = Pr$,

i.e. $$Pr = \sigma Z = 125 \times 10^6 \times \frac{0 \cdot 02 \times 0 \cdot 003^2}{6} = 3 \cdot 75 \text{ N m}$$

$$\therefore P = \frac{3 \cdot 75}{0 \cdot 10} = 37 \cdot 5 \text{ N}$$

$$\therefore \delta = \frac{2 \times 37 \cdot 5 \times 0 \cdot 10^3}{200 \times 10^9 \times \dfrac{0 \cdot 02 \times 0 \cdot 003^3}{12}} \left(1 + \frac{\pi}{4} \right)$$

$$= 0 \cdot 014 \text{ 9 m} \quad \text{or} \quad \underline{14 \cdot 9 \text{ mm}}$$

7. *A ring of mean radius R is made from a bar of uniform section with the two ends at C connected by a pin-joint. The ring is subjected to three radial forces arranged in equilibrium as shown in Fig. 8.13. Show that the force in the pin is*

$$F = \frac{2P}{3\pi}\{8 + 2(\pi - \alpha)\}. \qquad \text{(U. Lond.)}$$

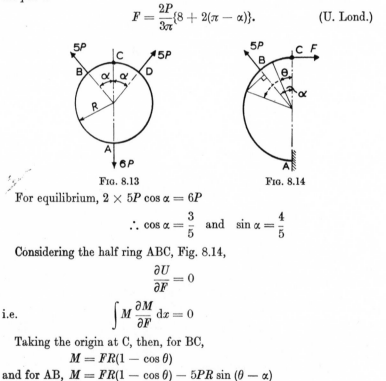

FIG. 8.13   FIG. 8.14

For equilibrium, $2 \times 5P \cos \alpha = 6P$

$$\therefore \cos \alpha = \frac{3}{5} \quad \text{and} \quad \sin \alpha = \frac{4}{5}$$

Considering the half ring ABC, Fig. 8.14,

$$\frac{\partial U}{\partial F} = 0$$

i.e. $$\int M \frac{\partial M}{\partial F} \, \mathrm{d}x = 0$$

Taking the origin at C, then, for BC,
$$M = FR(1 - \cos \theta)$$
and for AB, $M = FR(1 - \cos \theta) - 5PR \sin(\theta - \alpha)$

$$\frac{\partial M}{\partial F} = R(1 - \cos \theta) \quad \text{and} \quad \mathrm{d}x = R \, \mathrm{d}\theta$$

$$\therefore \int_0^\alpha FR(1 - \cos\theta) \times R(1 - \cos\theta) \times R\,d\theta$$

$$+ \int_\alpha^\pi \{FR(1 - \cos\theta) - 5PR\sin(\theta - \alpha)\} \times R(1 - \cos\theta) \times R\,d\theta = 0$$

i.e. $F\displaystyle\int_0^\pi (1 - \cos\theta)^2\,d\theta = 5P\int_\alpha^\pi \sin(\theta - \alpha)(1 - \cos\theta)\,d\theta$

i.e. $F\displaystyle\int_0^\pi (1 - 2\cos\theta + \cos^2\theta)\,d\theta$

$$= 5P\int_\alpha^\pi \{\sin(\theta - \alpha) - \tfrac{1}{2}\sin(2\theta - \alpha) + \tfrac{1}{2}\sin\alpha\}\,d\theta$$

i.e. $\quad F \times \dfrac{3\pi}{2} = 5P\left(\cos\alpha + 1 + \dfrac{\pi - \alpha}{2}\sin\alpha\right)$

$$= P\{8 + 2(\pi - \alpha)\}$$

$$\therefore F = \frac{2P}{3\pi}\{8 + 2(\pi - \alpha)\}$$

8. *A thin proving ring of radius r is subjected to a diametral tensile load W. Determine (a) the increase in diameter in the direction of W, (b) the decrease in diameter perpendicular to the direction of W.*

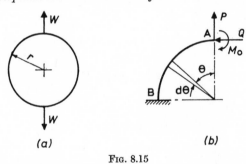

FIG. 8.15

It is sufficient to consider one quarter of the ring AB, Fig. 8.15(b), fixed at the mid-point of one of the sides and subjected to a force $P\ (= W/2)$ at the free end. Due to the continuity of the ring at A, however, the tangent there must remain horizontal and hence a moment M_0 must be applied for this purpose, the moment corresponding to the B.M. in the actual ring at that point.

The increase in the vertical diameter of the ring will be twice the deflection of A relative to B in the quadrant and the decrease in horizontal diameter will be twice the horizontal movement of A relative to B. For this purpose, it is necessary to add a horizontal force Q, of zero magnitude.

Taking the origin at A,

$$M = M_0 - Pr \sin \theta - Qr(1 - \cos \theta)$$

$$\frac{\partial M}{\partial M_0} = 1$$

$$\frac{\partial M}{\partial P} = -r \sin \theta$$

$$\frac{\partial M}{\partial Q} = -r(1 - \cos \theta)$$

and $$dx = r \, d\theta$$

There is no rotation in the direction of M_0,

$$\therefore \frac{\partial U}{\partial M_0} = \frac{1}{EI} \int_0^l M \frac{\partial M}{\partial M_0} \, dx = 0$$

i.e. $\displaystyle \int_0^{\pi/2} \{M_0 - Pr \sin \theta\} \times 1 \times r \, d\theta = 0$

from which $M_0 = \dfrac{2Pr}{\pi}$

$$\delta_v = 2 \frac{\partial U}{\partial P} = \frac{2}{EI} \int_0^l M \frac{\partial M}{\partial P} \, dx$$

$$= \frac{2}{EI} \int_0^{\pi/2} \left\{ \frac{2Pr}{\pi} - Pr \sin \theta \right\} \times \{-r \sin \theta\} \times r \, d\theta$$

$$= \frac{2Pr^3}{EI} \left(\frac{\pi}{4} - \frac{2}{\pi} \right) = \underline{0 \cdot 1484 \frac{Wr^3}{EI}}$$

$$\delta_h = 2 \frac{\partial U}{\partial Q} = \frac{2}{EI} \int_0^l M \frac{\partial M}{\partial Q} \, dx$$

$$= \frac{2}{EI} \int_0^{\pi/2} \left\{ \frac{2Pr}{\pi} - Pr \sin \theta \right\} \times \{-r(1 - \cos \theta)\} \times r \, d\theta$$

$$= \frac{2Pr^3}{EI} \left(\frac{2}{\pi} - \frac{1}{2} \right)$$

$$= \underline{0 \cdot 137 \frac{Wr^3}{EI}}$$

Note. Since $Q = 0$, the term involving Q may be omitted from all the integrals but it cannot be omitted from the original expression for M, otherwise no value for $\dfrac{\partial M}{\partial Q}$ will be obtained.

9. *Show that the maximum bending moment in the link shown in Fig.* 8.16
occurs at the centre of the curved portion and is given by

$$\frac{Wd}{2}\left(\frac{2r+d}{\pi r+d}\right)$$

Hence calculate the maximum tensile and compressive stresses when
$r = 25$ *mm*, $d = 50$ *mm and* $W = 10$ *kN, if the cross-section is a rectangle*
50 *mm* $\times$ 12·5 *mm, the latter dimension being in the plane of the figure.*

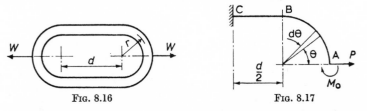

FIG. 8.16   FIG. 8.17

It is sufficient to consider one quarter of the link ABC, Fig. 8.17, fixed
at the mid-point of one of the sides and subjected to a force $P\ (= W/2)$ at
the free end. Due to the continuity of the link at A, however, the tangent
there must remain vertical and hence a moment M_0 must be applied for
this purpose, the moment corresponding to the B.M. in the actual link at
that point.

Since there is no rotation in the direction of M_0,

$$\frac{\partial U}{\partial M_0} = \frac{1}{EI}\int_0^l M\,\frac{\partial M}{\partial M_0}\,\mathrm{d}x = 0$$

For AB, taking the origin at A,

$$M = M_0 - Pr\sin\theta \quad \text{and} \quad \frac{\partial M}{\partial M_0} = 1$$

For BC, taking the origin at either end,

$$M = M_0 - Pr \qquad \text{and} \quad \frac{\partial M}{\partial M_0} = 1$$

$$\therefore \int_0^{\pi/2}(M_0 - Pr\sin\theta)r\,\mathrm{d}\theta + \int_0^{d/2}(M_0 - Pr)\,\mathrm{d}x = 0$$

i.e.

$$\left(M_0\frac{\pi}{2} - Pr\right)r + (M_0 - Pr)\frac{d}{2} = 0$$

from which

$$M_0 = Pr\left(\frac{2r+d}{\pi r+d}\right) = \frac{Wr}{2}\left(\frac{2r+d}{\pi r+d}\right)$$

At B,
$$M = M_0 - Pr = \frac{Wr}{2}\left(\frac{2r+d}{\pi r+d}\right) - \frac{Wr}{2}$$

$$= \frac{Wr}{2}\left(\frac{[\pi-2]r}{\pi r+d}\right), \quad \text{which is less than } M_0$$

The B.M. diagram, Fig. 8.18, is drawn to scale for the dimensions given, the B.M. at any point being measured perpendicular to the centre line of the link at that point (it is conventional to draw the diagram on the tension side).

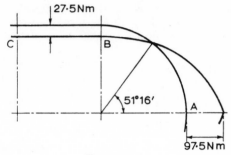

FIG. 8.18

At A, $\qquad M = M_0$

$$= \frac{10 \times 10^3 \times 0{\cdot}025}{2}\left(\frac{0{\cdot}05 + 0{\cdot}05}{\pi \times 0{\cdot}025 + 0{\cdot}05}\right) = 97{\cdot}5 \text{ N m}$$

At B, $\qquad M = M_0 - \dfrac{Wr}{2}$

$$= 97{\cdot}5 - \frac{10 \times 10^3 \times 0{\cdot}025}{2} = -27{\cdot}5 \text{ N m}$$

The point of inflexion is given by $M_0 - \dfrac{Wr}{2}\sin\theta = 0$

from which $\theta = 51° 16'$

At A, $\sigma = \pm\dfrac{M}{Z} = \pm\dfrac{97{\cdot}5 \times 6}{0{\cdot}05 \times 0{\cdot}012\,5^2} = \pm 74{\cdot}88 \text{ MN/m}^2$

At B, $\sigma = \dfrac{W}{2a} \pm \dfrac{M}{Z} = \dfrac{10 \times 10^3}{2 \times 0{\cdot}05 \times 0{\cdot}012\,5} \pm \dfrac{27{\cdot}5 \times 6}{0{\cdot}05 \times 0{\cdot}012\,5^2}$

$$= +29{\cdot}12 \quad \text{and} \quad -13{\cdot}12 \text{ MN/m}^2$$

Hence, maximum tensile and compressive stresses = <u>74·88 MN/m²</u>.

10. *A cantilever, lying in a horizontal plane, is in the shape of a quadrant of a circle of radius R, one end being firmly fixed. If a vertical load W is applied at the free end, find the vertical deflection under the load. The cantilever is of circular section, diameter d, and $G = 0{\cdot}4E$.*

$$\text{Total strain energy} = \frac{1}{2EI}\int_0^l M^2\,dx + \frac{1}{2GJ}\int_0^l T^2\,dx$$

$$\therefore \text{ vertical deflection} = \frac{1}{EI}\int_0^l M \frac{\partial M}{\partial W}\,\mathrm{d}x + \frac{1}{GJ}\int_0^l T \frac{\partial T}{\partial W}\,\mathrm{d}x$$

Taking the origin at the load point, Fig. 8.19,

$$M = WR\sin\theta \qquad \text{and} \qquad \frac{\partial M}{\partial W} = R\sin\theta$$

$$T = WR(1 - \cos\theta) \quad \text{and} \quad \frac{\partial T}{\partial W} = R(1 - \cos\theta)$$

$$\therefore \delta = \frac{1}{EI}\int_0^{\pi/2} WR\sin\theta \times R\sin\theta \times R\,\mathrm{d}\theta$$

$$+ \frac{1}{GJ}\int_0^{\pi/2} WR(1 - \cos\theta) \times R(1 - \cos\theta) \times R\,\mathrm{d}\theta$$

But $G = 0.4E$ and $J = 2I$

$$\therefore \delta = \frac{WR^3}{EI}\int_0^{\pi/2}\{\sin^2\theta + 1.25(1 - 2\cos\theta + \cos^2\theta)\}\,\mathrm{d}\theta$$

$$= \frac{WR^3}{EI}\left\{\frac{\pi}{4} + 1.25\left(\frac{3\pi}{4} - 2\right)\right\}$$

$$= \frac{64WR^3}{E\pi d^4}\left\{\frac{19}{16}\pi - 2.5\right\}$$

$$= 25.1\,\frac{WR^3}{Ed^4}$$

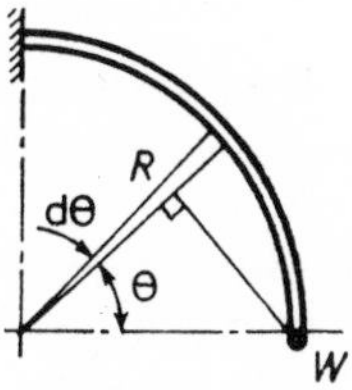

FIG. 8.19

11. A simply supported beam of rectangular cross-section carries a concentrated load P at the centre of the span. Determine the total internal energy of the beam in terms of the maximum bending stress and the volume of the beam.

Also show that the internal energy of the beam so obtained is only one-ninth as much as for a similar beam under uniform axial loading. (*U. Lond.*)

$$\left(Ans.: \frac{\sigma^2}{18E} \times \text{volume}\right)$$

12. A horizontal beam, simply supported at its ends, carries a total load wl uniformly distributed over its length l. Show that the total work done by the load in deflecting the beam is $w^2l^5/240EI$ where E is Young's Modulus for the material of the beam and I is the second moment of area of the cross-section.

Find the total strain energy in a rolled steel joist, 0·6 m long, carrying a uniformly distributed load of 35 kN/m run. $E = 200\,\text{GN/m}^2$ and $I = 5.66 \times 10^{-6}\,\text{mm}^4$.

(*Ans : 0·351 J*)

13. Solve Question No. 53, page 115, by strain energy.

14. A steel tube 50 mm internal diameter and 3 mm thick stands vertically up from a rigid base. At a distance of 0·9 m from the base the tube is bent into a quadrant of a circle of radius 0·6 m and at the end a vertical load of 2 kN is applied. Calculate the deflection of this load. $E = 200\,\text{GN/m}^2$. (*U. Lond.*)

(*Ans : 28·1 mm*)

15. A steel ring of rectangular cross-section 7·5 mm wide by 5 mm thick has a mean diameter of 300 mm. A narrow radial saw cut is made and tangential separating forces of 5 N each are applied at the cut in the plane of the ring.

Determine the additional separation due to these forces. $E = 200$ GN/m².
(*U. Lond.*)   (*Ans.:* 10·2 mm)

16. A steel bar 65 mm diameter is bent to the shape shown in Fig. 8.20 and the lower end is firmly fixed in the ground in a vertical position. A load of 1 kN is applied at the free end. Calculate the vertical deflection of the free end. $E = 200$ GN/m². (*U. Lond.*)   (*Ans.:* 12·95 mm)

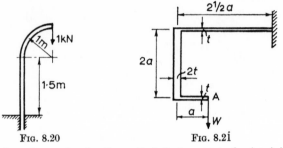

FIG. 8.20   FIG. 8.21

17. Obtain an expression for the vertical displacement of point A in the bent cantilever shown in Fig. 8.21, which is of uniform breadth b.

If $a = 50$ mm, $t = 6$ mm, $b = 25$ mm, and the bar is of steel, find the vertical displacement of A for $W = 20$ N. $E = 200$ GN/m². (*U. Lond.*)

$$\left(Ans.:\ \frac{24 \cdot 5\ Wa^3}{Ebt^3};\ 0 \cdot 0566\ \text{mm}\right)$$

18. A spring used in a measuring device is made of a rod of steel of diameter d bent to the form shown in Fig. 8.22 so that a force P applied to the ends of the spring will increase the distance between the ends by an amount δ. Show that the stiffness of the spring

$$s = \frac{P}{\delta} = \frac{3\pi E d^4}{32} \bigg/ (4L^3 + 6\pi R L^2 + 24 R^2 L + 3\pi R^3)$$

If s is to be 1·5 kN/m, $d = 6$ mm and $R = 40$ mm, find the length L. $E = 200$ GN/m². (*U. Lond.*)   (*Ans.:* 174 mm)

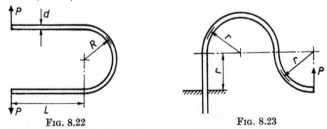

FIG. 8.22   FIG. 8.23

19. Fig. 8.23 shows the proportions of a spring made of material of uniform section. Derive an expression for the vertical movement of the free end due to the vertical force P.

A spring of these proportions is to be made of steel strip 0·6 mm thick and P is to have a maximum value of 5 N. Find the breadth of the strip and the mean radius r, given that the maximum bending stress due to P is not to exceed 150 MN/m² and the vertical deflection due to P is not to be more than 2·5 mm. $E = 200$ GN/m². (*U. Lond.*)   (*Ans.:* 23·92 Pr^3/EI; 18·7 mm; 11·2 mm)

20. The stiff frame shown in Fig. 8.24 is supported on a smooth surface and loaded at the centre of the span. Show that the deflection at the load due to bending is

$$\frac{Pa^3}{48EI}\left\{1 + 3\sqrt{2}\frac{b}{a} + 6\left(\frac{b}{a}\right)^2 + 4\left(\frac{b}{a}\right)^3\right\} \quad (U.\ Lond.)$$

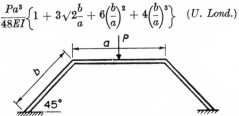

FIG. 8.24

21. A steel bar of constant section, second moment of area I is bent as shown in Fig. 8.25 and fixed at one end. Find the horizontal and vertical deflections at the free end. (*U. Lond.*)

$$\left(Ans.:\ \frac{Pa^2}{EI}\left(l + \frac{a}{3}\right);\ \frac{Pal^2}{2EI}\right)$$

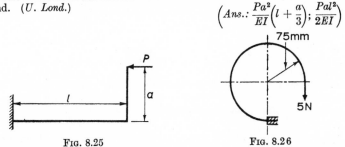

FIG. 8.25   FIG. 8.26

22. A steel spring is shown in Fig. 8.26. It is formed in a circular arc subtending an angle of 270° at the centre. The lower end is rigidly fixed and a vertical force of 5 N is applied at the free end.

If the section of the spring is 12 mm wide and 3 mm thick, calculate the vertical and horizontal displacements of the free end. $E = 200\ \text{GN/m}^2$. (*U. Lond.*)

(*Ans.*: 3·65 mm; 0·195 mm)

23. A steel tube having outside and inside diameters of 60 mm and 45 mm respectively, is bent into the form of a quadrant of 2 m radius. One end is rigidly attached to a horizontal base-plate to which a tangent to that end is perpendicular, and the free end supports a load of 500 N. Determine the vertical and horizontal deflections of the free end under this load. The dimensions of the cross-section may be considered as small relative to the radius of curvature. $E = 200\ \text{GN/m}^2$. (*U. Lond.*)   (*Ans.*: 36·1 mm; 23·0 mm)

24. A proving ring is 250 mm mean diameter, 40 mm wide and 6 mm thick. The maximum stress permitted is 550 MN/m². Find the load to cause this stress and the load to give 6 mm deflection of the ring in the direction of the loading.

Prove any formulae used which are particular to this problem. $E = 200\ \text{GN/m}^2$ (*U. Lond.*)   (*Ans.*: 3·325 kN; 2·98 kN)

25. A thin circular ring of mean radius R and uniform rectangular sections width b and thickness t is pulled by a load W along a diameter. Derive formulae for the maximum stress in the material and for the change in diameter along which the load is applied and along the diameter at right angles to this. (*U. Lond.*)

$$\left(Ans.:\ \frac{6WR}{\pi bt^2};\ \frac{WR^3}{EI}\left(\frac{\pi}{4} - \frac{2}{\pi}\right);\ \frac{WR^3}{EI}\left(\frac{2}{\pi} - \frac{1}{2}\right)\right)$$

26. Fig. 8.27 shows a steel rod, 10 mm diameter, with one end firmly fixed to a horizontal table. The remainder of the rod is bent into the form of three-quarters of a circle and the free end of the rod is constrained by guides to move in a vertical direction. If the mean radius to which the rod is bent is 150 mm, determine the vertical deflection of the free end when a 100 N load is gradually applied there. $E = 200$ GN/m².   (*U. Lond.*)   (*Ans.:* 8 mm)

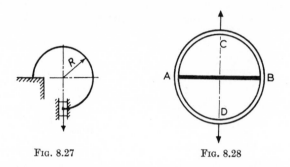

FIG. 8.27   FIG. 8.28

27. Fig. 8.28 shows a circular ring of mean radius R, made of material having a uniform section. The ring is fitted with a rigid bar across the diameter AB and transmits a pull W along the diameter CD which is at right angles to AB. Obtain the force in the bar in terms of W, and the change in the diameter CD in terms of W and the flexural rigidity EI of the ring.   (*U. Lond.*)

                                  (*Ans.:* 0·918 W; 0·0234 Wr^3/EI)

28. A chain link made of circular section rod has the dimensions shown in Fig. 8.29. Prove that if d, the diameter of the section, is assumed small compared with R, the mean radius of the curved ends, then the maximum bending moment occurs at the point of application of the load and is equal to

$$\frac{PR}{2}\left\{\frac{l + 2R}{l + \pi R}\right\}$$

If $R = 25$ mm, $d = 6$ mm and $l = 45$ mm, calculate the ratio of the maximum tensile stress at the section where the load is applied to that at the section half-way along the straight portion.   (*U. Lond.*)   (*Ans.:* 2·94)

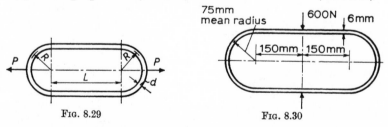

FIG. 8.29   FIG. 8.30

29. Fig. 8.30 shows a flat ring made of steel 25 mm wide by 6 mm thick, loaded with a central load of 600 N. Calculate the maximum bending moment in the ring.

Sketch the B.M. diagram and find the position of the points of inflexion.

Taking E as 200 GN/m², find the vertical deflection produced by the load of 600 N.   (*U. Lond.*)

        (*Ans.:* 38·7 Nm (at load point); 129 mm from load point; 8·9 mm)

30. A stiff rectangular steel frame is loaded as shown in Fig. 8.31. Show that the bending moment at the corners is

$$M = \frac{Ql^2 - Pd^2}{8(l + d)}$$

Sketch the bending moment diagram for a long and short side and calculate the deflection of the longer side when $P = 200 \text{ N}, Q = 100 \text{ N}, l = 300 \text{ mm}, d = 150 \text{ mm}$ and the section is rectangular 24 mm × 6 mm, the latter dimension in the plane of the rectangle. $E = 200 \text{ GN/m}^2$. (*U. Lond.*)   (*Ans.: 4·07 mm*)

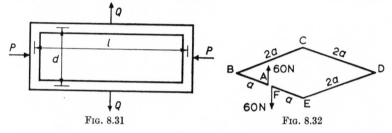

FIG. 8.31   FIG. 8.32

31. A 10 mm diameter steel rod is bent to form a square with sides $2a = 40$ mm long. The ends meet at the mid-point of one side and are separated by equal opposite forces of 60 N applied in a direction perpendicular to the plane of the square as shown in perspective in the Fig. 8.32. Calculate the amount by which they will be out of alignment. $E = 200 \text{ GN/m}^2; G = 80 \text{ GN/m}^2$. (*U. Lond.*)
(*Ans.: 9·78 mm*)

32. A cantilever forming a circular arc in plan, and subtending $\pi/3$ rad at the centre, has a circular cross-section of 50 mm diameter and the radius of the centre line is 0·75 m. Find the maximum deflection when a load of 400 N is acting at the free end. $E = 200 \text{ GN/m}^2; G = 80 \text{ GN/m}^2$. (*U. Lond.*)   (*Ans.: 2·75 mm*)

33. Fig. 8.33 shows the plan of a 25 mm diameter steel rod fixed at A. The rod is curved to a radius of 0·5 m and when unloaded lies in a horizontal plane. If a vertical load of 400 N is applied at B, find the maximum normal and shearing stresses on the cross-section of the rod at A, and the vertical deflection of the load. Take E as 200 GN/m^2 and G as 80 GN/m^2, and neglect the effect of the direct shearing force. (*U. Lond.*)
(*Ans.: 157·3 MN/m²; 92·1 MN/m² (see equations 12.21 and 12.23); 16·06 mm*)

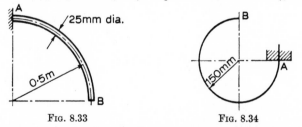

FIG. 8.33   FIG. 8.34

34. A circular steel wire 10 mm diameter is bent as shown in Fig. 8.34. It is rigidly held at the end A so that the centre line of the wire lies in the horizontal plane. Calculate the vertical deflection at the free end B when a vertical load of 20 N is placed there. $E = 200 \text{ GN/m}^2; G = 80 \text{ GN/m}^2$. (*U. Lond.*)
(*Ans.: 9·42 mm*)

CHAPTER 9

SPRINGS

9.1 Close-coiled helical spring with axial load. A close-coiled helical spring is one in which the obliquity of the wire is small; such a spring, under axial load, may be assumed to be subjected to torsion only, the effects of bending and direct shear being negligible.

Fig. 9.1 shows a close-coiled spring under an axial load W.

Let D = mean coil diameter,
                 d = wire diameter,
                 n = number of coils,
                 l = length of wire $\simeq \pi D n$,
                 δ = axial deflection.

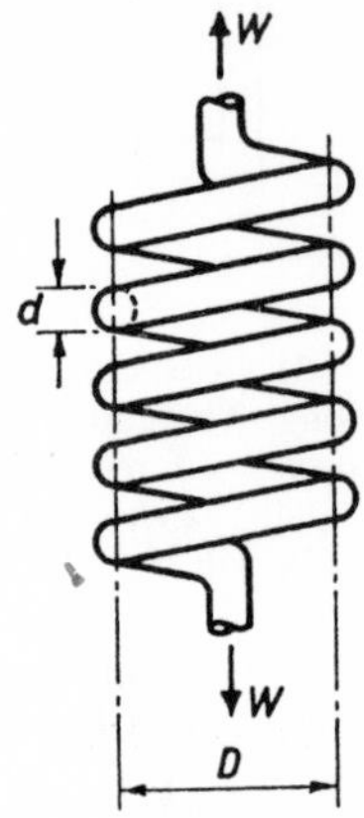

The torque on the wire at all sections $= W \times \dfrac{D}{2}$

Fig. 9.1

$\therefore$ maximum shear stress, $\tau = \dfrac{T}{Z}$

$$= \frac{\dfrac{WD}{2}}{\dfrac{\pi}{16} d^3}$$

$$= \frac{8WD}{\pi d^3} \quad . \quad . \quad . \quad . \quad . \quad (9.1)$$

The twist of one end of the wire relative to the other end is given by

$$\theta = \frac{Tl}{GJ} = \frac{\dfrac{WD}{2} \times \pi D n}{G \times \dfrac{\pi}{32} d^4}$$

$$= \frac{16 WD^2 n}{G d^4}$$

Axial movement of the free end $= \theta \times \dfrac{D}{2}$

i.e. $\delta = \dfrac{8 WD^3 n}{G d^4} \quad . \quad . \quad . \quad . \quad (9.2)$

Alternatively, equating the work done by the load to the strain energy in the wire,

$$\tfrac{1}{2}W\delta = \tfrac{1}{2}T\theta = \frac{T^2l}{2GJ}$$

$$= \tfrac{1}{2}\left(\frac{WD}{2}\right)^2 \frac{\pi Dn}{G \times \dfrac{\pi}{32}d^4} = \frac{4W^2D^3n}{Gd^4}$$

i.e.
$$\delta = \frac{8WD^3n}{Gd^4}$$

The strain energy $\dfrac{4W^2D^3n}{Gd^4}$ may be written as

$$U = \left(\frac{8WD}{\pi d^3}\right)^2 \times \frac{\pi^2Dnd^2}{16G}$$

$$= \frac{\tau^2}{4G} \times \pi Dn \times \frac{\pi}{4}d^2$$

$$= \frac{\tau^2}{4G} \times \text{volume} \ . \qquad . \qquad . \qquad . \qquad . \qquad (9.3)$$

This corresponds with the strain energy in pure torsion derived in **Art.** (4.4).

9.2 Close-coiled helical spring with axial couple. Fig. 9.2 shows a close-coiled helical spring under an axial couple M.

The bending moment on the wire at all sections $= M$

$\therefore$ maximum bending stress, $\sigma = \dfrac{M}{Z}$

$$= \frac{M}{\dfrac{\pi}{32}d^3}$$

$$= \frac{32M}{\pi d^3} \ . \qquad . \quad (9.4)$$

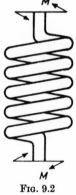

FIG. 9.2

Due to M, let the radius of curvature of the coils change from R to R' and the number of coils change from n to n'.

Then $\quad M = EI\left(\dfrac{1}{R'} - \dfrac{1}{R}\right)$, approximately

The length of wire, $l = 2\pi Rn = 2\pi R'n'$

$$\therefore \frac{1}{R} = \frac{2\pi n}{l} \qquad \text{and} \qquad \frac{1}{R'} = \frac{2\pi n'}{l}$$

$$\therefore M = EI \times \frac{2\pi}{l}(n' - n)$$

But $2\pi(n' - n)$ is the angle of twist of the spring, ϕ,

$$\therefore M = \frac{EI\phi}{l}$$

or

$$\phi = \frac{Ml}{EI} = \frac{M \times \pi Dn}{E \frac{\pi}{64} d^4}$$

$$= \frac{64MDn}{Ed^4} \qquad . \qquad . \qquad . \qquad . \quad (9.5)$$

Alternatively, since the bending moment is constant at all sections,

$$U = \frac{M^2 l}{2EI} \qquad . \qquad \text{from equation (8.1)}$$

Therefore, equating the work done by M to the strain energy in the wire,

$$\tfrac{1}{2}M\phi = \frac{M^2 l}{2EI}$$

$$\therefore \phi = \frac{Ml}{EI}, \quad \text{as before.}$$

The strain energy $\dfrac{M^2 l}{2EI}$ may be written as

$$U = \frac{32M^2 Dn}{Ed^4} = \left(\frac{32M}{\pi d^3}\right)^2 \frac{\pi^2 Dnd^2}{32E}$$

$$= \frac{\sigma^2}{8E} \times \pi Dn \times \frac{\pi}{4} d^2 = \frac{\sigma^2}{8E} \times \text{volume} \qquad . \quad (9.6)$$

9.3   Open-coiled helical springs. Let the helix angle of the wire be α and the mean radius of the coils be R. Then the length of wire,

$$l = 2\pi Rn \sec \alpha$$

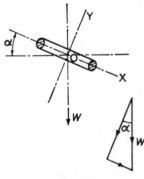

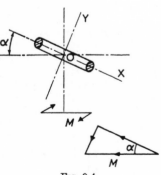

FIG. 9.3   FIG. 9.4

(a) *Axial load.* Fig. 9.3 shows part of the spring, subjected to an axial load W. The moment WR applied to the wire may be resolved into components perpendicular and parallel to the wire.

Component in plane OX $= WR \sin \alpha$, bending the wire.
Component in plane OY $= WR \cos \alpha$, twisting the wire.

Equating the work done by the load to the strain energy in the wire,

$$\tfrac{1}{2}W \delta = \frac{(WR \sin \alpha)^2 l}{2EI} + \frac{(WR \cos \alpha)^2 l}{2GJ}$$

$$\therefore \delta = WR^2 l \left\{ \frac{\sin^2 \alpha}{EI} + \frac{\cos^2 \alpha}{GJ} \right\} \qquad . \qquad . \qquad . \quad (9.7)$$

(b) *Axial couple.* Fig. 9.4 shows part of the spring, subjected to an axial couple M (this is regarded as positive if it increases the curvature of the wire, i.e. winding up the spring). This moment may be resolved into components perpendicular and parallel to the wire.

Component in plane OX $= M \cos \alpha$, bending the wire.
Component in plane OY $= M \sin \alpha$, twisting the wire.

Equating the work done by the couple to the strain energy in the wire,

$$\tfrac{1}{2}M\phi = \frac{(M \cos \alpha)^2 l}{2EI} + \frac{(M \sin \alpha)^2 l}{2GJ}$$

$$\therefore \phi = Ml \left\{ \frac{\cos^2 \alpha}{EI} + \frac{\sin^2 \alpha}{GJ} \right\} \qquad . \qquad . \qquad . \quad (9.8)$$

9.4 Composite action of axial load and couple. When an axial load is applied to an open-coiled spring, the spring winds up as well as extends and similarly, when a winding-up couple is applied, the spring extends as well as twists. These movements and the formulae already derived can be obtained by the application of Castigliano's Theorem.

If the load W and couple M are applied simultaneously,

total moment in plane OX $= -WR \sin \alpha + M \cos \alpha$, bending the wire
and
total moment in plane OY $=\ \ \ WR \cos \alpha + M \sin \alpha$, twisting the wire

$$\therefore U = \tfrac{1}{2}(-WR \sin \alpha + M \cos \alpha)^2 \frac{l}{EI} + \tfrac{1}{2}(WR \cos \alpha + M \sin \alpha)^2 \frac{l}{GJ}$$

$$= \frac{l}{2} \left\{ \frac{W^2 R^2 \sin^2 \alpha - WRM \sin 2\alpha + M^2 \cos^2 \alpha}{EI} \right.$$

$$\left. + \frac{W^2 R^2 \cos^2 \alpha + WRM \sin 2\alpha + M^2 \sin^2 \alpha}{GJ} \right\}$$

$$\delta = \frac{\partial U}{\partial W} = \frac{l}{2} \left\{ \frac{2WR^2 \sin^2 \alpha - RM \sin 2\alpha}{EI} + \frac{2WR^2 \cos^2 \alpha + RM \sin 2\alpha}{GJ} \right\}$$

$$= WR^2l\left\{\frac{\sin^2\alpha}{EI} + \frac{\cos^2\alpha}{GJ}\right\} + MRl\frac{\sin 2\alpha}{2}\left\{\frac{1}{GJ} - \frac{1}{EI}\right\} \qquad . \qquad (9.9)$$

$$\phi = \frac{\partial U}{\partial M} = \frac{l}{2}\left\{\frac{-WR\sin 2\alpha + 2M\cos^2\alpha}{EI} + \frac{WR\sin 2\alpha + 2M\sin^2\alpha}{GJ}\right\}$$

$$= Ml\left\{\frac{\cos^2\alpha}{EI} + \frac{\sin^2\alpha}{GJ}\right\} + WRl\frac{\sin 2\alpha}{2}\left\{\frac{1}{GJ} - \frac{1}{EI}\right\} \qquad . \qquad (9.10)$$

The additional terms obtained in equations (9.9) and (9.10) represent the extension due to M and the angle of twist due to W respectively.

If $\alpha \to 0$, these formulae reduce to those obtained for close-coiled springs.

9.5 Flat spiral springs. Fig. 9.5 shows a flat spiral spring, made of rectangular section strip, breadth b and thickness t. The winding torque T is applied at the central arbor O and the other end of the spring is pinned at the point A.

If the spring is tangential at A, the reaction there is purely horizontal.* If the force is P and the distance OA is h, then

$$T = Ph$$

The maximum B.M. occurs at the point B,

i.e. $M_{max} = P \times 2h$, assuming that $OB = OA$

$\therefore$ maximum bending stress, $\sigma = \dfrac{2Ph}{Z}$

$$= \frac{2T}{\dfrac{bt^2}{6}} = \frac{12T}{bt^2} \qquad . \qquad . \qquad . \qquad (9.11)$$

B.M. on element $dl = Px$

$$\therefore U = \int_0^l \frac{M^2\,dl}{2EI}$$

$$= \int_0^l \frac{P^2x^2}{2EI}\,dl$$

$$= \int_0^l \frac{T^2x^2}{2h^2EI}\,dl$$

$$\therefore \phi = \frac{\partial U}{\partial T} = \int_0^l \frac{Tx^2}{h^2EI}\,dl$$

$$= \frac{T}{h^2EI}\int_0^l x^2\,dl$$

$$= \frac{T}{h^2EI}\left(\frac{h^2}{4} + h^2\right)l,$$

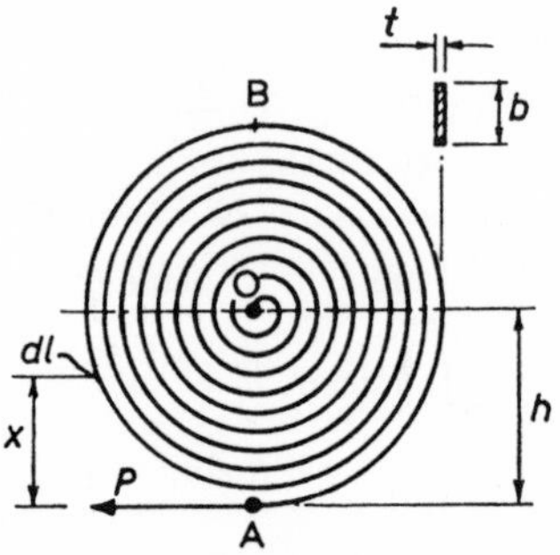

FIG. 9.5

assuming that the spring is equivalent to a disc,

* As the spring is wound up, the strip will become inclined to the line of action of P and the spring will become progressively stiffer.

$$= \frac{5Tl}{4EI} = \frac{15Tl}{Ebt^3} \qquad . \qquad . \qquad . \qquad . \qquad . \qquad (9.12)$$

The strain energy, $U = \frac{1}{2}T\phi$

$$= \frac{15}{2} \frac{T^2 l}{Ebt^3}$$

$$= \left(\frac{12T}{bt^2}\right)^2 \frac{5}{96} \frac{btl}{E} = \frac{5\sigma^2}{96E} \times \text{volume} . \qquad . \quad (9.13)$$

9.6   Leaf, laminated or carriage springs. The leaf spring is designed so that the maximum stress is the same in all plates at all sections, giving maximum utilization of material. The arrangement of the spring is shown in Fig. 9.6, each plate being free to slide relative to the adjacent plates as the spring deflects. The ends of each plate are tapered to provide a uniform change in effective breadth between the centre and the ends and if the plates were cut along their centre lines and placed side by side, they would form a diamond-shaped plate.

Let $b = $ breadth of plate
$\quad\quad\quad t = $ thickness of each plate
$\quad\quad\quad n = $ number of plates

Then effective width of plate at centre
$\quad\quad = nb$

At a section distance x from one end,

$$\sigma = \frac{M}{Z} = \frac{Wx/2}{\left(\dfrac{x}{l/2} \times nt\right) \times \dfrac{t^2}{6}}$$

$$= \frac{3Wl}{2nbt^2} \quad . \qquad . \qquad . \quad (9.14)$$

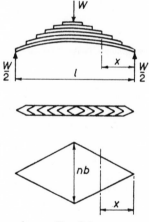

Fig. 9.6

It will be noted that this is independent of x, i.e. σ is constant at all sections.

At any section, M is proportional to x and I is proportional to x, so that M is proportional to I.

Therefore, since $\dfrac{M}{I} = \dfrac{E}{R}$, R is a constant. Thus, if the spring is to become flat when loaded, the plates must initially be bent in the arc of a circle.

The load which will cause the plates to become flat is called the *proof load*.

$$E\frac{\mathrm{d}^2 y}{\mathrm{d}x^2} = \frac{M}{I} = \frac{-Wx/2}{\left(\dfrac{x}{l/2} \times nb\right) \times \dfrac{t^3}{12}} = -\frac{3Wl}{nbt^3} \quad . \qquad . \quad (9.15)$$

$$\therefore E \frac{\mathrm{d}y}{\mathrm{d}x} = -\frac{3Wl}{nbt^3} x + A$$

When $x = \dfrac{l}{2}, \dfrac{\mathrm{d}y}{\mathrm{d}x} = 0, \therefore A = \dfrac{3Wl}{nbt^3} \cdot \dfrac{l}{2}$

$$\therefore Ey = -\frac{3Wl}{nbt^3}\left(\frac{x^2}{2} - \frac{l}{2} x\right) + B$$

When $x = 0, y = 0, \therefore B = 0.$

The maximum deflection occurs at the centre, where $x = \dfrac{l}{2}$,

i.e.
$$y_{\max} = \frac{3Wl^3}{8Enbt^3} \qquad . \qquad . \qquad . \qquad . \qquad . \quad (9.16)$$

Alternatively, from the geometry of the circle into which the plates are initially formed, Fig. 9.7,

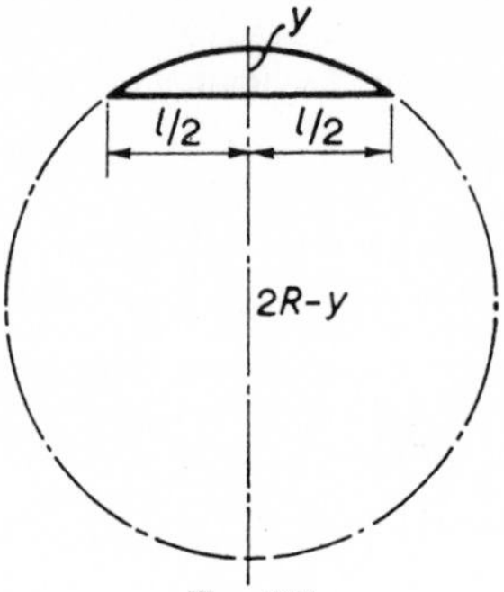

$$y(2R - y) = \left(\frac{l}{2}\right)^2$$

or
$$y = \frac{l^2}{8R}, \qquad . \qquad . \quad (9.17)$$

neglecting the term y^2 in comparison with $2Ry$,

$$= \frac{l^2}{8} \cdot \frac{M}{EI}$$

$$= \frac{3Wl^3}{8Enbt^3} \qquad . \qquad . \qquad . \qquad . \text{ from equation (9.15)}$$

Fig. 9.7

Alternatively
$$U = \int_0^l \frac{M^2}{2EI}\, \mathrm{d}x$$

$$= 2\int_0^{l/2} \frac{3Wl}{2Enbt^3} \cdot \frac{W}{2}\, x\, \mathrm{d}x \text{ from equation (9.15)}$$

i.e.
$$\tfrac{1}{2}Wy = \frac{3}{16} \frac{W^2l^3}{Enbt^3}$$

$$\therefore y = \frac{3Wl^3}{8Enbt^3}$$

The strain energy $\dfrac{3}{16} \dfrac{Wl^3}{Enbt^3}$ may be written as

$$U = \left(\frac{3Wl}{2nbt^2}\right)^2 \frac{nbtl}{12E}$$

$$= \frac{\sigma^2}{6E} \times \frac{nbtl}{2} = \frac{\sigma^2}{6E} \times \text{volume} \qquad . \qquad . \qquad . \quad (9.18)$$

9.7 Vibration of springs. (a) *Linear motion.* If a body of mass m, attached to a spring of stiffness S, is displaced a distance x from its equilibrium position, the restoring force is Sx.

When released, the acceleration of the body is given by

$$P = Sx = mf$$

or

$$\frac{x}{f} = \frac{m}{S}$$

The periodic time of the resulting vibration is then given by

$$t = 2\pi \sqrt{\frac{\text{displacement}}{\text{acceleration}}}$$

$$= 2\pi \sqrt{\frac{m}{S}} \quad . \qquad . \qquad . \qquad . \qquad (9.19)$$

For a close-coiled helical spring with a axial load,

$$S = \frac{W}{\delta} = \frac{Gd^4}{8D^3n} \qquad . \quad \text{from equation (9.2)}$$

For a leaf spring, $\qquad S = \dfrac{W}{y} = \dfrac{8Enbt^3}{3l^3} \qquad . \quad$ from equation (9.16)

(b) *Angular motion.* If a body of moment of inertia I, attached to a spring of torsional stiffness S, is displaced an angle ϕ from its equilibrium position, the restoring torque is $S\phi$.

When released, the acceleration of the body is given by

$$T = S\phi = I\alpha$$

or

$$\frac{\phi}{\alpha} = \frac{I}{S}$$

$$\therefore t = 2\pi \sqrt{\frac{I}{S}}, \quad \text{where } I = mk^2 \qquad . \qquad . \qquad (9.20)$$

For a close-coiled helical spring with an axial couple,

$$S = \frac{M}{\phi} = \frac{Ed^4}{64Dn} \qquad . \quad \text{from equation (9.5)}$$

For a flat spiral spring, $\quad S = \dfrac{T}{\phi} = \dfrac{Ebt^3}{15l} . \qquad . \quad$ from equation (9.12)

1. *A close-coiled helical spring is to have a stiffness of* 1 *kN/m of compression, a maximum load of* 50 *N and a maximum shearing stress of* 120 *MN/m². The solid length of the spring (i.e. when the coils are touching) is to be* 45 *mm.*

Find the diameter of the wire, the mean diameter of the coils and the number of coils required. $G = 50$ *GN/m².* (U. Lond.)

From equation (9.2), $\qquad S = \dfrac{W}{\delta} = \dfrac{Gd^4}{8D^3n}$

i.e. $$1\,000 = \frac{50 \times 10^9 \times d^4}{8D^3 n}$$

i.e. $$\frac{d^4}{D^3 n} = 0.16 \times 10^{-6} \qquad . \qquad . \qquad . \qquad (1)$$

From equation (9.1), $$\tau = \frac{8WD}{\pi d^3}$$

i.e. $$120 \times 10^6 = \frac{8 \times 50 \times D}{\pi d^3}$$

.e. $$\frac{D}{d^3} = 0.3 \times 10^6 \pi \qquad . \qquad . \qquad . \qquad (2)$$

Also $$nd = 0.045 \text{ m} \qquad . \qquad . \qquad . \qquad (3)$$

Therefore, from equations (1), (2) and (3),

$$d = 0.003\,4 \text{ m}, \quad D = 0.043\,6 \text{ m} \quad \text{and} \quad n = 12.54$$

---

2. *A composite spring has two close-coiled helical steel springs in series; each spring has a mean coil diameter of 8 times the diameter of its wire. One spring has 20 coils and wire diameter of 2·5 mm. Find the diameter of the wire in the other spring if it has 15 coils and the stiffness of the composite spring is 1·25 kN/m.*

Find the greatest axial load that can be applied to the spring and the corresponding extension for a maximum shearing stress of 300 MN/m². G = 80 GN/m². (U. Lond.)

Fig. 9.8 shows the arrangement of the two springs, which are subject to an axial load W.

$$d_1 = 0.002\,5 \text{ m} \qquad \therefore D_1 = 0.02 \text{ m}$$

$$\therefore S_1 = \frac{W}{\delta_1} = \frac{Gd_1^4}{8D_1^3 n_1} \qquad . \qquad . \qquad \text{from equation (9.2)}$$

$$= \frac{80 \times 10^9 \times 0.002\,5^4}{8 \times 0.02^3 \times 20} = 2.44 \text{ kN/m}$$

Total extension, $$\delta = \frac{W}{S_1} + \frac{W}{S_2}$$

$\therefore$ effective stiffness, $$S = \frac{W}{\dfrac{W}{S_1} + \dfrac{W}{S_2}} = \frac{S_1 S_2}{S_1 + S_2}$$

i.e. $$1.25 = \frac{2.44 S_2}{2.44 + S_2}$$

$$\therefore S_2 = 2.57 \text{ kN/m}$$

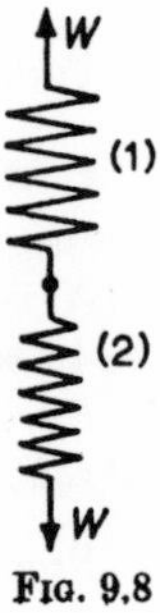

FIG. 9.8

$$\therefore 2 \cdot 57 \times 10^3 = \frac{80 \times 10^9 \times d_2^4}{8 \times (8d_2)^3 \times 15}$$

from which $\qquad d_2 = \underline{0 \cdot 001\ 975\ \text{m}}$

From equation (9.1), $\tau = \dfrac{8WD}{\pi d^3} = \dfrac{64W}{\pi d^2}$ . . . since $D = 8d$

The maximum shear stress therefore occurs in spring (2),

i.e. $\qquad 300 \times 10^6 = \dfrac{64W}{\pi \times 0 \cdot 001\ 975^2}$

$$\therefore W = \underline{57 \cdot 5\ \text{N}}$$

$$\delta = \frac{W}{S}$$

$$= \frac{57 \cdot 5}{1 \cdot 25 \times 10^3} = \underline{0 \cdot 046\ \text{m}}$$

3. *The spring load against which a valve is opened is provided by an inner helical spring arranged within and concentric with an outer helical spring. Both springs are of steel, close-coiled, and the free length of the inner spring is 6 mm longer than that of the outer spring. The outer spring has 12 coils of mean diameter 25 mm, diameter of wire 3 mm and an initial compression of 5 mm when the valve is closed. Find the stiffness of the inner spring if the greatest force required to open the valve 10 mm is 150 N.*

If the radial clearance between the springs is approximately 1·5 mm, find the diameter of the wire of the inner spring if it has 10 coils. $G = 80\ GN/m^2$.

(U. Lond.)

Fig. 9.9 shows the arrangement of the two springs.

$\qquad$ Initial compression of outer spring $= 5$ mm

$\qquad \therefore$ initial compression of inner spring $= 5 + 6$

$$= 11\ \text{mm}$$

When the valve is opened 10 mm,

$\qquad$ compression of outer spring $= 15$ mm

and compression of inner spring $= 22$ mm

Force exerted by outer spring $= \delta_1 \times \dfrac{Gd_1^4}{8D_1^3 n_1}$ $\qquad$ from equation (9.2)

$$= 0 \cdot 015 \times \frac{80 \times 10^9 \times 0 \cdot 003^4}{8 \times 0 \cdot 025^3 \times 12}$$

$$= 64 \cdot 8\ \text{N}$$

$\therefore$ force exerted by inner spring $= 150 - 64 \cdot 8 = 85 \cdot 2$ N

$\therefore$ stiffness of inner spring $= \dfrac{85 \cdot 2}{0 \cdot 022} = \underline{3\ 870\ \text{N/m}}$

$$D_2 = D_1 - (d_1 + d_2 + 2 \times 0{\cdot}001\ 5)$$
$$= 0{\cdot}025 - (0{\cdot}003 + d_2 + 0{\cdot}003)$$
$$= 0{\cdot}019 - d_2 \text{ m}$$

$$S_2 = \frac{W_2}{\delta_2} = \frac{Gd_2^4}{8D_2^3 n_2}$$

i.e. $$3\ 870 = \frac{80 \times 10^9 \times d_2^4}{8(0{\cdot}019 - d_2)^3 \times 10}$$

from which $d_2 = 0{\cdot}002\ 08$ m

or   2·08 mm

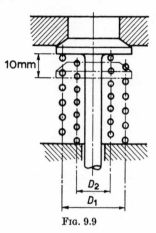

Fig. 9.9

4. *A close-coiled helical spring is made of steel wire 6 mm diameter coiled into 50 coils of mean diameter 50 mm. The modulus of rigidity of the steel is 80 GN/m². The spring is held fixed at the top and a mass of 15 kg is allowed to fall through a height of 50 mm before engaging with a hook at the lower end of the spring.*

Calculate (a) the maximum extension of the spring and (b) the maximum stress in the wire. (U. Lond.)

If the mass m drops through a height h before engaging with the hook and causes a maximum instantaneous extension δ, then

loss of potential energy of load $= mg(h + \delta)$.

This is stored in the spring as strain energy, neglecting loss of energy at impact. Thus, if the maximum instantaneous stress is τ,

$$mg(h + \delta) = \frac{\tau^2}{4G} \times \text{volume} . \quad \text{from equation (9.3)}$$

From equations (9.1) and (9.2),

$$\tau = \frac{8WD}{\pi d^3}$$

and $$\delta = \frac{8WD^3 n}{Gd^4}$$

where W is the maximum instantaneous force in the spring

$$\therefore \delta = \tau \times \frac{\pi D^2 n}{Gd}$$

$$= \tau \times \frac{\pi^2 \times 0{\cdot}05^2 \times 50}{80 \times 10^9 \times 0{\cdot}006} = 0{\cdot}817 \times 10^{-9}\tau \text{ m}$$

i.e.

$$15 \times 9 \cdot 81(0 \cdot 05 + 0 \cdot 817 \times 10^{-9}\tau) = \frac{\tau^2}{4 \times 80 \times 10^9} \times \frac{\pi}{4} \times 0 \cdot 006^2 \times \pi \times 0 \cdot 05 \times 50$$

from which

$$\tau^2 - 1 \cdot 733 \times 10^8 \tau - 1 \cdot 06 \times 10^{16} = 0$$

$$\therefore \tau = 221 \cdot 1 \ \text{MN/m}^2 *$$

$$\delta = 221 \cdot 1 \times 10^6 \times 0 \cdot 817 \times 10^{-9}$$

$$= 0 \cdot 180 \ 7 \ \text{m}$$

5. *A close-coiled helical spring is made of wire 2·5 mm diameter. The mean coil diameter is 25 mm and there are 20 coils. One end of the spring is rigidly fixed and a uniform disc 100 mm diameter and of mass 1 kg is rigidly attached to the other end so that the spring and disc are co-axial. Find the periodic time of small angular oscillations of the disc. $E = 200 \ GN/m^2$.*

If the amplitude of the oscillations is 30°, find the maximum bending stress in the wire.

From equation (9.20),

$$t = 2\pi \sqrt{\frac{I}{S}}$$

and from equation (9.5),

$$S = \frac{M}{\phi} = \frac{Ed^4}{64Dn}$$

$$\therefore t = 2\pi \sqrt{\frac{64Dn}{Ed^4} \times \frac{mr^2}{2}}$$

$$= 2\pi \sqrt{\frac{64 \times 0 \cdot 025 \times 20}{200 \times 10^9 \times 0 \cdot 002 \ 5^4} \times \frac{1 \times 0 \cdot 05^2}{2}}$$

$$= 0 \cdot 45 \ \text{s}$$

From equations (9.4) and (9.5),

$$\sigma = \frac{32M}{\pi d^3}$$

and

$$\phi = \frac{64MDn}{Ed^4}$$

$$\therefore \sigma = \phi \times \frac{Ed}{2\pi Dn}$$

$$= \frac{\pi}{6} \times \frac{200 \times 10^9 \times 0 \cdot 002 \ 5}{2\pi \times 0 \cdot 025 \times 20} \ \text{N/m}^2 = 83 \ \text{MN/m}^2$$

* The lower (negative) value for τ from the quadratic equation represents the instantaneous stress in the wire at the highest point of the rebound.

6. *Derive an expression for the axial stiffness (i.e. load per unit extension) of an open-coiled helical spring made of round wire of diameter d, the mean radius of the coils R and their inclination α. Calculate the percentage error in the value obtained for the stiffness if the inclination of the coils is neglected for a spring in which* α = 30°. *Take* E = 2·5G. (U. Lond.)

From equation (9.7),

$$\delta = WR^2 l \left\{ \frac{\sin^2 \alpha}{EI} + \frac{\cos^2 \alpha}{GJ} \right\}$$

where

$$l = 2\pi Rn \sec \alpha$$

But

$$E = 2\text{·}5G \quad \text{and for round wire, } J = 2I$$

$$\therefore \delta = \frac{2\pi WR^3 n}{GJ} \sec \alpha \left\{ \frac{\sin^2 \alpha}{1\text{·}25} + \cos^2 \alpha \right\}$$

$$\therefore S = \frac{W}{\delta} = \frac{GJ}{2\pi R^3 n \sec \alpha \left\{ \dfrac{\sin^2 \alpha}{1\text{·}25} + \cos^2 \alpha \right\}}$$

If the inclination of the wire is neglected, this reduces to

$$S = \frac{GJ}{2\pi R^3 n}$$

Thus, if the stiffness of the open-coiled and close-coiled springs are denoted by S_o and S_c respectively, the error involved by regarding the spring as close-coiled

$$= \frac{S_o - S_c}{S_o} = 1 - \frac{S_c}{S_o}$$

$$= 1 - \frac{1}{\sec 30° \left\{ \dfrac{\sin^2 30°}{1\text{·}25} + \cos^2 30° \right\}}$$

$$= 1 - 0\text{·}912 = 0\text{·}088 \quad \text{or} \quad \underline{8\text{·}8 \text{ per cent}}$$

7. *An open-coiled spring carries an axial, vertical load W. Derive ex-expressions for the vertical displacement and angular twist of the free end.*

Find the mean radius of an open-coiled spring (angle of helix, 30°) to give a vertical displacement of 25 mm and an angular rotation of the loaded end of 1·25° under an axial load of 40 N. The material available is steel rod of 6 mm diameter. E = 200 GN/m² *and* G = 80 GN/m². (U. Lond.)

From equations (9.9) and (9.10),

$$\delta = WR^2 l \left\{ \frac{\sin^2 \alpha}{EI} + \frac{\cos^2 \alpha}{GJ} \right\}$$

and

$$\phi = WRl \frac{\sin 2\alpha}{2} \left\{ \frac{1}{GJ} - \frac{1}{EI} \right\}$$

$$E = 2 \cdot 5G \quad \text{and for round wire } J = 2I$$

so that
$$EI = 1 \cdot 25GJ$$

$$\therefore \ 0 \cdot 025 = \frac{WR^2l}{GJ}\left\{\frac{\sin^2 30°}{1 \cdot 25} + \cos^2 30°\right\}$$

$$= \frac{WR^2l}{GJ} \times 0 \cdot 95$$

$$\therefore \ \frac{WR^2l}{GJ} = 0 \cdot 026\ 3 \qquad . \qquad . \qquad . \qquad . \qquad . \qquad (1)$$

and
$$1 \cdot 25 \times \frac{\pi}{180} = \frac{WRl}{GJ}\frac{\sin 60°}{2}\left\{1 - \frac{1}{1 \cdot 25}\right\}$$

$$= \frac{WRl}{GJ} \times 0 \cdot 086\ 6$$

$$\therefore \ \frac{WRl}{GJ} = 0 \cdot 252 \qquad . \qquad . \qquad . \qquad . \qquad . \qquad (2)$$

Therefore, from equations (1) and (2), $R = \dfrac{0 \cdot 026\ 3}{0 \cdot 252} = \underline{0 \cdot 104\ 4 \text{ m}}$

8. *An open-coiled helical spring made of 10 mm diameter rod has six free coils 100 mm mean diameter. The ends of the spring are fastened to two discs kept 0·75 m apart, which is the free length of the spring. Calculate the force on the discs, acting along the axis of the spring, when one disc is rotated through 10° to coil the spring. $E = 200$ GN/m² and $G = 80$ GN/m². (U. Lond.)*

$$\text{Pitch of coils} = \frac{0 \cdot 75}{6} = 0 \cdot 125 \text{ m}$$

$$\therefore \ \tan \alpha = \frac{0 \cdot 125}{0 \cdot 10\pi} = 0 \cdot 397\ 9$$

$$\therefore \ \alpha = 21° 42'$$

$$l = 2\pi Rn \sec \alpha$$

$$= 2\pi \times 0 \cdot 05 \times 6 \times \sec 21° 42' = 2 \cdot 03 \text{ m}$$

$$E = 2 \cdot 5G \text{ and } J = 2I, \text{ so that } EI = 1 \cdot 25GJ$$

From equation (9.9),

$$\delta = WR^2l\left\{\frac{\sin^2 \alpha}{EI} + \frac{\cos^2 \alpha}{GJ}\right\} + MRl\frac{\sin 2\alpha}{2}\left\{\frac{1}{GJ} - \frac{1}{EI}\right\} = 0$$

i.e. $W \times 0 \cdot 05\left\{\dfrac{0 \cdot 369\ 7^2}{1 \cdot 25} + 0 \cdot 929\ 1^2\right\} + M \times \dfrac{0 \cdot 687\ 1}{2}\left\{1 - \dfrac{1}{1 \cdot 25}\right\} = 0$

from which
$$M = -0 \cdot 707\ 5W$$

From equation (9.10),

$$\phi = Ml\left\{\frac{\cos^2 \alpha}{EI} + \frac{\sin^2 \alpha}{GJ}\right\} + WRl\frac{\sin 2\alpha}{2}\left\{\frac{1}{GJ} - \frac{1}{EI}\right\} = 10 \times \frac{\pi}{180}$$

i.e.

$$\frac{Wl}{GJ}\left[-0.707\ 5\left\{\frac{0.929\ 1^2}{1.25} + 0.369\ 7^2\right\} + 0.05 \times \frac{0.687\ 1}{2}\left\{1 - \frac{1}{1.25}\right\}\right] = \frac{\pi}{18}$$

i.e.

$$-\frac{W \times 2.03}{80 \times 10^9 \times \frac{\pi}{32} \times 0.01^4} \times 0.587\ 4 = \frac{\pi}{18}$$

from which $\qquad W = \underline{-11.5\ \text{N}}$ (i.e. compressive)

9. *A flat spiral spring is made of steel 12 mm broad and 0·5 mm thick. The end at the greatest radius is attached to a fixed point and the other end to a spindle. The length of the steel strip is 6 m.*

Determine: (a) the maximum turning moment which can be applied to the spindle if the stress in the strip is not to exceed 550 MN/m²; (b) the number of turns required to be given to the spindle; (c) the energy then stored in the spring. E = 200 GN/m². (U. Lond.)

(a) From equation (9.11), $\qquad \sigma = \dfrac{12T}{bt^2}$

i.e. $\qquad 550 \times 10^6 = \dfrac{12T}{0.012 \times 0.000\ 5^2}$

from which $\qquad T = \underline{0.137\ 5\ \text{N m}}$

(b) From equation (9.12), $\qquad \phi = \dfrac{15Tl}{Ebt^3}$

$$= \frac{15 \times 0.137\ 5 \times 6}{200 \times 10^9 \times 0.012 \times 0.000\ 5^3}$$

$$= 41.25\ \text{rad} = \underline{6.57\ \text{rev}}$$

(c) $\qquad U = \tfrac{1}{2}T\phi$

$$= \tfrac{1}{2} \times 0.137\ 5 \times 41.25 = \underline{2.84\ \text{J}}$$

10. *A laminated steel spring, simply supported at the ends and centrally loaded with a span of 0·75 m is required to carry a proof load of 7·5 kN and the central deflection is not to exceed 50 mm. The bending stress must not be greater than 400 MN/m². Plates are available in multiples of 1 mm for thickness and in multiples of 4 mm for width.*

Determine suitable values for the thickness, width and number of plates and the radius to which the plates should be formed.

Assume the width to be twelve times the thickness. E = 200 GN/m². (U. Lond.)

From equation (9.16), $\qquad y = \dfrac{3Wl^3}{8Enbt^3}$

i.e. $\qquad 0.05 = \dfrac{3 \times 7.5 \times 10^3 \times 0.75^3}{8 \times 200 \times 10^9 \times n \times 12t \times t^3}$

from which $\qquad nt^4 = 9.89 \times 10^{-9}$ $\qquad . \qquad . \qquad . \qquad .$ (1)

From equation (9.14), $\sigma = \dfrac{3Wl}{2nbt^2}$

i.e. $400 \times 10^6 = \dfrac{3 \times 7\cdot5 \times 10^3 \times 0\cdot75}{2 \times n \times 12t \times t^2}$

from which $nt^3 = 1\cdot758 \times 10^{-6}$.   .   .   . (2)

Therefore, from equations (1) and (2), $t = 0\cdot005\ 62$ m.
The nearest suitable thickness above this value is 6 mm

$$b = 12t = 12 \times 6 = 72\ \text{mm}$$

From equation (2), $n = \dfrac{1\cdot758 \times 10^{-6}}{0\cdot006^3} = 8\cdot13$

i.e.   9 plates are required

Actual deflection under load $= \dfrac{3 \times 7\cdot5 \times 10^3 \times 0\cdot75^3}{8 \times 200 \times 10^9 \times 9 \times 0\cdot072 \times 0\cdot006^3}$

$= 0\cdot042\ 4$ m

Hence, from equation (9.17),

$$0\cdot042\ 4 = \dfrac{0\cdot75^2}{8R} \quad \therefore R = 1\cdot66\ \text{m}$$

11. *A quarter-elliptic, i.e. cantilever, leaf spring has a length of* 0·5 *m and consists of plates each* 50 *mm wide and* 6 *mm thick. Find the least number of plates which can be used if the deflection under a gradually applied mass of* 200 *kg is not to exceed* 70 *mm.*

If, instead of being gradually applied, the mass of 200 *kg falls a distance of* 6 *mm on to the undeflected spring, find the maximum deflection and stress produced. What is then the frequency of the resulting vibrations?* $E = 200$ GN/m^2.

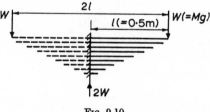

FIG. 9.10

The arrangement of the spring is shown in Fig. 9.10. The stress and end deflection are the same as in an ordinary leaf spring of span $2l$ and carrying a central load $2W$,

i.e.
$$\sigma = \frac{3(2W)(2l)}{2nbt^2} \qquad \text{from equation (9.14)}$$

$$= \frac{6Wl}{nbt^2} \qquad \qquad \qquad (1)$$

and
$$y = \frac{3(2W)(2l)^3}{8Enbt^3} \qquad \text{from equation (9.16)}$$

$$= \frac{6Wl^3}{Enbt^3} \qquad \qquad \qquad (2)$$

Thus, in equation (2),
$$0{\cdot}07 = \frac{6 \times 200 \times 9{\cdot}81 \times 0{\cdot}5^3}{200 \times 10^9 \times n \times 0{\cdot}05 \times 0{\cdot}006^3}$$

$$\therefore n = 9{\cdot}72$$

i.e.
<u>10 leaves are required</u>

When the mass is dropped on to the beam, the loss of potential energy of the mass is equal to the strain energy stored in the beam,

i.e.
$$mg(h + y) = \frac{\sigma^2}{6E} \times \text{volume} \qquad \text{from equation (9.18)}$$

But, from equations (1) and (2),
$$\sigma = y \times \frac{Et}{l^2}$$

$$\therefore mg(h + y) = \frac{y^2}{6E} \times \left(\frac{Et}{l^2}\right)^2 \times \tfrac{1}{2} \times nb \times l \times t$$

$$= y^2 \times \frac{Enbt^3}{12l^3}$$

i.e. $200 \times 9{\cdot}81(0{\cdot}006 + y) = y^2 \times \dfrac{200 \times 10^9 \times 10 \times 0{\cdot}05 \times 0{\cdot}006^3}{12 \times 0{\cdot}5^3}$

i.e. $7{\cdot}34y^2 - y - 0{\cdot}006 = 0$

from which
$$y = \underline{0{\cdot}142 \text{ m}}$$

$$\sigma = 0{\cdot}142 \times \frac{200 \times 10^9 \times 0{\cdot}006}{0{\cdot}5^2}$$

$$= \underline{682 \text{ MN/m}^2}$$

Periodic time of vibration,
$$t = 2\pi\sqrt{\frac{m}{S}} \qquad \text{from equation (9.19)}$$

$$= 2\pi\sqrt{\frac{y}{g}}$$

where y is the *static* deflection under the load.

With 10 leaves,

$$\text{actual deflection} = \frac{9\cdot72}{10} \times 0\cdot07 = 0\cdot068$$

$$\therefore t = 2\pi\sqrt{\frac{0\cdot068}{9\cdot81}} = 0\cdot522 \text{ s}$$

$$\therefore \text{ frequency, } N = \frac{1}{0\cdot522} = \underline{1\cdot915 \text{ Hz}}$$

12. A close-coiled helical spring is to have a stiffness of 70 kN/m and to exert a force of 2·25 kN. If the mean diameter of the coils is to be 90 mm, and the working stress 230 MN/m², find the required number of coils and the diameter of the steel rod from which the spring should be made. Take the modulus of rigidity as 80 GN/m². (*U. Lond.*)   (*Ans.:* 6·58; 13·55 mm)

13. A helical compression spring has a coil diameter of 75 mm and must carry a maximum load of 900 N with a compression of 100 mm. Calculate the diameter of the wire and the number of free turns required. Allow a maximum shearing stress of 400 MN/m² and G = 80 GN/m². (*U. Lond.*) (*Ans.:* 7·54 mm; 8·52)

14. A helical spring has 14 free coils of 16 mm diameter and is made of 2 mm diameter wire. Its original length is 60 mm. What compressive load will reduce the length to 43 mm? Calculate the stress in the wire at this load. G = 75 GN/m². (*U. Lond.*)   (*Ans.:* 44·4 N; 226 MN/m²)

15. A close-coiled helical spring is to have a stiffness of 80 kN/m and to exert a force of 2·7 kN. If the mean diameter of the coils is to be 75 mm and the maximum stress is not to exceed 250 MN/m², calculate the required number of coils and the diameter of the steel rod from which the spring should be made. The modulus of rigidity of the material is 80 GN/m². (*I.C.E.*)   (*Ans.:* 8; 12·74 mm)

16. A close-coiled helical spring made of round steel wire is required just to fit over a rod 30 mm diameter and to carry an axial load of 120 N without causing the deflection to exceed 20 mm. The maximum allowable shearing stress is 200 MN/m² and G for the steel is 80 GN/m². Find the diameter of the wire, the mean diameter of the coil and the number of turns. (*U. Lond.*)
                  (*Ans.:* 3·72 mm; 33·72 mm; 8·52)

17. Close-coiled helical springs having n turns are made of round wire such that the mean diameter of the coils, D (m), is 10 times the diameter of the wire. Show that the 'stiffness' in N/m for any such spring is $D/n \times$ a constant, and determine the constant if the modulus of rigidity of the material is 80 GN/m².

Such a spring is required to support a load of 900 N with an extension of 100 mm and a maximum shearing stress of 350 MN/m². Calculate (*i*) its mass, (*ii*) the mean diameter of the coils, and (*iii*) the number of turns. The material has a density of 7·8 Mg/m³. (*U. Lond.*)   (*Ans.:* 10⁶; 0·91 kg; 80·84 mm; 8·98)

18. A composite spring has two close-coiled helical springs connected in series; each spring has 12 coils at a mean diameter of 25 mm. Find the diameter of the wire in one of the springs if the diameter of the wire in the other spring is 2·5 mm and the stiffness of the composite spring is 700 N/m.

Estimate the greatest load that can be carried by the composite spring and the corresponding extension for a maximum shearing stress of 180 MN/m². G = 80 GN/m². (*U. Lond.*)   (*Ans.:* 2·11 mm; 26·55 N; 37·9 mm)

19. Two close-coiled helical springs are arranged, one inside the other, about the same longitudinal axis. Both springs have the same number of effective coils and the same overall length, but the mean coil diameter of the outer spring, which is made of steel wire, is twice that of the inner spring, which is made of bronze wire. The springs are designed to act together when a tensile force is applied, so that both suffer the same change in length and each carries half the force.

Determine the ratio of the wire diameters, and the ratio of the stresses produced in the wires, if the modulus of rigidity of steel is twice that of bronze. (*I.C.E.*)

$$\left(Ans.: \frac{d_\text{s}}{d_\text{b}} = \sqrt{2}; \frac{\sigma_\text{s}}{\sigma_\text{b}} = \frac{1}{\sqrt{2}} \right)$$

20. In a compound helical spring the inner spring is arranged within and concentric with the outer one but is 10 mm shorter. The outer spring as 10 coils of mean diameter 25 mm and the diameter of the wire is 3 mm. Find the stiffness of the inner spring if an axial load of 150 N causes the outer one to compress 20 mm. If the radial clearance between the two springs is to be 1·6 mm, find the diameter of the wire of the inner spring when it has 8 coils. $G = 80$ GN/m^2 for both springs. (*U. Lond.*) (*Ans.:* 4·62 kN/m; 2·04 mm)

21. An axially loaded close-coiled helical spring whose free length is to be 50 mm is required to have a strain energy of 0·45 J when the maximum shearing stress is 140 MN/m^2 and the spring is fully compressed (i.e. coils touching).

Assuming a mean coil diameter of 25 mm, find the diameter of the steel wire and the number of coils required. $G = 80$ GN/m^2. (*U. Lond.*)

(*Ans.:* 3·19 mm; 11·7)

22. Derive a formula for the strain energy stored per unit volume in a circular section rod subjected to pure torsion.

A closely-coiled helical spring of circular section is required to absorb 270 J of energy without the stress exceeding 350 MN/m^2. If the steel has a density of 7·8 Mg/m^3, calculate the mass of the spring.

If the maximum load is 1·8 kN and the mean diameter of the coils is 100 mm, calculate the diameter of the rod. Take $G = 75$ GN/m^2. (*U. Lond.*)

(*Ans.:* 5·16 kg; 10·94 mm)

23. Prove that the energy stored per unit volume of a compressed helical spring made of round wire is $\tau^2/4G$, where τ is the maximum shearing stress in the wire and G is the modulus of rigidity.

Determine the mass of such a spring which requires a force of 9 kN to produce a compression of 140 mm, the maximum shearing stress being 450 MN/m^2.

Density of material = 7·8 Mg/m^3; $G = 80$ GN/m^2. (*U. Lond.*)

(*Ans.:* 7·76 kg)

24. A helical spring of mean diameter 75 mm consists of 8 coils of steel wire 6 mm diameter. The spring is mounted with its axis vertical. A mass of 5 kg is dropped 50 mm on to the top of the spring. Estimate the maximum deflection of the spring and the instantaneous maximum shearing stress. Treat as a close-coiled spring, but assume that the coils do not quite close up tight as the result of the impact. $G = 80$ GN/m^2. (*U. Lond.*) (*Ans.:* 50·6 mm; 171·7 MN/m^2)

25. A close-coiled helical spring consists of 5 mm diameter wire made up into 10 coils of mean diameter 50 mm. A mass of 3 kg falls from a height of 25 mm before it reaches the top of the spring and compresses it. Calculate the stiffness of the spring and hence the maximum deflection and shear stress due to the falling mass if the modulus of rigidity is 80 GN/m^2. (*U. Lond.*)

(*Ans.:* 5 kN/m; 24 mm; 122 MN/m^2)

26. A vertical rod, 3 m long, 25 mm in diameter, fixed at the top end, is provided with a collar at the bottom end. A helical spring of mean diameter 240 mm, consisting of 5 coils of 40 mm diameter steel, is mounted on the collar. A sliding mass of 550 kg is dropped down the rod on to the spring. Find the height, measured from the top of the uncompressed spring, from which the weight should be dropped to produce an instantaneous stress of 70 MN/m² in the rod.

Find also the maximum shearing stress in the spring.

Take E for the rod as 70 GN/m² and G for the spring as 80 GN/m². Assume the spring close-coiled, but not quite closed up tight by the action of the falling weight. (*U. Lond.*) (*Ans.:* 223 mm; 328·5 MN/m²)

27. A close-coiled helical spring is subjected to an axial load W and an axial couple M. Derive expressions for the extensions and angle of twist produced.

A close-coiled helical spring is to be made of wire 5 mm diameter for which $E = 200$ GN/m² and $G = 80$ GN/m². It is required to extend 28 mm for an axial load of 100 N and to twist 0·22 radian for an axial couple of 1 Nm. Find the mean diameter of the coils and the number of coils required. (*U. Lond.*)

(*Ans.:* 42·34 mm; 23)

28. A helical spring of 100 mm mean diameter has 15 turns of 6 mm diameter wire. The spring is mounted with its axis vertical, fixed at the top, and a mass of 1·8 kg of which the radius of gyration is 65 mm, is attached at the lower end. When given a small angular displacement in a horizontal plane, the weight makes 100 oscillations about the vertical axis in 33 s. Calculate the modulus of elasticity of the spring, treating it as closely coiled.

Find also what angular displacement of the weight will produce a maximum bending stress of 165 MN/m². (*U. Lond.*) (*Ans.:* 204·8 GN/m²; 72·6°)

29. A closely coiled spring is made of 4·8 mm diameter wire and has 16 free coils. It is of the helical type, but the coil radius increases uniformly from 25 mm at one end to 50 mm at the other end. Determine the deflection per newton. $G = 80$ GN/m². (*U. Lond.*) (*Ans.:* 1·41 mm)

30. Obtain an expression for the elongation of an open-coiled helical spring made of wire of circular section.

Calculate the pitch angle of the coils of an open-coiled helical spring for which the elongation is 2 per cent greater than that of a close-coiled spring otherwise similar in every respect. (*U. Lond.*) (*Ans.:* 15° 21′)

31. A helical spring is made of circular section wire 12 mm diameter and wound for 30 coils at a pitch of 50 mm. The mean diameter of the coils is 75 mm. Working from the fundamental formula used for beams and shafts, calculate the extension of the spring under a load of 500 N and find the angular rotation of the load in degrees. $E = 200$ GN/m²; $G = 80$ GN/m². (*U. Lond.*)

(*Ans.:* 28·8 mm; 0·0338 rad)

32. An open-coiled helical spring is made of wire 6 mm diameter and wound to a mean-coiled diameter of 50 mm. The pitch of the coils is 25 mm and there are 10 complete turns. If a pure axial twisting moment of 7 N m is applied to the spring, calculate the resulting angle of twist and the extension. Work from first principles or prove formulae used. $E = 200$ GN/m²; $G = 80$ GN/m². (*U. Lond.*)

(*Ans.:* 50·5°; 0·847 mm)

33. Derive an expression for the axial extension of an open-coiled helical spring produced by an axial twisting couple.

A helical spring has a mean diameter of 65 mm, and consists of 12 turns of 6 mm diameter wire. Initially the inclination of the turns is 7°. Calculate the axial and angular deformations caused by an axial 'winding-up' couple of 9 N m. Explain carefully any approximations made. $E = 200 \text{ GN/m}^2$; $G = 80 \text{ GN/m}^2$. (*U. Lond.*)   (*Ans.:* 1·72 mm; 1·754 rad)

34. An open coiled spring of 125 mm mean diameter has 10 coils of 12 mm diameter wire, at a slope of 30° to the horizontal when the coil axis is vertical. Find expressions for the longitudinal extensions δ and the rotation θ for the joint application of an axial load W and an axial torque T. Hence, find the axial load and torque necessary to extend the spring 5 mm if rotation is prevented, indicating whether the torque tends to wind up or unwind the spring. $E = 200 \text{ GN/m}^2$; $G = 80 \text{ GN/m}^2$. (*U. Lond.*)   (*Ans.:* 48·9 N; 0·312 N m, unwinding)

35. A flat spiral spring is 6 mm wide and 0·25 mm thick, the length being 2·5 m. Assuming the maximum stress of 800 MN/m² to occur at the point of greatest bending moment, calculate the torque, the work that can be stored in the spring, and the number of complete turns to wind up the spring. Take $E = 200 \text{ GN/m}^2$. (*U. Lond.*)   (*Ans.:* 0·025 N m; 0·625 J; 7·96 rev)

36. An instrument control spring is made of phosphor-bronze 1 mm wide and 0·1 mm radial thickness. It is to be formed into a flat spiral spring pinned at the outer end and at the inner end attached to the collet on the instrument arbor.

Calculate the necessary length of spring so that a torque of 45 μN m will cause a rotation of 90°.

If the moving parts have a mass of 6 g and the radius of gyration is taken as 14 mm, calculate the periodic time of free vibration.

The beam formula as applied to a spiral spring must be proved, and the assumptions stated. $E = 120 \text{ GN/m}^2$. (*U. Lond.*)   (*Ans.:* 279·2 mm; 1·14 s)

37. Obtain from first principles an expression for the energy stored in a flat spiral spring per unit volume of material in terms of the maximum bending stress, which is assumed to occur at the point of greatest bending moment, and the elastic modulus.

Hence, find the necessary length of a spring 25 mm wide and 0·5 mm thick which will store 7·5 J for a limiting stress of 800 MN/m². Find also the torque required, and the number of turns of the winding-spindle necessary to wind up the spring. $E = 200 \text{ GN/m}^2$. (*U. Lond.*) (*Ans.:* 3·6 m; 0·4167 N m; 5·73 rad)

38. A laminated spring, made of 12 steel plates, is 0·9 m long. The maximum central load is 7·2 kN. If the maximum allowable stress in the steel is 230 MN/m² and the maximum deflection approximately 38 mm, calculate the width and thickness of the plates. $E = 200 \text{ GN/m}^2$.
Either work from first principles, or prove any formulae used. (*U. Lond.*)
     (*Ans.:* 93·8 mm; 6·13 mm)

39. A leaf spring is required to satisfy the following specification: $L = 0·75$ m; $W = 5$ kN; $b = 75$ mm; maximum stress, 210 MN/m²; maximum deflection, 25 mm; $E = 200 \text{ GN/m}^2$. Find the number of leaves and their thickness. If the leaves become straight when this load is applied, find the initial radius of curvature.
     (*Ans.:* 10; 6 mm; 2·8 m)

40. Deduce an expression for the central deflection of a carriage spring when simply supported at the ends and loaded in the centre so that the plates become straight. Such a spring has 12 plates each 65 mm wide by 6 mm thick, and the longest plate is 0·8 m long. The greatest bending stress is not to exceed 185 MN/m² and the central deflection when the spring is fully loaded is not to exceed 20 mm. Estimate the magnitude of the greatest central load that can be applied to the spring. $E = 200 \text{ GN/m}^2$. (*U. Lond.*)   (*Ans.:* 3·51 kN)

41. A quarter-elliptic or cantilever leaf spring of length l with n plates each of breadth b and thickness t is so shaped that circular bending occurs. Derive expressions (a) for the maximum stress due to bending and (b) for the maximum deflection due to an end load W.

If the maximum allowable bending stress is 400 MN/m² and the spring has 5 plates each 70 mm wide by 10 mm thick with the length of the longest plate 0·4 m, find (c) the maximum value for the load W and (d) the deflection at the end. Assuming that the spring just straightens under these conditions, determine the initial radius of curvature of the plates. For steel $E = 200$ GN/m². ($U.\ Lond.$)

$(Ans.:\ 5·833$ kN; 32 mm; 2·5 m)

42. Deduce an expression for the resilience of a loaded carriage spring, the maximum bending stress being given.

A carriage spring 1·35 m long has leaves of 100 × 12·5 mm section. The maximum bending stress is 150 MN/m² and the spring must absorb 125 J when straightened. Calculate the number of leaves and their initial curvature. $E = 200$ GN/m². ($U.\ Lond.$)

$(Ans.:\ 8;\ 8·43$ m)

43. A carriage spring, centrally loaded and simply supported at the ends, has 10 steel plates, each 50 mm wide by 6 mm thick. If the longest plate is 0·75 m long, find the initial radius of curvature of the plates when the greatest bending stress is 150 MN/m² and the plates are finally straight. Neglecting the loss of energy at impact, determine the greatest height from which a mass of 23 kg may be dropped centrally on the spring without exceeding the limiting bending stress of 150 MN/m². $E = 200$ GN/m². ($U.\ Lond.$)

$(Ans.:\ 4$ m; 75·9 mm)

44. A mass of 20 kg is dropped from a height of 100 mm on to the centre of a carriage spring which is simply supported at its ends. The spring has 10 steel plates each 50 mm wide and 6 mm thick, the longest plate being 0·75 m. Calculate the maximum instantaneous stress in the plates and the initial radius of curvature of the spring if the impact just flattens the spring. $E = 200$ GN/m². ($U.\ Lond.$)

$(Ans.:\ 158$ MN/m²; 3·81 m)

CHAPTER 10

SHEAR STRESS IN BEAMS

10.1 Shear stress distribution. When a shearing force is applied to a beam, the shear stress on the cross-section produces sliding of transverse elements of the beam and the complementary shear stress (of equal magnitude to the transverse shear stress*) produces sliding of longitudinal elements.†

The mean shear stress on a transverse section is the shearing force divided by the cross-sectional area but this stress is not uniform across the section, being zero at the top and bottom of the section. It may also vary across the width of the section but in the following analysis, the shear stress is assumed to be uniform on planes parallel with the neutral axis.

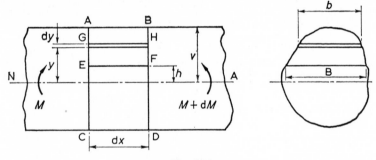

Fɪɢ. 10.1

Let AC and BD, Fig. 10.1, be two cross-sections of a beam, distance dx apart, subjected to bending moments M and $M + dM$ respectively, and let the shear force on AC be F.

It is required to obtain an expression for the shear stress at the layer EF, of breadth B, at a distance h from N A.

Bending stress at distance y from N A $= \dfrac{M}{I} \cdot y$

∴ horizontal force on end G of element GH

$$= \frac{M}{I} \cdot y \times b\, dy$$

---

* See Art. 1.3.

† This effect is apparent in wooden beams tested to destruction; shearing occurs along the grain, parallel to the neutral axis, the wood being weaker in this direction than perpendicular to the grain.

Similarly, horizontal force on end H $= \dfrac{M + \mathrm{d}M}{I} \cdot y \times b \, \mathrm{d}y$

$\therefore$ net horizontal force on element $= \dfrac{\mathrm{d}M}{I} \, by \, \mathrm{d}y$

$\therefore$ total horizontal force on cross-section between AB and EF

$$= \int_h^v \dfrac{\mathrm{d}M}{I} \, by \, \mathrm{d}y$$

$\therefore$ shear stress on EF $= \dfrac{\dfrac{\mathrm{d}M}{I}\displaystyle\int_h^v by \, \mathrm{d}y}{B \, \mathrm{d}x}$

i.e. $\qquad\qquad \tau = \dfrac{F}{IB}\displaystyle\int_h^v by \, \mathrm{d}y \quad$ since $\dfrac{\mathrm{d}M}{\mathrm{d}x} = F \quad$. $\quad$. $\quad$. (10.1)

This is the horizontal shear stress, and hence the transverse shear stress, at a distance h from N A.

If the area of the cross-section between AB and EF is a and the distance of the centroid of this area from N A is $\bar{y}$, then

$$\int_h^v by \, \mathrm{d}y = a\bar{y}$$

so that $\qquad\qquad \tau = \dfrac{F}{IB} a\bar{y} \quad$. $\quad$. $\quad$. $\quad$. $\quad$. $\quad$. (10.2)

For a rectangular cross-section, Fig. 10.2(a),

$$\tau = \dfrac{F}{\dfrac{bd^3}{12} b} \cdot b\left(\dfrac{d}{2} - h\right) \times \tfrac{1}{2}\left(\dfrac{d}{2} + h\right)$$

$$= \dfrac{6F}{bd^3}\left(\dfrac{d^2}{4} - h^2\right) \qquad . \quad . \quad . \quad . \quad . (10.3)$$

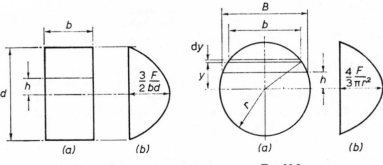

FIG. 10.2   FIG. 10.3

This is a parabolic distribution, as shown in Fig. 10.2(*b*), the maximum ordinate being $\dfrac{3}{2}\dfrac{F}{bd}$ when $h = 0$. Thus the maximum shear stress is $\dfrac{3}{2}$ times the mean shear stress.

For a circular section, Fig. 10.3(*a*),

$$\tau = \frac{F}{\dfrac{\pi}{4} r^4 . B} \int_h^r y \times 2\sqrt{r^2 - y^2} \, dy$$

$$= \frac{4F}{\pi r^4 \times 2\sqrt{r^2 - h^2}} \left[-\frac{2}{3}(r^2 - h^2)^{3/2} \right]_h^r$$

$$= \frac{4}{3} . \frac{F}{\pi r^4}(r^2 - h^2) \qquad . \qquad . \qquad . \qquad . \qquad . \qquad (10.4)$$

This is again a parabolic distribution, as shown in Fig. 10.3(*b*), the maximum ordinate being $\dfrac{4}{3}\dfrac{F}{\pi r^2}$ when $h = 0$. Thus the maximum shear stress is $\dfrac{4}{3}$ times the mean shear stress.

In the case of an I-beam or a T-beam, it is evident that the shear stress in the web at the junction with the flange cannot be transmitted to the flange in such a way as to give a uniform shear stress along the inside surface of the flange. The shear stress in the flange at the junction with the web will approximate to that in the web at that point and will fall away rapidly as the horizontal distance from the web increases, being zero at the outside edges of the flange. The plane of shear, away from the web, has thus become vertical instead of horizontal.

The shear stress in the flange of a beam is extremely small, however (see Example 1), and thus this error is of little consequence but in all cases of suddenly or rapidly changing width of section, the assumption that the shear stress is constant across any layer parallel to the neutral axis is unrealistic.

Example 1 shows that most of the shear force is carried by the web of an I-beam and the maximum shear stress approximates closely to that obtained by dividing the shearing force by the area of the web.

10.2   Built-up girders. Large girders are usually built up by welding or riveting the flange plates to the web. The weld or rivets must therefore transfer the horizontal shear force between the web and flange. Thus, if the shear stress at the top and bottom of the web is τ, the horizontal force in a welded joint, per unit length of beam, is

$$\tau \times t \times 1$$

In the case of a riveted girder, Fig. 10.4, let S be the strength of a rivet in double shear. Then, if the pitch of the rivets in the web is p,

$$S = \tau \times t \times p$$

or
$$p = \frac{S}{\tau t} \ . \qquad . \qquad . \qquad . \qquad . \qquad . \qquad (10.5)$$

Between the angles and the flange are rivets in single shear on either side of the web, thus having the same resistance to shear as the single rivets in double shear between the angles and the web. Thus the same pitch is required for the flange rivets as for the web rivets.

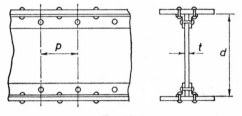

FIG. 10.4

As an approximation, τ may be taken as $\dfrac{F}{t \times d}$

10.3 Deflection due to shear. The sliding of successive elements of a beam due to transverse shear produces a deflection which is additional to that caused by bending. This deflection is usually negligible in comparison with that due to bending except for very short stiff beams and may well be less than the errors inherent in the simple theory of bending.

Case (a)—cantilever of rectangular section with concentrated end load, Fig. 10.5.

From equation (10.3),

$$\tau = \frac{6W}{bd^3}\left(\frac{d^2}{4} - h^2\right)$$

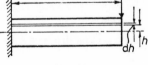

FIG. 10.5

$\therefore$ shear strain energy in elementary strip parallel to the neutral axis

$$= \frac{\tau^2}{2G} \times \text{volume}$$

$$= \left\{\frac{6W}{bd^3}\left(\frac{d^2}{4} - h^2\right)\right\}^2 \times \frac{bl\,\mathrm{d}h}{2G}$$

$\therefore$ total shear strain energy in beam

$$= 2\int_0^{d/2} \frac{18W^2l}{Gbd^6}\left(\frac{d^4}{16} - \frac{d^2h^2}{2} + h^4\right)\mathrm{d}h = \frac{3}{5}\frac{W^2l}{Gbd}$$

This is equal to the work done by the load W moving down through the shear deflection, y_s,

i.e. $$\tfrac{1}{2}Wy_s = \frac{3}{5}\frac{W^2l}{Gbd}$$

from which $$y_s = \frac{6}{5}\frac{Wl}{Gbd} \qquad . \qquad . \qquad . \qquad . \quad (10.6)$$

Since the shearing force is constant at all sections, the slope of the beam is uniform, as shown in Fig. 10.6.

Thus, $$\phi = \frac{6}{5}\frac{W}{Gbd}$$

If the shear stress were uniformly distributed over the section, then

$$\phi = \frac{\tau}{G} = \frac{W}{Gbd}$$

Thus the actual shear deflection is $\dfrac{6}{5}$ times that obtained if the shear stress is assumed to be uniform.

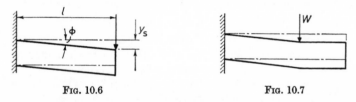

FIG. 10.6   FIG. 10.7

If the load is not at the free end, the form of the deflected beam is as shown in Fig. 10.7, the beam remaining horizontal between the load and the free end.

Case (b)—cantilever of rectangular section with uniformly distributed load, Fig. 10.8.

At a section distance x from the free end,

$$F = wx$$

∴ shear deflection over length $dx = \dfrac{6}{5}\dfrac{wx\,dx}{Gbd}$

from equation (10.6)

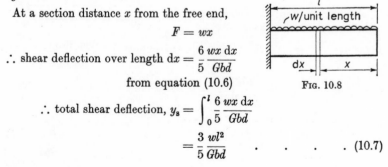

FIG. 10.8

∴ total shear deflection, $y_s = \displaystyle\int_0^l \frac{6}{5}\frac{wx\,dx}{Gbd}$

$$= \frac{3}{5}\frac{wl^2}{Gbd} \qquad . \qquad . \qquad . \qquad . \quad (10.7)$$

Case (c)—simply supported beam of rectangular section with central concentrated load, Fig. 10.9.

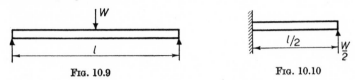

FIG. 10.9   FIG. 10.10

The central deflection is the same as the end deflection of a cantilever of length $\frac{l}{2}$, carrying an upward end load $\frac{W}{2}$, Fig. 10.10,

i.e.
$$y_s = \frac{\frac{6}{5}\left(\frac{W}{2}\right)\left(\frac{l}{2}\right)}{Gbd} = \frac{3}{10}\frac{Wl}{Gbd} \qquad . \qquad . \qquad . \ (10.8)$$

Case (d)—simply supported beam of rectangular section with uniformly distributed load, Fig. 10.11.

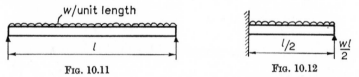

FIG. 10.11   FIG. 10.12

The central deflection is the same as the end deflection of a cantilever of length $\frac{l}{2}$, carrying a downward uniformly distributed load w/unit length and an upward end load, $\frac{wl}{2}$, Fig. 10.12,

i.e.
$$y_s = \frac{6}{5}\frac{\left(\frac{wl}{2}\right)\left(\frac{l}{2}\right)}{Gbd} - \frac{3}{5}\frac{w\left(\frac{l}{2}\right)^2}{Gbd} = \frac{3}{20}\frac{wl^2}{Gbd}. \qquad . \qquad (10.9)$$

Case (e)—simply supported beam of rectangular section with concentrated load not at centre, Fig. 10.13.

The deflection under the load is the same as the end deflection of either a cantilever of length a carrying an end load $\frac{Wb}{l}$ or of a cantilever of length b carrying an end load $\frac{Wa}{l}$.

Thus, in either case,

$$y_s = \frac{6}{5}\frac{Wab}{Gbdl} \qquad (10.10)$$

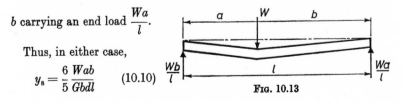

FIG. 10.13

Case (f)—cantilever of circular section with concentrated end load, Fig. 10.14.

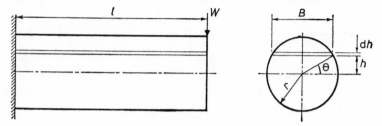

Fig. 10.14

From equation (10.4),

$$\tau = \frac{4}{3}\frac{W}{\pi r^4}(r^2 - h^2)$$

∴ shear strain energy in elementary strip parallel to the neutral axis

$$= \left\{\frac{4}{3}\frac{W}{\pi r^4}(r^2 - h^2)\right\}^2 \times \frac{Bl\,\mathrm{d}h}{2G}$$

$$= \frac{16}{9}\frac{W^2 l}{\pi^2 r^8 G}(r^2 - h^2)^2 \times \sqrt{r^2 - h^2}\,\mathrm{d}h$$

∴ total shear strain energy in beam

$$= 2 \times \frac{16}{9}\frac{W^2 l}{\pi^2 r^8 G}\int_0^r (r^2 - h^2)^{5/2}\,\mathrm{d}h$$

i.e.

$$\tfrac{1}{2}Wy_s = \frac{32}{9}\frac{W^2 l}{\pi^2 r^8 G} \times \frac{15}{96}\pi r^6 {}^*$$

from which

$$y_s = \frac{10}{9}\frac{Wl}{\pi r^2 G} \qquad . \qquad . \qquad . \qquad . \qquad . \qquad (10.11)$$

Other cases of circular beams may be derived from this equation in the same way as for rectangular beams.

10.4　Total deflection. The total deflection is the sum of the deflections due to bending and shearing. Thus, for a cantilever of rectangular section carrying a concentrated end load,

---

* $h = r \sin\theta$　　　　　∴ $\mathrm{d}h = r\cos\theta\,\mathrm{d}\theta$

$$\therefore \int_0^r (r^2 - h^2)^{5/2}\,\mathrm{d}h = \int_0^{\pi/2} (r^2\cos^2\theta)^{5/2} \times r\cos\theta\,\mathrm{d}\theta$$

$$= r^6 \int_0^{\pi/2} \cos^6\theta\,\mathrm{d}\theta$$

$$= r^6 \times \frac{5}{6}\cdot\frac{3}{4}\cdot\frac{1}{2}\cdot\frac{\pi}{2} = \frac{15}{96}\pi r^6$$

$$y = \frac{Wl^3}{3EI} + \frac{6}{5}\frac{Wl}{Gbd}$$

$$= \frac{4Wl^3}{Ebd^3}\left\{1 + \frac{3E}{10G}\left(\frac{d}{l}\right)^2\right\}$$

$$= \frac{4Wl^3}{Ebd^3}\left\{1 + \frac{3}{4}\left(\frac{d}{l}\right)^2\right\} \quad \text{if} \quad \frac{E}{G} = \frac{5}{2}$$

The shear deflection is therefore only of importance in cases where the ratio $\frac{d}{l}$ is relatively large.

1. *An I-beam, 350 mm × 200 mm, has a web thickness of 12·5 mm and a flange thickness of 25 mm. Calculate the ratio of maximum to mean shearing stress in the section and the percentage of the total shear carried by the web.*

$$I_{NA} = \frac{0\cdot2 \times 0\cdot35^3}{12} - \frac{0\cdot187\,5 \times 0\cdot3^3}{12}$$

$$= 293 \times 10^{-6}\,\text{m}^4$$

From equation (10.2),

$$\tau = \frac{F}{IB}\,a\bar{y}$$

$$\therefore \tau_{max} = \frac{F(0\cdot2 \times 0\cdot025 \times 0\cdot162\,5 + 0\cdot15 \times 0\cdot012\,5 \times 0\cdot075)}{293 \times 10^{-6} \times 0\cdot012\,5}$$

$$= 260F$$

$$\tau_{mean} = \frac{F}{0\cdot35 \times 0\cdot2 - 0\cdot3 \times 0\cdot187\,5}$$

$$= 72\cdot75F$$

$$\therefore \frac{\tau_{max}}{\tau_{mean}} = \frac{260}{72\cdot75} = 3\cdot57$$

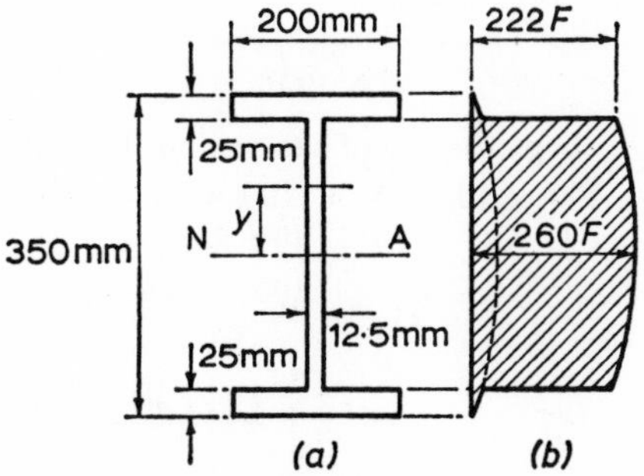

Fig. 10.15

At the top and bottom of the web,

$$\tau = \frac{F \times 0\cdot2 \times 0\cdot025 \times 0\cdot162\,5}{293 \times 10^{-6} \times 0\cdot012\,5} = 222F$$

Therefore force carried by web, represented by the shaded area in Fig. 10.15(b)

$$= \{222 + \tfrac{2}{3}(260 - 222)\} \times F \times 0\cdot3 \times 0\cdot012\,5$$
$$= 0\cdot929F$$

∴ percentage of shear force carried by web

$$= \underline{92\cdot9}$$

NOTE. Assuming that the whole of the shear force is carried by the web alone,

$$\tau_{\text{mean}} = \frac{F}{0\cdot3 \times 0\cdot012\,5} = 266F$$

which is very close to the maximum shear stress.

2. *A T-section beam, symmetrical about a vertical axis, is made with a top flange 100 mm wide and 14 mm thick to which a vertical web plate, 150 mm deep and 10 mm wide is welded.*

At a certain section, the total shearing force is 40 kN. Calculate the percentage shear carried by the vertical web and the shearing force per metre run in the welded connection. (U. Lond.)

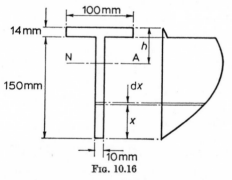

FIG. 10.16

Taking moments about the top of the section, Fig. 10.16,
$$100 \times 14 \times 7 + 150 \times 10 \times 89 = (100 \times 14 + 150 \times 10)h$$
$$\therefore h = 49\cdot4 \text{ mm}$$

$$I_{\text{NA}} = \frac{100 \times 14^3}{12} + 100 \times 14 \times 42\cdot4^2$$
$$+ \frac{10 \times 150^3}{12} + 10 \times 150 \times 39\cdot6^2$$
$$= 7\cdot708 \times 10^6 \text{ mm}^4$$

At a distance x m from the bottom of the web,

$$\tau = \frac{40 \times 10^3}{7 \cdot 708 \times 10^{-6} \times 0 \cdot 01} \times 0 \cdot 01 x\left(0 \cdot 114\ 6 - \frac{x}{2}\right) \text{N/m}^2$$

$$= 2\ 593 x(0 \cdot 229\ 2 - x)\ \text{MN/m}^2$$

∴ shear force carried by element $= 2\ 593 x(0 \cdot 229\ 2 - x) \times 0 \cdot 01\ dx$

∴ total shear force carried by web $= 25 \cdot 93 \displaystyle\int_0^{0 \cdot 15} (0 \cdot 229\ 2x - x^2)\ dx$

$$= 0 \cdot 037\ 7\ \text{MN} = \underline{37 \cdot 7\ \text{kN}}$$

∴ percentage of shear force carried by web

$$= \frac{37 \cdot 7}{40} \times 100 = \underline{94 \cdot 2}$$

Shear stress at top of web $\quad = 2\ 593 \times 0 \cdot 15(0 \cdot 229\ 2 - 0 \cdot 15)$

$$= 30 \cdot 8\ \text{MN/m}^2$$

∴ shear force per metre in welded connection

$$= 30 \cdot 8 \times 10^6 \times 0 \cdot 01 \times 1\ \text{N}$$

$$= \underline{308\ \text{kN}}$$

3. *Assuming the commonly accepted theory of distribution of shearing stress in beams and starting from first principles, derive a formula for the intensity of shearing stress at any distance from the neutral axis in a hollow circular section.*

Hence or otherwise show that in a very thin hollow rivet, the maximum shearing stress tends to twice the mean shearing stress. (U. Lond.)

The cross-section of the beam is shown in Fig. 10.17.

From equation (10.1),

$$\tau = \frac{F}{IB} \int_h^v by\ dy$$

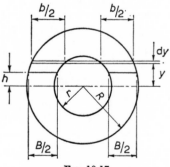

FIG. 10.17

$0 < h < r$

$$\tau = \frac{F}{I \times 2(\sqrt{R^2 - h^2} - \sqrt{r^2 - h^2})}\left\{\int_h^r 2(\sqrt{R^2 - y^2} - \sqrt{r^2 - y^2})\ y\ dy \right.$$

$$\left. + \int_r^R 2\sqrt{R^2 - y^2}\ y\ dy\right\}$$

$$= \frac{F}{3I}\left\{\frac{(R^2 - h^2)^{3/2} - (r^2 - h^2)^{3/2}}{\sqrt{R^2 - h^2} - \sqrt{r^2 - h^2}}\right\}$$

$\underline{r < h < R}$

$$\tau = \frac{F}{I \times 2\sqrt{R^2 - h^2}} \int_h^R 2\sqrt{R^2 - y^2}\, y\, dy = \frac{F}{3I}(R^2 - h^2)$$

The maximum shear stress occurs when $h = 0$,

i.e.
$$\tau_{max} = \frac{F}{3I} \cdot \frac{R^3 - r^3}{R - r} = \frac{4F}{3\pi(R^4 - r^4)} \cdot \frac{R^3 - r^3}{R - r}$$

$$\tau_{mean} = \frac{F}{\pi(R^2 - r^2)}$$

$$\therefore \frac{\tau_{max}}{\tau_{mean}} = \frac{4}{3(R^4 - r^4)} \cdot \frac{R^3 - r^3}{R - r} \times (R^2 - r^2)$$

$$= \frac{4}{3} \cdot \frac{R^2 + Rr + r^2}{R^2 + r^2}$$

As $r \to R$,
$$\frac{\tau_{max}}{\tau_{mean}} \to \frac{4}{3} \cdot \frac{3R^2}{2R^2}$$

$$\to \underline{2}$$

4. *A transverse shear force F and a bending moment Fl are applied to a uniform beam having the symmetrical cross-section shown in Fig. 10.18. If the ratio of the transverse shear stress at the neutral axis to the maximum direct stress due to bending is not to be less than 0·5, determine the maximum permissible value of l in terms of a.* (U. Lond.)

From equation (10.2),

$$\tau = \frac{F}{IB} \cdot a\bar{y}$$

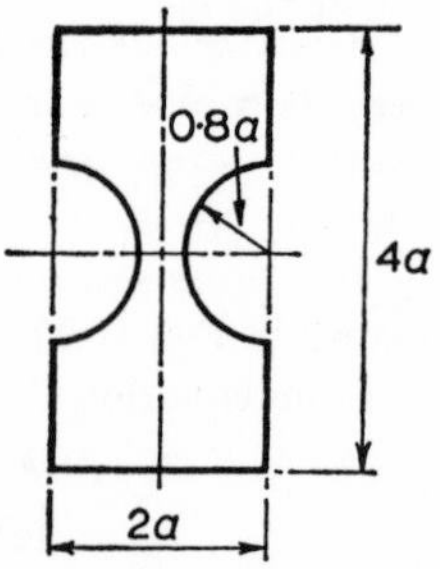

$$\therefore \tau_{max} = \frac{F}{I} \cdot \frac{2a \times 2a \times a - \frac{\pi}{2}(0 \cdot 8a)^2 \times \frac{4 \times 0 \cdot 8a}{3\pi}}{0 \cdot 4a}$$

$$= 9 \cdot 15 \frac{Fa^2}{I}$$

$$\sigma = \frac{M}{I} \cdot y$$

Fig. 10.18

$$\therefore \sigma_{max} = \frac{Fl}{I} \cdot 2a$$

$$\therefore 9 \cdot 15 \frac{Fa^2}{I} = 0 \cdot 5 \times \frac{Fl}{I} 2a$$

$$\therefore l = \underline{9 \cdot 15a}$$

5. *A beam of square section is placed so that the plane of bending is parallel to a diagonal; the side of the square is s and the shear force is F. Plot the shear stress distribution curve.*

Find the mean intensity and the maximum intensity and where it occurs.

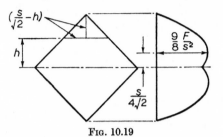

FIG. 10.19

Referring to Fig. 10.19,

$$\tau = \frac{F}{IB}\, a\bar{y}$$

$$= \frac{F}{I}\, \frac{\left(\dfrac{s}{\sqrt{2}} - h\right)^2 \times \left(h + \left[\dfrac{s}{\sqrt{2}} - h\right]\Big/3\right)}{2\left(\dfrac{s}{\sqrt{2}} - h\right)}$$

$$= \frac{F}{6I}\left(\frac{s}{\sqrt{2}} - h\right)\left(2h + \frac{s}{\sqrt{2}}\right)$$

For the maximum shear stress, $\dfrac{\mathrm{d}\tau}{\mathrm{d}h} = 0$,

i.e.
$$\left(\frac{s}{\sqrt{2}} - h\right) \times 2 + \left(2h + \frac{s}{\sqrt{2}}\right) \times (-1) = 0$$

from which
$$h = \frac{s}{4\sqrt{2}}$$

$$\therefore \tau_{\max} = \frac{F}{6 \times \dfrac{s^4}{12}}\left(\frac{s}{\sqrt{2}} - \frac{s}{4\sqrt{2}}\right)\left(\frac{s}{2\sqrt{2}} + \frac{s}{\sqrt{2}}\right) = \frac{9}{8}\frac{F}{s^2}$$

NOTE. Using the equimomental system (Art. 3.5), the square may be replaced by the system shown in Fig. 10.20, whence

$$I_{\mathrm{NA}} = 4 \times \frac{s^2}{6} \times \left(\frac{s}{2\sqrt{2}}\right)^2 = \frac{s^4}{12}$$

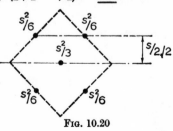

FIG. 10.20

6. *A beam having a uniform rectangular cross-section of breadth b and depth d is simply supported at the ends of a span L. It carries a uniformly distributed load of w per unit length on the whole span and two equal point loads each W at L/6 on either side of mid-span.*

Determine in terms of the given symbols and the elastic constants, the deflection at mid-span due to (a) bending, and (b) shear. (U. Lond.)

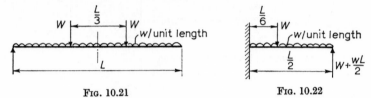

Fig. 10.21   Fig. 10.22

The beam is shown in Fig. 10.21; the central deflection is the same as the end deflection of the cantilever shown in Fig. 10.22.

(a) *Bending deflection.* From the equations of Art. 5.2,

$$y_b = \frac{\left(W + \frac{wL}{2}\right)\left(\frac{L}{2}\right)^3}{3EI} - \frac{W\left(\frac{L}{6}\right)^3}{3EI} - \frac{W\left(\frac{L}{6}\right)^2}{2EI} \times \frac{L}{3} - \frac{w\left(\frac{L}{2}\right)^4}{8EI}$$

$$= \frac{L^3}{2Ebd^3}\left\{\frac{23}{27}W + \frac{5}{16}wL\right\}$$

(b) *Shear deflection.* From the equations of Art. 10.3,

$$y_s = \frac{6}{5}\frac{\left(W + \frac{wL}{2}\right)\left(\frac{L}{2}\right)}{Gbd} - \frac{6}{5}\frac{W\left(\frac{L}{6}\right)}{Gbd} - \frac{3}{5}\frac{w\left(\frac{L}{2}\right)^2}{Gbd}$$

$$= \frac{L}{20Gbd}\{8W + 3wL\}$$

7. *A cantilever of length l and with a constant width b is subjected to a vertical load W at its tip. If the maximum stress due to bending is to be constant along the length of the beam, find the equation relating depth of beam at any section distance x from the built-in end to the depth d_0 at the built-in end.*

Also calculate the deflection at the tip of the cantilever due to shear alone. (I.Mech.E.)

Referring to Fig. 10.23,

$$\sigma = \frac{M}{Z}$$

$$= \frac{Wx}{\frac{bd^2}{6}} = \frac{6Wx}{bd^2}$$

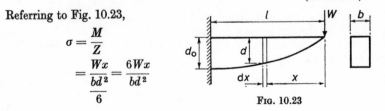

Fig. 10.23

If σ is to be constant, equal to that at the fixed end,

$$\frac{x}{d^2} = \frac{l}{d_0^2}$$

$$\therefore d = d_0 \sqrt{\frac{x}{l}}$$

Shear deflection over length $dx = \dfrac{6}{5} \dfrac{W \, dx}{Gbd} = \dfrac{6}{5} \dfrac{W\sqrt{l} \, dx}{Gbd_0\sqrt{x}}$

$\therefore$ total shear deflection at free end $= \dfrac{6W\sqrt{l}}{5Gbd_0} \displaystyle\int_0^l \dfrac{dx}{\sqrt{x}}$

$$= \frac{12}{5} \frac{Wl}{Gbd_0}$$

8. *The deflection of an I-section beam due to shear is commonly calculated by assuming the shearing stress uniformly distributed over a rectangle formed by the web thickness and the overall depth. Determine the percentage error in this assumption for a 240 mm $\times$ 120 mm I-section beam. The web is 10 mm thick and the flanges are 20 mm thick.*

The usual formula for shear stress distribution can be assumed.

(U. Lond.)

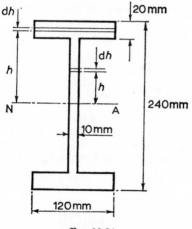

FIG. 10.24

Referring to Fig. 10.24,

$$I = \frac{0.12 \times 0.24^3}{12} - \frac{0.11 \times 0.20^3}{12} = 64.81 \times 10^{-6} \text{ m}^4$$

The shear stress in the flange at a distance h from N A is given by

$$\tau = \frac{F}{IB} a\bar{y}$$

$$= \frac{F}{I} \frac{(0{\cdot}12 - h) \times 0{\cdot}12 \times \frac{1}{2}(0{\cdot}12 + h)}{0{\cdot}12}$$

$$= \frac{F}{I} \frac{0{\cdot}014\ 4 - h^2}{2} \ \text{N/m}^2$$

$\therefore$ shear strain energy in one flange

$$= \int_{0{\cdot}10}^{0{\cdot}12} \left(\frac{F}{I} \frac{0{\cdot}014\ 4 - h^2}{2}\right)^2 \times \frac{0{\cdot}12 \times l \times \mathrm{d}h}{2G}$$

$$= 2{\cdot}026 \times 10^{-9} \frac{F^2 l}{GI^2} \ \text{J}$$

The shear stress in the web at a distance h from N A is given by

$$\tau = \frac{F}{I} \frac{0{\cdot}12 \times 0{\cdot}02 \times 0{\cdot}11 + (0{\cdot}10 - h) \times 0{\cdot}01 \times \frac{1}{2}(0{\cdot}10 + h)}{0{\cdot}01}$$

$$= \frac{F}{I} \frac{0{\cdot}062\ 8 - h^2}{2} \ \text{N/m}^2$$

$\therefore$ shear strain energy in one half of web

$$= \int_{0}^{0{\cdot}10} \left(\frac{F}{I} \frac{0{\cdot}062\ 8 - h^2}{2}\right)^2 \times \frac{0{\cdot}01 \times l \times \mathrm{d}h}{2G}$$

$$= 443{\cdot}147 \times 10^{-9} \frac{F^2 l}{GI^2} \ \text{J}$$

$\therefore$ total shear strain energy in beam

$$= 2(2{\cdot}026 + 443{\cdot}147) \times 10^{-9} \frac{F^2 l}{GI^2}$$

$$= 890{\cdot}346 \times 10^{-9} \frac{F^2 l}{G \times (64{\cdot}81 \times 10^{-6})^2} = 211{\cdot}9 \frac{F^2 l}{G} \ \text{J}$$

Assuming that the shear stress is uniformly distributed over an area $0{\cdot}24 \ \text{m} \times 0{\cdot}01 \ \text{m}$,

$$\tau = \frac{F}{0{\cdot}002\ 4} \ \text{N/m}^2$$

$$\therefore U = \left(\frac{F}{0{\cdot}002\ 4}\right)^2 \times \frac{0{\cdot}24 \times 0{\cdot}01 \times l}{2G} = 208{\cdot}3 \frac{F^2 l}{G} \ \text{J}$$

$$\therefore \text{error} = \frac{211{\cdot}9 - 208{\cdot}3}{211{\cdot}9} \times 100$$

$$= \underline{1{\cdot}7 \ \text{per cent}}$$

9. An R.S.J. is of I-section of overall height 200 mm and flange width 125 mm. The web thickness is 7 mm and the flange thicknesses 11 mm. The standard taper on the flanges may be neglected and all corners may be assumed sharp. The beam is subjected to transverse loads acting parallel to the web, and at one section the shear force is 100 kN. Determine the maximum vertical shearing stress in the web at this section.

What proportion of the total shear force is carried by the web?   (*U. Lond.*)
(*Ans.:* 80·8 MN/m²; 94·8%)

10. A cast iron beam with flange and web section is 250 mm deep overall. The top flange is 125 mm × 50 mm deep, the bottom flange 200 mm × 50 mm deep and the web is 40 mm thick. If the transverse shearing force is 140 kN, calculate the consequent shear stress in the web at the top and bottom junctions with flanges and the maximum shear stress and sketch a diagram showing the variation of shear stress over the depth of the beam.   (*U. Lond.*)
(*Ans.:* 15 MN/m²; 18·5 MN/m²; 17·1 MN/m²)

11. State the formula giving the shearing stress at any depth in the section of a beam subjected to a shearing force S. Define the symbols used and show them on a sketch. State clearly the assumptions made in deriving the formula and criticise these assumptions.

A 350 mm × 150 mm I-beam is subjected to a shearing force S and a bending moment M. Determine (*a*) the percentage of the shearing force carried by the web, and (*b*) the percentage of the bending moment carried by the flanges. The flanges are 17·5 mm thick and the web is 10 mm thick. $I_{xx} = 173 \times 10^{-6}$ m⁴. Assume all corners square and the flanges to be rectangles.   (*U. Lond.*)
(Ans.: 94·5%; 83·8%)

12. A cantilever of I-section 200 mm × 100 mm has rectangular flanges 10 mm thick and web 75 mm thick. It carries a uniformly distributed load. Determine the length of the cantilever if the maximum bending stress is three times the maximum shearing stress. What is the ratio of the stresses half-way along the length of the cantilever?   (*U. Lond.*)   (*Ans.:* 1 m; 1·5)

13. Fig. 10.25 shows the section of a Tee-beam, made of a uniform material, which is subjected to a shear force of 200 kN and a bending moment of 25 kN m. Calculate (*a*) the maximum bending stress and (*b*) the maximum shear stress giving sketches to show the form of stress distribution in each case.   (*U. Lond.*)
(*Ans.:* 137·5 MN/m²; 65·3 MN/m²)

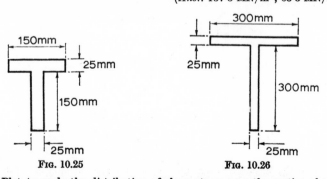

FIG. 10.25   FIG. 10.26

14. Plot to scale the distribution of shear stress over the section shown in Fig. 10.26, which is subjected to a shearing force of 300 kN, giving essential numerical values.   (*U. Lond.*)   (*Ans.:* $\tau_{max} = 51·5$ MN/m²)

15. A rod of circular section is subjected to a shearing force on a plane perpendicular to its axis. Find the maximum shearing stress in terms of the shearing force and the rod diameter.

If the rod is as a beam with free ends and a central concentrated load, express the free length in terms of the diameter for which the maximum shearing stress, due to shearing force, is half the maximum direct stress. (*U. Lond.*)

$$\left(Ans.: \frac{16F}{3\pi D^2}; \frac{L}{D} = \frac{2}{3}\right)$$

16. A hollow steel cylinder, 200 mm external and 100 mm internal diameter, acting as a beam, is subjected to a shearing force F newtons perpendicular to the axis.

Determine the mean shearing stress across the section, and, making the usual assumptions, the average shearing stress at the neutral axis and at sections 25, 50 and 75 mm from the neutral axis as fractions of the mean value.

Draw a diagram to show the variation of average shearing stress across the section of the cylinder. (*U. Lond.*) $\left(Ans.: \dfrac{F}{0 \cdot 03\ \pi}\ N/m^2;\ 1 \cdot 65,\ 0 \cdot 80,\ 0 \cdot 467\right)$

17. Derive a formula for the intensity of shearing stress at any point in the cross-section of a uniform beam, due to the shearing force. Criticise the assumptions made and point out when these would lead to serious errors.

Assuming your method can be applied to circular sections, find the maximum intensity of shearing stress in a hollow circular section 100 mm external diameter and 75 mm internal diameter when subjected to a total shearing force of 160 kN. (*U. Lond.*) (*Ans.:* 91·7 MN/m²)

18. A steel bar rolled to the section shown in Fig. 10.27 is subjected to a shearing force of 200 kN applied in the direction YY. Making the usual assumptions, determine the average shearing stress at the sections A, B, C and D, and find the ratio of the maximum to the mean shearing stress in the section.

Draw, to scale, a diagram to show the variation of the average shearing stress across the section. (*U. Lond.*) (*Ans.:* 0, 10·35, 44·5, 71·1 MN/m²; 3·875)

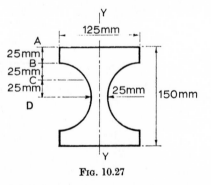

Fig. 10.27

19. State the formula which is generally used to give the intensity of the shearing stress at any depth in the section of a beam due to the shearing force. Make a critical statement pointing out the weakness of the method used to derive the formula.

A beam has a symmetrical triangular section of breadth B and depth D and is subjected at a certain section to a vertical shearing force S acting in the direction of the axis of symmetry. Deduce in terms of B, D and S the mean shearing stress τ at any depth d from the vertex of the triangular section. Plot a graph showing how τ varies over the depth of the section and find the ratio of the average shearing stress over the section to the maximum shearing stress.   (*U. Lond.*)

$$\left(Ans.: \frac{12Sd(D - d)}{BD^3} ; \frac{2}{3}\right)$$

20. A bar of hexagonal cross-section and of side length 25 mm is used as a cantilever, one diagonal being horizontal. A load hung from the bar subjects it to a shearing force of 20 kN. Plot the shear stress distribution diagram. (*U. Lond.*)

$$\left(Ans.: \tau = 0.0315 \frac{20{,}300 - 65h^2 + h^3}{44.3 - h} \text{ N/mm}^2, \text{ where } h \text{ is in mm}\right)$$

21. A tube of hollow square section, 50 mm square outside and 6 mm uniform thickness, is subjected to a shearing force of 50 kN acting in the direction of a diagonal. Find the maximum shearing stress produced.

Make a sketch showing the approximate distribution of shearing stress over the cross-section.   (*U. Lond.*)

$(Ans.: \tau = 0.0715 (617 - h^2) \text{ N/mm}^2, \text{ where } h \text{ is in mm}; 106 \text{ N/mm}^2)$

22. Derive an expression for the deflection due to shear in a cantilever of rectangular section, loaded with a concentrated load at the free end. The usual parabolic distribution of shearing stress over the cross-section may be assumed.

A cantilever of length L, rectangular in section, of depth d and breadth b, carries two point loads, each W, one at the free end and the other half-way along its length. If E/G is 2·5, find the ratio of d to L for which the deflection at the end due to shear will be 1/100 of that due to bending. (*U. Lond.*)

$(Ans.: 0.108)$

23. For a given cantilever of rectangular cross-section, length l, depth d and carrying a concentrated load at the free end, show that

$$\frac{\text{deflection due to shearing strain}}{\text{bending deflection}} = \text{constant} \times \left(\frac{d}{l}\right)^2,$$

and find the value of the constant for a steel cantilever. Hence find the least value of l/d if the deflection due to shearing strain is not to exceed 1 per cent of the total deflection. $E = 200$ GN/m^2; $G = 76.5$ GN/m^2.   (*U. Lond.*)

$(Ans.: 0.783; 8.79)$

24. A simply supported rectangular beam of depth d, breadth b and span L is loaded at the centre with a concentrated load W. Show that the deflection due to shear is $3WL/10Gbd$.

Hence, making reasonable assumptions, deduce the ratio of deflection due to shear to the deflection due to bending in the case of an I-section beam, 400 mm × 150 mm, simply supported on a span of 2·4 m and carrying a central load.

$I_{xx} = 283 \times 10^{-6}$ m^4; mean flange thickness 21·2 mm; web thickness 13·8 mm. $E/G = 2.7$.   (*U. Lond.*)

$(Ans.: 3.87, \text{ basing shear deflection on web area only})$

25. A beam of span l and of constant rectangular section rests upon two supports and has a uniformly distributed load of w per unit length. If the ratio of E/G is $2\frac{1}{2}$ for the material of the beam, show that the ratio of the shear to the bending deflection is given by $c(k/l)^2$ where k is the relevant radius of gyration of the section, and find the value of c.   (*U. Lond.*) $(Ans.: 28.8)$

26. A simply supported beam of rectangular cross-section and length l is subjected to a uniform distributed load of 150 N/m. Find from first principles the length of the beam in terms of its depth, such that the central deflection due to bending is ten times that due to shear. It may be assumed that the maximum shear stress is $1\cdot5$ × the mean shear stress acting on a given section. $E = 200 \text{ GN/m}^2$ and $G = 80 \text{ GN/m}^2$. (*I. Mech. E.*)   (*Ans.*: $l = 4\cdot9\ d$)

27. A circular shaft carries a transverse shearing force. Making normal assumptions, which must be stated, prove: (*a*) the maximum intensity of shearing stress is 4/3 times the mean shearing stress; (*b*) the total shear strain energy per unit length is 10/9 times that calculated by taking the mean intensity of shearing stress as uniform throughout.

A circular shaft 100 mm diameter carries an over-hung load of 100 kN. If this load is considered concentrated at a section 125 mm from a rigid bearing, calculate the deflection due to the effects of bending and shear. $E = 200 \text{ GN/m}^2$ and $G = 80 \text{ GN/m}^2$. (*U. Lond.*) (*Ans.*: $y_b = 0\cdot066\ 25$ mm; $y_s = 0\cdot005\ 52$ mm)

28. An I-section cantilever 120 mm deep and 100 mm wide having flanges and web 10 mm thick, is $1\cdot2$ m long and carries an end load of 30 kN. Find the total shearing resilience of the cantilever and hence determine its deflection due to shear.
I for the section $= 6\cdot9 \times 10^{-6}$ m^4. Take $G = 80 \text{ GN/m}^2$. (*U. Lond.*)
          (*Ans.*: $5\cdot74$ J; $0\cdot382\ 5$ mm)

29. A cast iron cantilever, $0\cdot6$ m long, consists of an I-section 120 mm deep and 80 mm wide, having flanges 20 mm deep and a web thickness of 10 mm. If a load of 20 kN is supported at the free end, find, by graphical integration or otherwise, the deflection due to shear. Neglect the effect of fillets, and take $G = 40 \text{ GN/m}^2$.
(*U. Lond.*)   (*Ans.*: $0\cdot248$ mm)

30. A 250 mm × 150 mm R.S.J. with web 10 mm and flanges 18 mm thick has one end built firmly into a wall so that it can act as a horizontal cantilever $3\cdot6$ m long. It carries a load of 20 kN placed $1\cdot8$ m from the end. Assuming that the shearing force is carried by the web only, the shearing stress being uniformly distributed over the web, calculate the deflection produced at the end of the cantilever. Take $E = 200 \text{ GN/m}^2$ and $G = 80 \text{ GN/m}^2$. (*U. Lond.*)
          (*Ans.*: $y_s = 0\cdot21$ mm; $y_b = 6$ mm)

CHAPTER 11

UNSYMMETRICAL BENDING

11.1 Principal axes and principal moments of inertia. In the simple theory of bending (Art. 3.1), it is assumed that the section is symmetrical about the plane of bending.

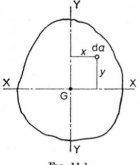

Fig. 11.1

If a bending moment is applied in the plane YY, Fig. 11.1, and no bending is to take place about that axis, then

$$\int \sigma \, da \times x = 0,$$

where σ is the stress on the element da due to bending about **XX**.

But
$$\sigma = \frac{M}{I_{XX}} \times y$$

$$\therefore \int xy \, da = 0$$

The quantity $\int xy \, da$ is called the *product of inertia* of the area about the axes **XX** and **YY** and the condition for pure bending is therefore that the product of inertia about the axes through the centroid in, and perpendicular to, the plane of bending shall be zero. Such axes are called the *principal axes* of the section and the moments of inertia (strictly *second moments of area*) about the principal axes are the principal moments of inertia, being respectively the greatest and least moments of inertia about any axis passing through G.

If a figure has an axis of symmetry, that axis is a principal axis.

11.2 Determination of principal axes and principal moments of inertia. Fig. 11.2 shows a figure of area A in which the principal axes through the centroid G are UU and VV: XX and YY are another pair of perpendicular axes passing through G, making an angle α with the principal axes. The element da in the positive quadrant has co-ordinates u and v relative to VV and UU and x and y relative to YY and XX respectively.

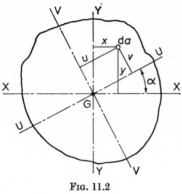

Fig. 11.2

Given the moments and product of inertia about XX and YY, it is required to find the principal moments of inertia and the direction of the principal axes.

$$u = x \cos \alpha + y \sin \alpha$$
$$v = y \cos \alpha - x \sin \alpha$$

$$I_{UU} = \int v^2 \, da = \int (y^2 \cos^2 \alpha - 2xy \sin \alpha \cos \alpha + x^2 \sin^2 \alpha) \, da$$
$$= I_{XX} \cos^2 \alpha - I_{XY} \sin 2\alpha + I_{YY} \sin^2 \alpha \qquad . \qquad . \quad (11.1)$$

$$I_{VV} = \int u^2 \, da = \int (x^2 \cos^2 \alpha + 2xy \sin \alpha \cos \alpha + y^2 \sin^2 \alpha) \, da$$
$$= I_{XX} \sin^2 \alpha + I_{XY} \sin 2\alpha + I_{YY} \cos^2 \alpha \qquad . \qquad . \quad (11.2)$$

$$I_{UV} = \int uv \, da = \int \{xy(\cos^2 \alpha - \sin^2 \alpha) + (y^2 - x^2) \sin \alpha \cos \alpha\} \, da$$
$$= I_{XY} \cos 2\alpha + (I_{XX} - I_{YY}) \frac{\sin 2\alpha}{2} = 0$$

$$\therefore \tan 2\alpha = \frac{2I_{XY}}{I_{YY} - I_{XX}} \cdot \qquad . \qquad . \qquad . \qquad . \qquad . \qquad . \quad (11.3)$$

Equation (11.3) gives two values of 2α differing by π, i.e. two values of α differing by $\pi/2$.

Given the principal moments of inertia, it is required to find the moments of inertia about XX and YY.

$$x = u \cos \alpha - v \sin \alpha$$
$$y = v \cos \alpha + u \sin \alpha$$

$$I_{XX} = \int y^2 \, da = \int (v^2 \cos^2 \alpha + uv \sin 2\alpha + u^2 \sin^2 \alpha) \, da$$
$$= I_{UU} \cos^2 \alpha + I_{VV} \sin^2 \alpha \quad (\text{since } I_{UV} = 0) \ . \quad (11.4)$$

$$I_{YY} = \int x^2 \, da = \int (u^2 \cos^2 \alpha - uv \sin 2\alpha + v^2 \sin^2 \alpha) \, da$$
$$= I_{VV} \cos^2 \alpha + I_{UU} \sin^2 \alpha \ . \qquad . \qquad . \qquad . \quad (11.5)$$
$$\therefore I_{XX} + I_{YY} = I_{UU} + I_{VV} \ (= J) \ . \qquad . \qquad . \qquad . \quad (11.6)$$

11.3 Momental ellipse.

Set off $Ga = \dfrac{1}{k_{UU}}$ and $Gb = \dfrac{1}{k_{VV}}$, Fig. 11.3, and draw an ellipse with Ga and Gb as the major and minor semi-axes.

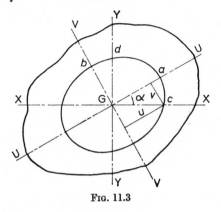

FIG. 11.3

Then $Gc = \dfrac{1}{k_{XX}}$ and $Gd = \dfrac{1}{k_{YY}}$.

Proof: From the equation of the ellipse,

$$\frac{u^2}{(1/k_{UU})^2} + \frac{v^2}{(1/k_{VV})^2} = 1$$

But $\qquad\qquad u = Gc \cos\alpha$ and $v = Gc \sin\alpha$

$$\therefore\ Gc^2\, k_{UU}{}^2 \cos^2\alpha + Gc^2\, k_{VV}{}^2 \sin^2\alpha = 1$$

$$\therefore\ A\, k_{UU}{}^2 \cos^2\alpha + A\, k_{VV}{}^2 \sin^2\alpha = \frac{A}{Gc^2}$$

i.e. $\qquad I_{UU} \cos^2\alpha + I_{VV} \sin^2\alpha = \dfrac{A}{Gc^2} = I_{XX}$ $\qquad$ from equation (11.4)

$$\therefore\ Gc = \frac{1}{k_{XX}}$$

For any figure having more than two axes of symmetry, such as a circle, square, equilateral triangle or other regular polygon, the momental ellipse becomes a circle and hence the moment of inertia about *any* axis through G is the same as about the principal axes.

11.4 Theorem of perpendicular axes for product of inertia. In Fig. 11.4, XX and YY are perpendicular axes through the centroid G and it is required to find the product of inertia about the parallel axes OO and QQ.

Product of inertia of element about OO and QQ

$$= (x + h)(y + k)\,\mathrm{d}a$$
$$= (xy + xk + yh + hk)\,\mathrm{d}a$$

Therefore, for the whole area,

$$I_{OQ} = \int xy\,\mathrm{d}a + k\int x\,\mathrm{d}a + h\int y\,\mathrm{d}a + hk\int \mathrm{d}a$$
$$= I_{XY} + Ahk \qquad . \qquad . \qquad . \qquad . \qquad . \qquad . \quad (11.7)$$

since $\int x\,\mathrm{d}a$ and $\int y\,\mathrm{d}a$ are both zero.

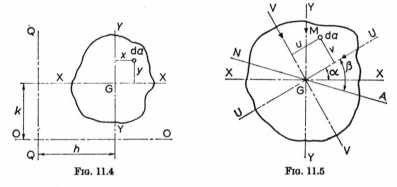

Fig. 11.4   Fig. 11.5

11.5   Beam with unsymmetrical bending moment. Fig. 11.5 shows the cross-section of a beam in which the applied bending moment acts in the plane YY, inclined at an angle α to the principal axis VV.

If the applied bending moment is M,

$$\text{component in plane VV} = M\cos\alpha$$
and $$\text{component in plane UU} = M\sin\alpha$$

Therefore stress on element $\mathrm{d}a$, of co-ordinates u and v relative to the principal axes,

$$= \frac{M\cos\alpha}{I_{UU}} \times v + \frac{M\sin\alpha}{I_{VV}} \times u$$

i.e. $$\sigma = M\left(\frac{v\cos\alpha}{I_{UU}} + \frac{u\sin\alpha}{I_{VV}}\right) \qquad . \qquad . \qquad . \quad (11.8)$$

Equation (11.8) applies to all points in the cross-section provided that the appropriate signs are ascribed to the co-ordinates u and v.

For points on the neutral axis, $\sigma = 0$

i.e. $$\frac{v\cos\alpha}{I_{UU}} = -\frac{u\sin\alpha}{I_{VV}}$$

i.e. $$v = -\left(\frac{I_{UU}}{I_{VV}}\tan\alpha\right) \times u \qquad . \qquad . \quad (11.9)$$

This is a straight line of slope $-\dfrac{I_{UU}}{I_{VV}} \tan \alpha$. If β is the inclination of this axis to UU, then

$$\beta = -\tan^{-1}\left(\frac{I_{UU}}{I_{VV}} \tan \alpha\right) \qquad . \qquad . \qquad (11.10)$$

The most highly stressed point is that which is farthest from the neutral axis. The stress at this point is then obtained by substituting the appropriate values of u and v in equation (11.8).

Deflection. If the load applied in plane YY is W, Fig. 11.6,

component in plane VV $= W \cos \alpha$

and   component in plane UU $= W \sin \alpha$

$\therefore$ deflection along VV, $\delta_{VV} = \dfrac{(W \cos \alpha)l^3}{kEI_{UU}}$

and deflection along UU, $\delta_{UU} = \dfrac{(W \sin \alpha)l^3}{kEI_{VV}}$

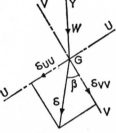

Fig. 11.6

where k is a constant depending on the position of the load and the end-fixing conditions.

$\therefore$ resultant deflection, $\delta = \sqrt{\delta_{VV}{}^2 + \delta_{UU}{}^2}$

$$= \frac{Wl^3}{kE} \sqrt{\left(\frac{\cos \alpha}{I_{UU}}\right)^2 + \left(\frac{\sin \alpha}{I_{VV}}\right)^2} \quad (11.11)$$

The inclination of the resultant deflection to VV

$$= \tan^{-1}\left(\frac{\delta_{UU}}{\delta_{VV}}\right) = \tan^{-1}\left(\frac{I_{UU}}{I_{VV}} \tan \alpha\right) \qquad . \qquad (11.12)$$

From equation (11.10), this is the angle β, thus confirming that the deflection is in a direction perpendicular to the neutral axis.

11.6 Short column with unsymmetrical load. Fig. 11.7 shows a short column with a load W which is eccentric to both principal axes of the section. Let the co-ordinates of the load point relative to VV and UU be a and b respectively.

Then the given load is equivalent to a load W at G, together with a moment Wa causing bending about VV and a moment Wb causing bending about UU. Thus the stress on an element da, of co-ordinates u and v relative to the principal axes

$$= \frac{W}{A} + \frac{Wa}{I_{VV}} \times u + \frac{Wb}{I_{UU}} \times v$$

i.e.
$$\sigma = W\left(\frac{1}{A} + \frac{au}{I_{VV}} + \frac{bv}{I_{UU}}\right) \qquad . \qquad . \qquad . \qquad (11.13)$$

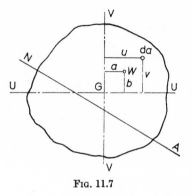

FIG. 11.7

The element da has been taken in the same quadrant as the load point and equation (11.13) then applies to all points in the cross-section provided that the appropriate signs are ascribed to the co-ordinates u and v.

The equation of the neutral axis is given by

$$\frac{1}{A} + \frac{au}{I_{VV}} + \frac{bv}{I_{UU}} = 0$$

from which
$$v = -\left(\frac{a}{b}\frac{I_{UU}}{I_{VV}}\right) \times u - \frac{I_{UU}}{Ab} \qquad . \qquad (11.14)$$

1. (a) *Find the product of inertia of the quadrant of a circle shown in Fig. 11.8 about the axes OX and OY.*

(b) *Find the principal moments of inertia and the directions of the principal axes of the angle section shown in Fig. 11.9.*

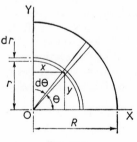

FIG. 11.8

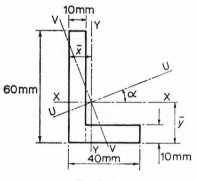

FIG. 11.9

(a) Product of inertia of element about OX and OY

$$= r\,\mathrm{d}\theta\,\mathrm{d}r \times x \times y$$
$$= r\,\mathrm{d}\theta\,\mathrm{d}r \times r\sin\theta \times r\cos\theta$$

Therefore, for the whole area,

$$I_{XY} = \int_0^{\pi/2}\int_0^R r^3 \sin\theta \cos\theta\,\mathrm{d}\theta\,\mathrm{d}r$$

$$= \frac{R^4}{4}\int_0^{\pi/2}\frac{\sin 2\theta}{2}\,\mathrm{d}\theta = \frac{R^4}{8}$$

(b) Taking moments about the left-hand side and base,

$$\bar{x} = \frac{70}{6}\ \text{mm} \quad \text{and} \quad \bar{y} = \frac{130}{6}\ \text{mm}$$

$$\therefore I_{XX} = \frac{10\times 60^3}{12} + 10\times 60\times\left(\frac{50}{6}\right)^2 + \frac{30\times 10^3}{12} + 30\times 10\times\left(\frac{100}{6}\right)^2$$

$$= \frac{11\cdot07}{36}\times 10^6\ \text{mm}^4$$

$$I_{YY} = \frac{60\times 10^3}{12} + 60\times 10\times\left(\frac{40}{6}\right)^2 + \frac{10\times 30^3}{12} + 10\times 30\times\left(\frac{80}{6}\right)^2$$

$$= \frac{3\cdot87}{36}\times 10^6\ \text{mm}^4$$

$$I_{XY} = 0 + 10\times 60\times\left(\frac{50}{6}\right)\times\left(-\frac{40}{6}\right) + 0 + 30\times 10\times\left(-\frac{100}{6}\right)\times\left(\frac{80}{6}\right)^*$$

$$= -0\cdot10\times 10^6\ \text{mm}^4$$

$$\therefore \tan 2\alpha = \frac{2\times(-0\cdot10)}{\dfrac{3\cdot87}{36} - \dfrac{11\cdot07}{36}} \quad . \quad \text{from equation (11.3)}$$

$$= 1$$

$$\therefore \alpha = \underline{22\tfrac{1}{2}^\circ}$$

$$\therefore I_{UU} = \frac{11\cdot07}{36}\cos^2 22\tfrac{1}{2}^\circ + 0\cdot10\sin 45^\circ + \frac{3\cdot87}{36}\sin^2 22\tfrac{1}{2}^\circ$$

from equation (11.1)

$$= \underline{349\,000\ \text{mm}^4}$$

and $I_{VV} = \dfrac{11\cdot07}{36}\sin^2 22\tfrac{1}{2}^\circ - 0\cdot10\sin 45^\circ + \dfrac{3\cdot87}{36}\cos^2 22\tfrac{1}{2}^\circ$

from equation (11.2)

$$= \underline{65\,800\ \text{mm}^4}$$

* Note that the product of inertia of each of the rectangles about its own axes is zero.

2. *A 80 mm × 80 mm angle as shown in Fig. 11.10 is used as a freely supported beam with one leg vertical.* $I_{XX} = I_{YY} = 0.873\ 6 \times 10^{-6}\ m^4$. *When a bending moment is applied in the vertical plane YY, the mid-section of the beam deflects in the direction AA at 30° 15′ to the vertical. Calculate the second moments of area of the section about its principal axes.*

Find also the bending stress at the corner B if the bending moment is 2 kN m.

(U. Lond.)

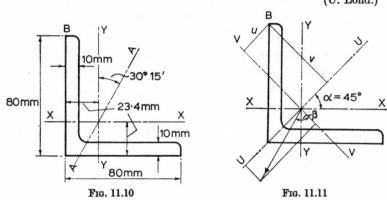

FIG. 11.10   FIG. 11.11

Since the angle has an axis of symmetry, that axis (UU in Fig. 11.11) is a principal axis and $\alpha = 45°$.

From equations (11.6) and (11.12),

$$I_{UU} + I_{VV} = I_{XX} + I_{YY} = 2 \times 0.873\ 6 \times 10^{-6} = 1.747\ 2 \times 10^{-6}\ m^4 \qquad (1)$$

and $\quad \tan \beta = \dfrac{I_{UU}}{I_{VV}^{a}} \tan \alpha = \dfrac{I_{UU}}{I_{VV}}, \quad$ since $\tan \alpha = 1$

$$\therefore \frac{I_{UU}}{I_{VV}} = \tan(45° + 30° 15′) = 3.79 \ . \qquad . \qquad . \qquad . \qquad (2)$$

Therefore, from equations (1) and (2),

$$I_{UU} = \underline{1.382 \times 10^{-6}\ m^4} \quad \text{and} \quad I_{VV} = \underline{0.365 \times 10^{-6}\ m^4}$$

By drawing or calculation, $u = 23.5$ mm and $v = 56.56$ mm.

$$\therefore \sigma = M\left(\frac{v \cos \alpha}{I_{UU}} + \frac{u \sin \alpha}{I_{VV}}\right) \qquad . \qquad . \qquad \text{from equation (11.8)}$$

$$= 2 \times 10^3\left(\frac{0.056\ 56 \cos 45°}{1.382 \times 10^{-6}} + \frac{0.023\ 5 \sin 45°}{0.365 \times 10^{-6}}\right) \text{N/m}^2$$

$$= \underline{149\ \text{MN/m}^2}$$

3. *Fig. 11.12 shows an unequal angle section, for which* $I_{XX} = 0.8 \times 10^{-6}\ m^4$ *and* $I_{YY} = 0.382 \times 10^{-6}\ m^4$. *Find the moments of inertia about the principal axes UU and VV, given that the angle between the axes UU and XX is* $28\frac{1}{2}°$.

If the angle, with the 80 mm leg vertical, is used as a beam, freely supported on a span of 2 m carrying a vertical load of 2 kN at the centre, find: (a) the maximum bending stress at the point A; (b) the direction and magnitude of the maximum deflection.

Neglect the weight of the beam and take E = 200 GN/m².   (U. Lond.)

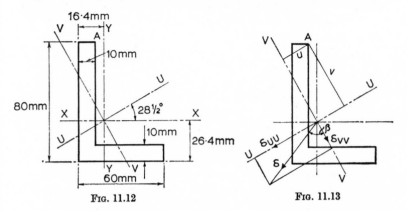

FIG. 11.12   FIG. 11.13

From equation (11.6),

$$I_{UU} + I_{VV} = I_{XX} + I_{YY}$$
$$= (0 \cdot 8 + 0 \cdot 382) \times 10^{-6} = 1 \cdot 132 \times 10^{-6} \text{ m}^4 \quad (1)$$

From equations (11.4) and (11.5),

$$I_{XX} - I_{YY} = I_{UU}(\cos^2 \alpha - \sin^2 \alpha) + I_{VV}(\sin^2 \alpha - \cos^2 \alpha)$$
$$= (I_{UU} - I_{VV}) \cos 2\alpha$$

$$\therefore I_{UU} - I_{VV} = \frac{I_{XX} - I_{YY}}{\cos 2\alpha} = \frac{(0 \cdot 8 - 0 \cdot 382) \times 10^{-6}}{\cos 57^\circ} = 0 \cdot 767 \ 5 \times 10^{-6} \text{ m}^4 \quad (2)$$

Therefore, from equations (1) and (2),

$$I_{UU} = \underline{0 \cdot 974 \ 8 \times 10^{-6} \text{ m}^4} \quad \text{and} \quad I_{VV} = \underline{0 \cdot 207 \ 2 \times 10^{-6} \text{ m}^4}$$

Alternatively I_{XY} can be determined from equation (11.3) and substituted in equations (11.1) and (11.2).

(a)   Maximum B.M. $= \dfrac{Wl}{4} = \dfrac{2 \times 10^3 \times 2}{4} = 1 \ 000$ N m

By drawing or calculation, $u = 20$ mm and $v = 50$ mm, Fig. 11.13,

$$\therefore \sigma = M\left(\frac{v \cos \alpha}{I_{UU}} + \frac{u \sin \alpha}{I_{VV}}\right) \qquad . \qquad . \qquad \text{from equation (11.8)}$$

$$= 1 \ 000\left(\frac{0 \cdot 05 \cos 28\frac{1}{2}^\circ}{0 \cdot 974 \ 8 \times 10^{-6}} + \frac{0 \cdot 02 \times \sin 28\frac{1}{2}^\circ}{0 \cdot 207 \ 2 \times 10^{-6}}\right) \text{ N/m}^2$$

$$= \underline{91 \cdot 2 \text{ MN/m}^2}$$

(b) From equation (11.11),

$$\delta = \frac{Wl^3}{48E}\sqrt{\left(\frac{\cos\alpha}{I_{UU}}\right)^2 + \left(\frac{\sin\alpha}{I_{VV}}\right)^2}$$

$$= \frac{2\times10^3\times2^3}{48\times200\times10^9}\sqrt{\left(\frac{\cos 28\frac{1}{2}°}{0.974\,8\times10^{-6}}\right)^2 + \left(\frac{\sin 28\frac{1}{2}°}{0.207\,2\times10^{-6}}\right)^2}$$

$$= 0.004\,125 \text{ m} \quad \text{or} \quad \underline{4.125 \text{ mm}}$$

From equation (11.12),

$$\beta = \tan^{-1}\left(\frac{I_{UU}}{I_{VV}}\tan\alpha\right)$$

$$= \tan^{-1}\left(\frac{0.974\,8}{0.207\,2}\tan 28\frac{1}{2}°\right) = 68°\,48'$$

∴ angle to vertical
$$= 68°\,48' - 28°\,30' = \underline{40°\,18'}$$

4. *A cantilever consists of a 60 mm × 60 mm × 10 mm angle with the top face AB horizontal, Fig. 11.14. It carries a load of 800 N at a distance of 1 m from the fixed end, the line of action of the load passing through the centroid of the section and inclined at 30° to the vertical.*

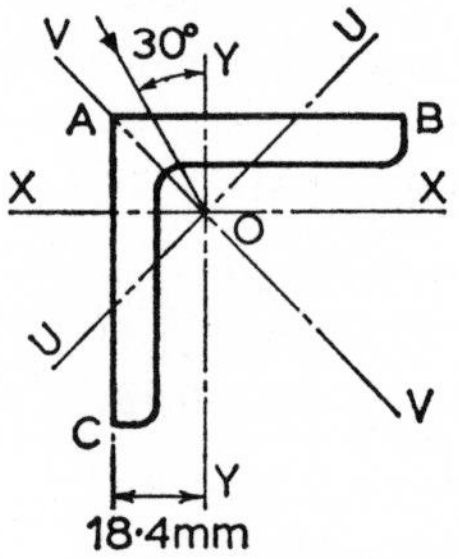

Fig. 11.14

Determine the stress at the corners A, B and C at the fixed end and also the position of the neutral axis.

$$I_{XX} = I_{YY} = 0.348\,8\times10^{-6} \; m^4;$$
$$I_{UU} = 0.147\,2\times10^{-6} \; m^4;$$
$$I_{VV} = 0.550\,6\times10^{-6} \; m^4. \qquad \text{(U. Lond.)}$$

B.M. at wall $= 800\times1 = 800$ N m

$$\therefore \sigma = M\left(\frac{v\cos\alpha}{I_{UU}} + \frac{u\sin\alpha}{I_{VV}}\right)$$

$$= 800\left(\frac{v\cos 15°}{0.147\,2\times10^{-6}} + \frac{u\sin 15°}{0.550\,6\times10^{-6}}\right) \text{ N/m}^2$$

$$= 5\,250v + 376u \text{ MN/m}^2$$

At the neutral axis, $\sigma = 0$, so that

$$v = -\frac{376}{5\ 250}\,u = -0.071\ 7u$$

Thus $\beta = \tan^{-1}(-0.071\ 7) = \underline{-4°\ 6'}$

i.e. the neutral axis is inclined at 4° 6′ clockwise from UU.

At A, $v = +26$ mm   and $u = 0$
∴ $\sigma = 5\ 250 \times 0.026$
$= 136.5$ MN/m² (tensile)

At B, $v = -16.4$ mm   and $u = +42$ mm
∴ $\sigma = -5\ 250 \times 0.016\ 4 + 376 \times 0.042$
$= -70.4$ MN/m² (compressive)

At C, $v = -16.4$ mm   and $u = -42$ mm
∴ $\sigma = -5\ 250 \times 0.016\ 4 - 376 \times 0.042$
$= -102.0$ MN/m² (compressive)

5. *A 150 mm × 60 mm I-beam is used as a column to carry a load acting in a direction parallel with the longitudinal axis of the column but not passing through either of the principal axes of the section. The magnitude and line of action of the load are such that the stresses at the corners A, B and C are as shown in Fig. 11.15. Determine the magnitude and location of the load, the stress at D and the position of the neutral axis and make a diagram of the section showing these values and the reference letters.*

For a 150 mm × 60 mm I-beam, $I_{XX} = 4.919 \times 10^{-6}\ m^4$;
$I_{YY} = 0.198\ 7 \times 10^{-6}\ m^4$;
$A = 1\ 324 \times 10^{-6}\ m^2.$

(U. Lond.)

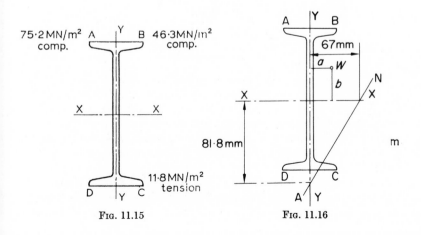

FIG. 11.15   FIG. 11.16

If the load point has co-ordinates a and b relative to XX and YY, Fig. 11.16, then, from equation (11.13),

$$\sigma = W\left(\frac{1}{A} + \frac{ax}{I_{YY}} + \frac{by}{I_{XX}}\right)$$

where x and y are the distances of an element from YY and XX respectively.

Taking compression as positive,

stress at A = 75·2

$$= W\left(\frac{1}{1\,324 \times 10^{-6}} - \frac{0·03a}{0·198\,7 \times 10^{-6}} + \frac{0·075b}{4·919 \times 10^{-6}}\right) \text{MN/m}^2 \quad (1)$$

stress at B = 46·3

$$= W\left(\frac{1}{1\,324 \times 10^{-6}} + \frac{0·03a}{0·198\,7 \times 10^{-6}} + \frac{0·075b}{4·919 \times 10^{-6}}\right) \text{MN/m}^2 \quad (2)$$

and

stress at C = −11·8

$$= W\left(\frac{1}{1\,324 \times 10^{-6}} + \frac{0·03a}{0·1987 \times 10^{-6}} - \frac{0·075b}{4·919 \times 10^{-6}}\right) \text{MN/m}^2 \quad (3)$$

Therefore, from equations (1), (2) and (3),

$$\underline{W = 42 \text{ kN}, \quad a = -2·278 \text{ mm} \quad \text{and} \quad b = 45·4 \text{ mm}}$$

Stress at D

$$= 42 \times 10^3\left(\frac{1}{1\,324 \times 10^{-6}} + \frac{0·03 \times 0·002\,278}{0·198\,7 \times 10^{-6}} - \frac{0·075 \times 0·045\,4}{4·919 \times 10^{-6}}\right) \text{N/m}^2$$

$$= \underline{17·02 \text{ MN/m}^2 \text{ (compressive)}}$$

At the neutral axis, $\sigma = 0$,

i.e.
$$\frac{0·045\,4y}{4·919 \times 10^{-6}} = \frac{0·002\,278x}{0·198\,7 \times 10^{-6}} - \frac{1}{1\,324 \times 10^{-6}}$$

from which
$$\underline{y = 1·24x - 0·081\,8 \text{ m}}$$

6. *A 300 mm × 150 mm I-beam is used as a stanchion to carry two loads, W and 2W, which act in directions parallel with the axis of the stanchion. The load W acts on the YY axis and 200 mm from the XX axis.*

(a) Find the boundary within which 2W must act if there is to be no tension.

(b) If 2W acts on the XX axis, find the magnitude of W and the position of the line of action of 2W if the greatest and least stresses are 105 MN/m² and 7·5 MN/m², both compressive.

$I_{XX} = 146·8 \times 10^{-6} \text{ m}^4$; $I_{YY} = 11·05 \times 10^{-6} \text{ m}^4$; $A = 9·932 \times 10^{-3} \text{ m}^2$.

Make a diagram of the section showing the load positions and the boundary required. (U. Lond.)

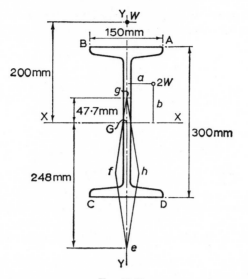

FIG. 11.17

(*a*) The load W is equivalent to a load W at G, Fig. 11.17, together with a moment $0.2W$ causing bending about XX.

The load $2W$ is equivalent to a load $2W$ at G, together with a moment $2Wb$ causing bending about XX and a moment $2Wa$ causing bending about YY.

Thus, on an element whose co-ordinates are x and y relative to YY and XX respectively,

$$\sigma = \frac{3W}{A} + \frac{(0 \cdot 2 + 2b)W}{I_{XX}} \times y + \frac{2aW}{I_{YY}} \times x$$

$$= W \left\{ 302 + \frac{0 \cdot 1 + b}{73 \cdot 4 \times 10^{-6}} \times y + \frac{a}{5 \cdot 525 \times 10^{-6}} \times x \right\}$$

For no stress at A,

$$302 + \frac{0 \cdot 1 + b}{73 \cdot 4 \times 10^{-6}} \times 0 \cdot 15 + \frac{a}{5 \cdot 525 \times 10^{-6}} \times 0 \cdot 075 = 0$$

from which $b = -6 \cdot 64a - 0 \cdot 248$ m

For no stress at D,

$$302 - \frac{0 \cdot 1 + b}{73 \cdot 4 \times 10^{-6}} \times 0 \cdot 15 + \frac{a}{5 \cdot 525 \times 10^{-6}} \times 0 \cdot 075 = 0$$

from which $b = 6 \cdot 64a + 0 \cdot 047\ 7$ m

These equations are represented by *ef* and *fg* respectively in Fig. 11.17 and *gh* and *he* represent the corresponding relations between a and b for no stress at C and B respectively.

(b) If the load $2W$ is on the XX axis and is to the right of YY, then the greatest compressive stress occurs at A and the least compressive stress occurs at C,

i.e. $105 \times 10^6 = W\left(302 + \dfrac{0 \cdot 1}{73 \cdot 4 \times 10^{-6}} \times 0 \cdot 15 + \dfrac{a}{5 \cdot 525 \times 10^{-6}} \times 0 \cdot 075\right)$ (1)

and $7 \cdot 5 \times 10^6 = W\left(302 - \dfrac{0 \cdot 1}{73 \cdot 4 \times 10^{-6}} \times 0 \cdot 15 - \dfrac{a}{5 \cdot 525 \times 10^{-6}} \times 0 \cdot 075\right)$ (2)

Therefore, from equations (1) and (2),

$$W = \underline{186 \cdot 3 \text{ kN}} \quad \text{and} \quad a = \underline{4 \cdot 225 \text{ mm}}$$

7. *A short length of bar having the section shown in Fig.* 11.18 *is subjected to a non-axial force at right angles to the plane of the section. Determine the boundary within which the force must act if there is to be no reversal of stress on the section.*

Make a sketch of the section showing the boundary and its dimensions.

(U. Lond.)

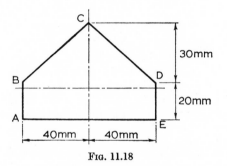

Fig. 11.18

Area of section $= 80 \times 20 + \frac{1}{2} \times 80 \times 30 = 2\ 800 \text{ mm}^2$.

By taking moments about the base, $\bar{y} = 18 \cdot 56$ mm.

By use of the equimomental system (Art. 3.5), or otherwise,

$$I_{\text{XX}} = 0 \cdot 388\ 3 \times 10^6 \text{ mm}^4 \quad \text{and} \quad I_{\text{YY}} = 1 \cdot 173 \times 10^6 \text{ mm}^4$$

If the load W has co-ordinates a and b relative to YY and XX respectively, Fig. 11.19,

$$\sigma = W\left(\frac{1}{A} + \frac{ax}{I_{\text{YY}}} + \frac{by}{I_{\text{XX}}}\right) \qquad . \qquad . \quad \text{from equation (11.13)}$$

$$= W\left(\frac{1}{2\ 800} + \frac{ax}{1 \cdot 173 \times 10^6} + \frac{by}{0 \cdot 388\ 3 \times 10^6}\right)$$

$$= \frac{W}{100}\left(\frac{1}{28} + \frac{ax}{11\ 730} + \frac{by}{3\ 883}\right) \text{ N/mm}^2$$

For no stress at A, $\dfrac{1}{28} - \dfrac{a \times 40}{11\,730} - \dfrac{b \times 18\cdot56}{3\,883} = 0$

from which $b = -0\cdot713a + 7\cdot48$ mm

For no stress at B, $\dfrac{1}{28} - \dfrac{a \times 40}{11\,720} + \dfrac{b \times 1\cdot44}{3\,883} = 0$

from which $b = 9\cdot2a - 96\cdot3$ mm

For no stress at C, $\dfrac{1}{28} + \dfrac{a \times 0}{11\,730} + \dfrac{b \times 31\cdot44}{3\,883} = 0$

from which $b = -4\cdot4$ mm

The boundary represented by these equations and the corresponding equations for no stress at D and E are shown in Fig. 11.19.

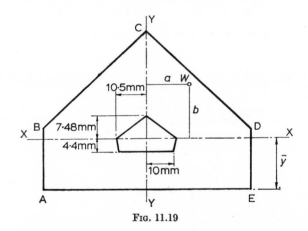

Fig. 11.19

8. A steel beam 50 mm × 25 mm in cross-section is supported over a span of 1 m with one 50 mm face inclined at 30° to the vertical. A load of 600 N acts vertically at the centre of the span. Neglecting the weight of the beam, and assuming that the ordinary beam theory applies, find (a) the maximum stress in the beam due to bending; (b) the magnitude and direction of the maximum deflection. $E = 200$ GN/m². (U. Lond.)

(Ans.: 26·9 MN/m²; 0·523 mm at 36° 35' to vertical)

9. A steel bar of rectangular section 100 mm × 40 mm is supported in bearings and carries a load of 10 kN at mid-span. If as indicated in Fig. 11.20 the beam is rotated slowly, find the inclination θ when the bending stress in the bar reaches its greatest value. Determine the value of the greatest bending stress and the vertical deflection at mid-span when this stress occurs. Assume the bar is direction-free at the supports. $E = 200$ GN/m². (U. Lond.)

(Ans.: 21° 48'; 121 MN/m²; 3·12 mm)

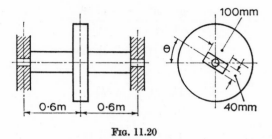

Fig. 11.20

10. An 80 mm × 80 mm × 10 mm angle is used as a beam simply supported at each end over a span of 2 m with one leg of the section horizontal and the other vertically upwards. It is loaded at the centre of the span with a vertical load which may be assumed to pass through the centroid of the section. The principal second moments of area for the section are $1 \cdot 38 \times 10^{-6}$ m⁴ and $0 \cdot 36 \times 10^{-6}$ m⁴. The distance of the centroid from the outside edge is $23 \cdot 5$ mm and toe has a radius of $5 \cdot 6$ mm.

Find the position of the neutral axis and calculate the safe load if the maximum stress is not to exceed 120 MN/m². Graphical constructions may be used.
(*U. Lond.*)   (*Ans.*: 3·02 kN)

11. An 80 mm × 80 mm × 10 mm steel angle is used as a cantilever of length 0·8 m and carries an end load. One leg of the angle is horizontal and the load at the end is vertical with its line of action passing through the centroid of the section. Determine the maximum allowable load if the bending stress is not to exceed 120 MN/m² and find also the vertical deflection at the end due to this load. Assume all corners of the angle to be left square. $E = 200$ GN/m². (*U. Lond.*)
(*Ans.*: 1·82 kN; 2·66 mm)

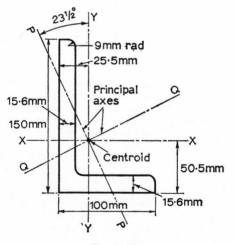

Fig. 11.21

12. A beam of the angle section shown in Fig. 11.21 is freely supported on a span of 2 m with the 150 mm leg vertical. A vertical load of 20 kN is applied at the centre of the span. Find (a) the maximum bending stress; (b) the direction and magnitude of the deflection at the centre. Neglect the weight of the beam itself, and neglect twisting effects and deflection due to shear.

The properties of the section are: $I_{XX} = 8\cdot12 \times 10^{-6}\,\text{m}^4$, $I_{YY} = 2\cdot88 \times 10^{-6}\,\text{m}^4$, $I_{PP} = 1\cdot675 \times 10^{-6}\,\text{m}^4$. $E = 200\ \text{GN/m}^2$. (*U. Lond.*)

(*Ans.:* 153 MN/m²; 67° 33′ to PP; 4·29 mm)

13. A rectangular bar of 80 mm × 40 mm cross-section has a pull of W N applied parallel to the axis of the bar, the point of application being 15 mm from one of the longer edges and 30 mm from one of the shorter edges of the section. If the tensile stress in the material is to be limited to 150 MN/m², determine the value of W and the stresses at the four corners of the section.

Find the area within which W must be situated if there is to be no compressive stress in the material. Show your results on a diagram of the cross-section and indicate the position of the neutral axis. (*U. Lond.*)

$$\left(Ans.:\ 192\ \text{kN};\ -30,\ +60,\ +150,\ +60\ \text{MN/m}^2;\ y = \pm\frac{x}{2} \pm \frac{20}{3};\right.$$
$$\left. y = -\frac{x}{2} - \frac{80}{3}\ (\text{mm units})\right)$$

14. A short column has a solid cross-section in the form of an equilateral triangle. Determine the shape and dimensions of the area within which the resultant compressive load must be applied if there is to be no tension on the cross-section of the column. The line of action of the load is parallel to the axis of the column. Calculate the stress at each of the three corners of an equilateral triangular column of 50 mm side when a compressive load of 80 kN acts at the position P shown in Fig. 11.22. (*U. Lond.*)

(*Ans.:* Equilateral triangle of side *s*/4; 140·5, 51·9, 23·6 MN/m²)

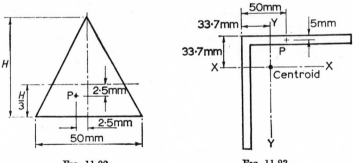

Fɪɢ. 11.22   Fɪɢ. 11.23

15. A length of 120 mm × 120 mm × 10 mm angle of the section shown in Fig. 11.23 transmits a longitudinal pull which passes through the point P. Determine (a) the position of the line of zero stress, (b) the maximum value of the pull if the stress on the section is not to exceed 100 MN/m². Assume all corners square. $I_{XX} = I_{YY} = 3\cdot184 \times 10^{-6}\,\text{m}^4$. (*U. Lond.*)

(*Ans.:* $y = -0\cdot567\ 5x - 48\cdot5$ (mm units)); 85 kN

16. A tie-bar of rectangular section, originally 75 mm wide by 25 mm thick, has these dimensions reduced by $1/n$th of the original values by the removal of material from two adjacent faces. If an axial tensile load of 100 kN is applied to the bar through the centre of the original section, find the value of $1/n$ for a maximum tensile stress of 120 MN/m². Determine also the magnitude of the least tensile stress. (*U. Lond.*)   (*Ans.:* 0·114; 15·49 MN/m²)

17. Fig. 11.24 shows the cross-section of a short column, made from a 160 mm × 120 mm I-section, with a 200 mm × 10 mm plate welded to one flange. A vertical load of 25 kN acts at P, the line of thrust passing 40 mm from the XX axis and 20 mm from the YY axis of the I-section. Calculate the maximum stress developed in the section. For the 160 mm × 120 mm I-section, area = 4.12×10^{-3} m², $I_{XX} = 18.42 \times 10^{-6}$ m⁴ and $I_{YY} = 4.61 \times 10^{-6}$ m⁴. (*I.C.E.*)   (*Ans.:* 11·56 MN/m²)

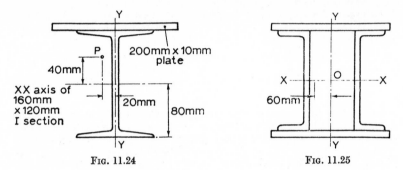

FIG. 11.24   FIG. 11.25

18. A compound compression member consists of two 325 mm × 100 mm channels and two plates each 400 mm × 20 mm, as shown in Fig. 11.25. The line of action of the load is parallel to the longitudinal axis of the member and passes through the XX axis at 60 mm from the centre O. Determine the least distance between the backs of the channels if there is to be no tension in the section.

If for the section found, the load can be applied at any point, show on a sketch the area within which it can act without causing tension anywhere in the section.

For one channel, cross-sectional area = 6.1×10^{-3} m², the centroid is 26 mm from the back of the channel and the principal second moments of area of the section are 96.5×10^{-6} m⁴ and 4.98×10^{-6} m⁴. (*U. Lond.*)

(*Ans.:* 142·2 mm; $y = \pm 2.165x \pm 130$ (mm units))

CHAPTER 12

COMPLEX STRESS AND STRAIN

12.1 Stresses on an oblique section. Fig. 12.1(*a*) shows a piece of material subjected to a tensile force P. If the cross-sectional area is a, the tensile stress on the cross-section, $\sigma = P/a$.

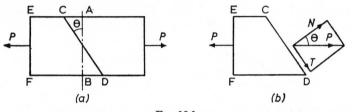

(a)   (b)

Fɪɢ. 12.1

The part CDEF, Fig. 12.1(*b*), is in equilibrium under the forces acting upon it, so that the resultant force on CD is equal and opposite to the applied force P. This can be resolved into normal and tangential components, N and T, producing direct and shear stresses σ_θ and τ_θ respectively. The area of the oblique section CD is $a \sec \theta$, so that

$$\sigma_\theta = \frac{N}{a \sec \theta} = \frac{P \cos \theta}{a \sec \theta} = \sigma \cos^2 \theta \qquad . \qquad . \qquad . \quad (12.1)$$

$$\tau_\theta = \frac{T}{a \sec \theta} = \frac{P \sin \theta}{a \sec \theta} = \sigma \sin \theta \cos \theta$$

$$= \frac{\sigma}{2} \sin 2\theta \qquad . \qquad . \qquad . \quad (12.2)$$

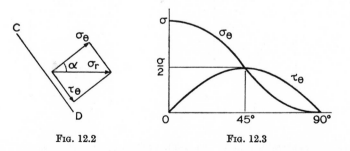

Fɪɢ. 12.2   Fɪɢ. 12.3

The resultant stress, σ_r, Fig. 12.2, is given by $\sigma_r = \sqrt{\sigma_\theta^2 + \tau_\theta^2}$, since each of the stresses acts on the same area, and $\alpha = \tan^{-1}(\tau_\theta/\sigma_\theta)$ (in the simple case considered, $\alpha = \theta$).

The variations in σ_θ and τ_θ are shown in Fig. 12.3. σ_θ has a maximum value σ when $\theta = 0$ and τ_θ has a maximum value $\sigma/2$ when $\theta = 45°$. Thus any material whose ultimate shear stress is less than half the ultimate stress in tension (or compression), will fail due to shear when subjected to a tensile (or compressive) load.

It is usual to work in terms of the applied and induced *stresses* rather than *forces* and to assume the material to be of unit thickness.

12.2 Material subjected to two perpendicular stresses. Fig. 12.4 shows an element of a material of unit thickness which is subjected to perpendicular tensile stresses σ_x and σ_y. The wedge ABC is in equilibrium under the forces acting upon it, so that, resolving forces normal to AC,

$$\sigma_\theta \times AC = \sigma_x \times AB \cos\theta + \sigma_y \times BC \sin\theta$$
$$\therefore \sigma_\theta = \sigma_x \cos^2\theta + \sigma_y \sin^2\theta$$
$$= \frac{\sigma_x + \sigma_y}{2} + \frac{\sigma_x - \sigma_y}{2}\cos 2\theta \quad . \quad . \quad . \quad (12.3)$$

The maximum value is σ_x or σ_y, whichever is greater and the minimum value is σ_x or σ_y, whichever is smaller.

Resolving forces parallel to AC,

$$\tau_\theta \times AC = \sigma_x \times AB \sin\theta - \sigma_y \times BC \cos\theta$$
$$\therefore \tau_\theta = (\sigma_x - \sigma_y)\sin\theta\cos\theta$$
$$= \frac{\sigma_x - \sigma_y}{2}\sin 2\theta \quad . \quad . \quad . \quad . \quad (12.4)$$

The maximum value is $\dfrac{\sigma_x - \sigma_y}{2}$ when $\theta = 45°$

If $\sigma_x = \sigma_y$, $\tau_\theta = 0$ for all values of θ.

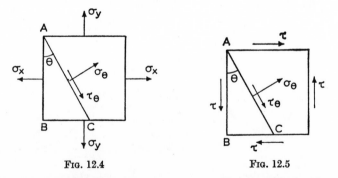

FIG. 12.4   FIG. 12.5

12.3 Material subjected to shear stress. If a material is subjected to pure shear on one plane, an equal shear stress is induced on the perpendicular plane to prevent rotation of the element (Art. 1.3); such a state is shown in Fig. 12.5.

Resolving forces normal to AC,

$$\sigma_\theta \times AC = \tau \times AB \sin\theta + \tau \times BC \cos\theta$$
$$\therefore \sigma_\theta = \tau \cos\theta \sin\theta + \tau \sin\theta \cos\theta$$
$$= \tau \sin 2\theta \quad . \quad . \quad . \quad . \quad . \quad (12.5)$$

The maximum value is τ when $\theta = 45°$.

Resolving forces parallel to AC,

$$\tau_\theta \times AC = -\tau \times AB \cos\theta + \tau \times BC \sin\theta$$
$$\therefore \tau_\theta = -\tau \cos^2\theta + \tau \sin^2\theta$$
$$= -\tau \cos 2\theta \quad . \quad . \quad . \quad . \quad . \quad (12.6)$$

The maximum value is τ when $\theta = 0$ or $90°$.

Shear stress induces numerically equal tensile and compressive stresses on planes at 45° to the planes of the shear stress, as shown in Fig. 12.6.

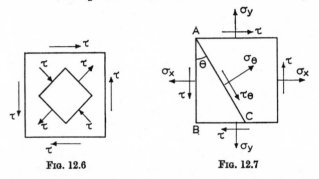

FIG. 12.6   FIG. 12.7

12.4 Material subjected to direct and shear stresses. Fig. 12.7 shows the most general case of stresses in two dimensions, since any system of stresses in two dimensions can be reduced to this form.

From the combination of previous formulae,

$$\sigma_\theta = \frac{\sigma_x + \sigma_y}{2} + \frac{\sigma_x - \sigma_y}{2} \cos 2\theta + \tau \sin 2\theta \quad . \quad . \quad (12.7)$$

and

$$\tau_\theta = \frac{\sigma_x - \sigma_y}{2} \sin 2\theta - \tau \cos 2\theta \quad . \quad . \quad . \quad (12.8)$$

For σ_θ to be a maximum or minimum, $\dfrac{d\sigma_\theta}{d\theta} = 0$

i.e.

$$-(\sigma_x - \sigma_y) \sin 2\theta + 2\tau \cos 2\theta = 0$$

$$\therefore \tan 2\theta = \frac{2\tau}{\sigma_x - \sigma_y} \quad . \quad . \quad (12.9)$$

Hence, from Fig. 12.8, $\sin 2\theta = \dfrac{2\tau}{\sqrt{(\sigma_x - \sigma_y)^2 + 4\tau^2}}$ $\quad . \quad (12.10)$

and

$$\cos 2\theta = \frac{\sigma_x - \sigma_y}{\sqrt{(\sigma_x - \sigma_y)^2 + 4\tau^2}} \quad . \quad (12.11)$$

∴ maximum and minimum values of σ_θ

$$= \frac{\sigma_x + \sigma_y}{2} + \frac{\sigma_x - \sigma_y}{2} \cdot \frac{\sigma_x - \sigma_y}{\sqrt{(\sigma_x - \sigma_y)^2 + 4\tau^2}} + \tau \frac{2\tau}{\sqrt{(\sigma_x - \sigma_y)^2 + 4\tau^2}}$$

$$= \tfrac{1}{2}\{(\sigma_x + \sigma_y) \pm \sqrt{(\sigma_x - \sigma_y)^2 + 4\tau^2}\} \quad . \quad . \quad . \quad (12.12)$$

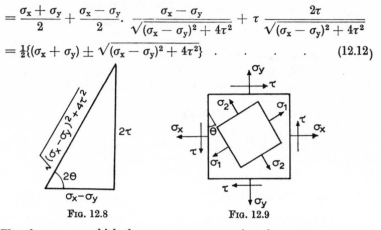

FIG. 12.8   FIG. 12.9

The planes upon which these stresses act are given by

$$\theta = \tfrac{1}{2} \tan^{-1} \frac{2\tau}{\sigma_x - \sigma_y} \quad \text{and} \quad \tfrac{1}{2}(\tan^{-1} \frac{2\tau}{\sigma_x - \sigma_y} + 180°)$$

i.e.
$$\tfrac{1}{2} \tan^{-1} \frac{2\tau}{\sigma_x - \sigma_y} + 90°$$

Thus the planes of maximum and minimum stress are mutually perpendicular; one of these stresses acts on one plane and the other stress acts on the perpendicular plane. The association between the stresses and planes is usually evident by considering the equilibrium of the wedge ABC but when in doubt, a unique solution for θ can be obtained from either of equations (12.14) and (12.15), Art. 12.5.

Substituting the values of sin 2θ and cos 2θ from equations (12.10) and (12.11) into the expression for τ_θ, equation (12.8) gives $\tau_\theta = 0$ on these planes. Such planes are referred to as the *principal planes* and the direct stresses acting on them are the *principal stresses*.

Thus, at any point in a stressed material, there are always mutually perpendicular planes upon which the stresses are wholly tensile or compressive and these are respectively the greatest and least direct stresses at that point.

Such an arrangement is shown in Fig. 12.9, where σ_1 and σ_2 are the principal stresses and θ is the angle given by equation (12.9).

Since this system of stress is identical with that shown in Fig. 12.4, it follows from equation (12.4) that the maximum shear stress in the body is given by

$$\tau_{max} = \frac{\sigma_1 - \sigma_2}{2}, \text{ acting on planes at } 45° \text{ to the principal planes}$$

Thus $\tau_{\max} = \frac{1}{2}[\frac{1}{2}\{(\sigma_x + \sigma_y) + \sqrt{(\sigma_x - \sigma_y)^2 + 4\tau^2}\}$
$$-\frac{1}{2}\{(\sigma_x + \sigma_y) - \sqrt{(\sigma_x - \sigma_y)^2 + 4\tau^2}\}]$$

$$= \frac{1}{2}\sqrt{(\sigma_x - \sigma_y)^2 + 4\tau^2} \quad . \quad . \quad . \quad . \quad (12.13)$$

12.5 Alternative derivation of principal stresses and planes. Since there is no shear stress on a principal plane, then if AC is such a plane, Fig. 12.10, the only stress acting on it is the principal stress, σ.

Hence, resolving forces horizontally,

$$\sigma \times AC \cos\theta = \sigma_x \times AB + \tau \times BC$$
$$\therefore \sigma = \sigma_x + \tau \tan\theta$$

or $\sigma - \sigma_x = \tau \tan\theta$.   (12.14)

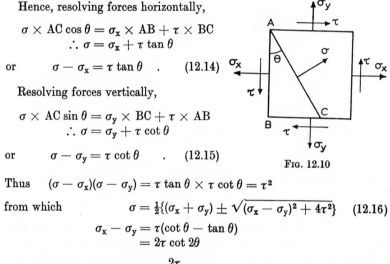

Resolving forces vertically,

$$\sigma \times AC \sin\theta = \sigma_y \times BC + \tau \times AB$$
$$\therefore \sigma = \sigma_y + \tau \cot\theta$$

or $\sigma - \sigma_y = \tau \cot\theta$.   (12.15)

Fig. 12.10

Thus $(\sigma - \sigma_x)(\sigma - \sigma_y) = \tau \tan\theta \times \tau \cot\theta = \tau^2$

from which $\sigma = \frac{1}{2}\{(\sigma_x + \sigma_y) \pm \sqrt{(\sigma_x - \sigma_y)^2 + 4\tau^2}\}$ (12.16)

$$\sigma_x - \sigma_y = \tau(\cot\theta - \tan\theta)$$
$$= 2\tau \cot 2\theta$$

$$\therefore \tan 2\theta = \frac{2\tau}{\sigma_x - \sigma_y} . \quad . \quad . \quad . \quad . \quad (12.17)$$

In the case of one direct stress only,

$$\sigma = \frac{1}{2}(\sigma_x \pm \sqrt{\sigma_x^2 + 4\tau^2}) \quad . \quad . \quad (12.18)$$

$$\tan 2\theta = \frac{2\tau}{\sigma_x} \quad . \quad . \quad . \quad . \quad (12.19)$$

and $\tau_{\max} = \frac{1}{2}\sqrt{\sigma_x^2 + 4\tau^2}$.   .   .   .   (12.20)

12.6 Mohr's Stress Circle. The results derived in Art. 12.2 can be represented graphically as follows:

From a point O, Fig. 12.11, set off $OA = \sigma_x$ and $OB = \sigma_y$. Draw a circle with AB as diameter and set off QC at an angle 2θ to QA.

Then $OQ = \dfrac{\sigma_x + \sigma_y}{2}$ and $QA = \dfrac{\sigma_x - \sigma_y}{2}$

so that $$OD = \frac{\sigma_x + \sigma_y}{2} + \frac{\sigma_x - \sigma_y}{2} \cos 2\theta = \sigma_\theta$$

and $$CD = \frac{\sigma_x - \sigma_y}{2} \sin 2\theta \qquad = \tau_\theta$$

The resultant stress is represented by OC and the angle QOC is the angle which the resultant makes with the normal to the plane.

Fig. 12.11 has been based on the assumption that σ_x and σ_y are both tensile (or compressive). If, however, σ_x is tensile and σ_y is compressive (or vice versa), the point O lies inside the circle, as shown in Fig. 12.12.

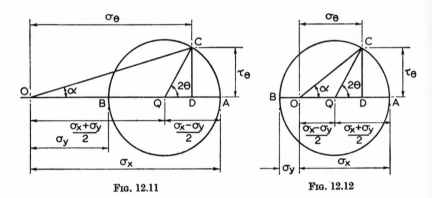

FIG. 12.11   FIG. 12.12

In the more general case dealt with in Art. 12.4, set off $OA = \sigma_x$, $OB = \sigma_y$ and $AM = BN = \tau$, Fig. 12.13. Draw a circle with MN as diameter and set off QC at an angle 2θ to QM.

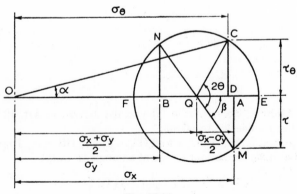

FIG. 12.13

Radius of circle, $R = QM = \sqrt{QA^2 + AM^2} = \sqrt{\left(\dfrac{\sigma_x - \sigma_y}{2}\right)^2 + \tau^2}$

Hence

$$OE = OQ + R = \frac{\sigma_x + \sigma_y}{2} + \sqrt{\left(\frac{\sigma_x - \sigma_y}{2}\right)^2 + \tau^2}$$

and $\quad OF = OQ - R = \dfrac{\sigma_x + \sigma_y}{2} - \sqrt{\left(\dfrac{\sigma_x - \sigma_y}{2}\right)^2 + \tau^2}$

Thus, by comparison with equations (12.12), OE and OF are the principal stresses, σ_1 and σ_2.

$$\begin{aligned}
OD = OQ + QD &= OQ + R \cos (2\theta - \beta) \\
&= OQ + R \cos 2\theta \cos \beta + R \sin 2\theta \sin \beta \\
&= \frac{\sigma_x + \sigma_y}{2} + \frac{\sigma_x - \sigma_y}{2} \cos 2\theta + \tau \sin 2\theta = \sigma_\theta
\end{aligned}$$

$$\begin{aligned}
CD = R \sin (2\theta - \beta) &= R \sin 2\theta \cos \beta - R \cos 2\theta \sin \beta \\
&= \frac{\sigma_x - \sigma_y}{2} \sin 2\theta - \tau \cos 2\theta = \tau_\theta
\end{aligned}$$

12.7 Combined bending and twisting. A common application of combined stresses is that of a shaft subjected to bending and twisting and it is often convenient to express the resulting direct and shear stresses directly in terms of the applied moment and torque.

If the bending moment is M and the torque is T, Fig. 12.14(a), then the

FIG. 12.14

stresses acting on an element on the upper surface are as shown in the plan view, Fig. 12.14(b) (those on the lower surface are the same, except that σ_x is compressive).

From equations (3.4) and (4.2),

$$\sigma_x = \frac{M}{\frac{\pi}{32} d^3} \quad \text{and} \quad \tau = \frac{T}{\frac{\pi}{16} d^3}, \text{ assuming a solid shaft.*}$$

* For a hollow shaft of outer and inner diameters D and d respectively, equations (12.21) and (12.23) become

$$\frac{\pi}{32} \frac{D^4 - d^4}{D} \sigma_1 = \tfrac{1}{2}\{M + \sqrt{M^2 + T^2}\} \text{ and } \frac{\pi}{16} \frac{D^4 - d^4}{D} \tau_{max} = \sqrt{M^2 + T^2}$$

Equations (12.22) and (12.24) are unaffected.

Thus the maximum principal stress, σ_1, is given by

$$\sigma_1 = \tfrac{1}{2}\{\sigma_x + \sqrt{\sigma_x^2 + 4\tau^2}\}$$

$$= \frac{1}{2}\left\{\frac{M}{\dfrac{\pi}{32}d^3} + \sqrt{\left(\frac{M}{\dfrac{\pi}{32}d^3}\right)^2 + 4\left(\frac{T}{\dfrac{\pi}{16}d^3}\right)^2}\right\}$$

i.e. $$\frac{\pi}{32}d^3\sigma_1 = \tfrac{1}{2}\{M + \sqrt{M^2 + T^2}\} \quad . \qquad . \qquad . \qquad . \qquad (12.21)$$

The quantity $\dfrac{\pi}{32}d^3\sigma_1$ is evidently the equivalent bending moment, i.e. that bending moment which, acting alone, would produce the same maximum direct stress as M and T acting together,

i.e. $$M_e = \tfrac{1}{2}\{M + \sqrt{M^2 + T}\} \qquad . \qquad . \qquad (12.22)$$

$$\tau_{max} = \tfrac{1}{2}\sqrt{\sigma_x^2 + 4\tau^2} \quad . \qquad . \quad \text{from equation (12.20)}$$

$$= \frac{1}{2}\sqrt{\left(\frac{M}{\dfrac{\pi}{32}d^3}\right)^2 + 4\left(\frac{T}{\dfrac{\pi}{16}d^3}\right)^2}$$

i.e. $$\frac{\pi}{16}d^3\tau_{max.} = \sqrt{M^2 + T^2} \quad . \qquad . \qquad . \qquad . \qquad (12.23)$$

The quantity $\dfrac{\pi}{16}d^3\tau_{max.}$ is evidently the equivalent torque, i.e. that torque which, acting alone, would produce the same maximum shear stress as M and T acting together,

i.e. $$T_e = \sqrt{M^2 + T^2} \qquad . \qquad . \qquad . \qquad (12.24)$$

12.8 Principal strains. The principal strains are the strains in the direction of the principal stresses. If the principal stresses on an element are σ_x and σ_y, Fig. 12.15,

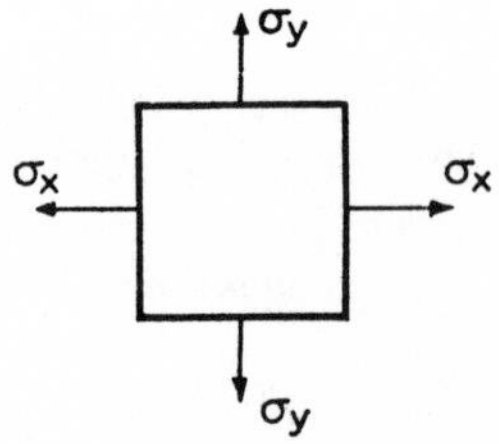

FIG. 12.15

then strain in direction of σ_x due to $\sigma_x = \dfrac{\sigma_x}{E}$

and strain in direction of σ_x due to $\sigma_y = -\nu\dfrac{\sigma_y}{E}$

$\therefore$ resultant strain in x direction, $\varepsilon_x = \dfrac{\sigma_x}{E} - \nu\dfrac{\sigma_y}{E}$ (12.25)

Similarly,   resultant strain in y direction, $\varepsilon_y = \dfrac{\sigma_y}{E} - \nu\dfrac{\sigma_x}{E}$ (12.26)

If these strains are measured and it is required to find the corresponding stresses, then, multiplying equation (12.26) by ν and adding to equation (12.25),

$$\varepsilon_x + \nu\varepsilon_y = \frac{\sigma_x}{E}(1 - \nu^2)$$

$$\therefore \; \sigma_x = \frac{E}{1 - \nu^2}(\varepsilon_x + \nu\varepsilon_y) \quad . \quad . \quad (12.27)$$

Similarly,
$$\sigma_y = \frac{E}{1 - \nu^2}(\varepsilon_y + \nu\varepsilon_x) \quad . \quad . \quad (12.28)$$

12.9 Strains on an oblique section. Fig. 12.16 shows an element ABCD which is subjected to pure strains ε_x and ε_y, the distorted shape relative to the point F being shown dotted. The line FG, inclined at θ to AB moves to the position FG′, the displacements of G in the x and y directions being dx and dy respectively.

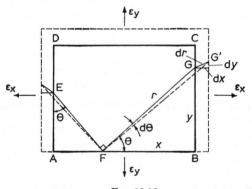

Fɪɢ. 12.16

Since the movement of G is very small, the distance GG′ may be regarded as the change in the length of FG, so that the strain on FG,

$$\varepsilon_\theta = \frac{\mathrm{d}r}{r}$$

$$r^2 = x^2 + y^2$$
$$\therefore \; 2r\,\mathrm{d}r = 2x\,\mathrm{d}x + 2y\,\mathrm{d}y$$
$$\therefore \; \frac{\mathrm{d}r}{r} = \frac{\mathrm{d}x}{x}\left(\frac{x}{r}\right)^2 + \frac{\mathrm{d}y}{y}\left(\frac{y}{r}\right)^2$$

i.e.
$$\varepsilon_\theta = \varepsilon_x \cos^2\theta + \varepsilon_y \sin^2\theta$$

$$= \frac{\varepsilon_x + \varepsilon_y}{2} + \frac{\varepsilon_x - \varepsilon_y}{2}\cos 2\theta \quad . \quad (12.29)$$

Similarly, it can be shown that the strain on FE is

$$\frac{\varepsilon_x + \varepsilon_y}{2} - \frac{\varepsilon_x - \varepsilon_y}{2} \cos 2\theta$$

$$\tan \theta = \frac{y}{x}$$

$$\therefore \sec^2 \theta \, d\theta = \frac{x \, dy - y \, dx}{x^2}$$

$$= \frac{dy}{y} \cdot \frac{y}{x} - \frac{dx}{x} \cdot \frac{y}{x}$$

$$= (\varepsilon_y - \varepsilon_x) \tan \theta$$

$$\therefore d\theta = (\varepsilon_y - \varepsilon_x) \sin \theta \cos \theta$$

$$= -\frac{\varepsilon_x - \varepsilon_y}{2} \sin 2\theta$$

The negative sign indicates that when $\varepsilon_x > \varepsilon_y$, as assumed in Fig. 12.16, the angle θ *decreases*.

A similar analysis on the triangle AFE shows that FE also rotates through the same angle as FG, so that the total change in the right angle EFG is $2 \, d\theta$. This is the shear strain in directions inclined at angle θ to the faces of ABCD,

i.e. $$\phi_\theta = (\varepsilon_x - \varepsilon_y) \sin 2\theta \quad . \qquad . \qquad . \qquad (12.30)$$

Equations (12.29) and (12.30) are similar to equations (12.3) and (12.4) and they can therefore be represented by a similar graphical construction. Fig. 12.17 shows Mohr's strain circle, in which OA represents ε_x, OB represents ε_y and the angle AQC is 2θ. Then OD and CD represent respectively ε_θ and $\phi_\theta/2$.

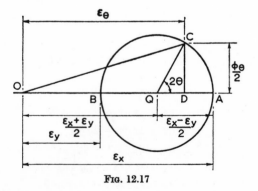

Fig. 12.17

12.10 Electric resistance strain gauges. The strain on the surface of a stressed body is usually determined by an electric resistance strain gauge, which consists of a piece of fine wire, bent as shown in Fig. 12.18 and firmly fixed to a paper backing. The gauge is cemented to the surface to be investigated and distortion of the body in the direction of the axis of the gauge then produces corresponding distortion in the length and cross-section of the wire, which affects its electrical resistance.

This change is registered by a Wheatstone Bridge arrangement, Fig. 12.19; a 'dummy' gauge, identical with the 'active' gauge, is attached to a piece of the same material and kept in close proximity with the body under test so that the effect of changes of resistance due to temperature variation are eliminated.

The active and dummy gauges are represented by resistances R_2 and R_3 respectively, R_1 is a variable resistance and R_4 is a fixed resistance. When the active gauge is unstrained and no current is passing through the galvanometer, R_1 is equal to R_4.

When the active gauge is strained, the galvanometer is balanced by means of the variable resistance and then

$$\frac{R_2}{R_3} = \frac{R_1}{R_4}$$

or
$$\frac{R_2 - R_3}{R_3} = \frac{R_1 - R_4}{R_4} \qquad . \qquad . \qquad . \qquad (12.31)$$

i.e. fractional change in gauge resistance = fractional change in R_1.

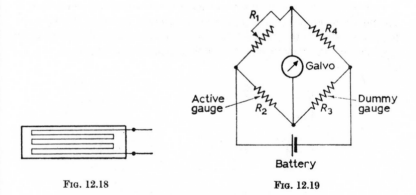

FIG. 12.18   FIG. 12.19

The ratio $\dfrac{\text{fractional change in gauge resistance}}{\text{fractional change in length of wire}}$ is called the *gauge factor*.

If R is the resistance of the wire, l is its length, d is its diameter and ρ is the specific resistance of the material, then

$$R = \rho \frac{l}{a} = \frac{4}{\pi} \frac{\rho l}{d^2}$$

$$\therefore \log R = \log \frac{4}{\pi} + \log \rho + \log l - 2 \log d$$

$$\therefore \frac{\mathrm{d}R}{R} = \frac{\mathrm{d}\rho}{\rho} + \frac{\mathrm{d}l}{l} - 2\frac{\mathrm{d}d}{d}$$

But
$$\frac{\mathrm{d}d}{d} = -\nu\frac{\mathrm{d}l}{l}$$

$$\therefore \frac{\mathrm{d}R}{R} = \frac{\mathrm{d}\rho}{\rho} + \frac{\mathrm{d}l}{l}(1 + 2\nu)$$

Therefore the gauge factor,

$$\frac{\mathrm{d}R}{R} \bigg/ \frac{\mathrm{d}l}{l} = (1 + 2\nu) + \frac{\mathrm{d}\rho}{\rho} \bigg/ \frac{\mathrm{d}l}{l} \qquad . \qquad . \qquad . \qquad (12.32)$$

If ρ is a constant, the gauge factor is $(1 + 2\nu)$ but by experimental calibration, it is usually about 30 per cent greater, implying that ρ changes.

12.11 Determination of principal strains. From equations (12.29),

$$\varepsilon = \frac{\varepsilon_x + \varepsilon_y}{2} + \frac{\varepsilon_x - \varepsilon_y}{2}\cos 2\theta$$

$$= m + n\cos 2\theta \quad \text{where} \quad m = \frac{\varepsilon_x + \varepsilon_y}{2} \quad \text{and} \quad n = \frac{\varepsilon_x - \varepsilon_y}{2}$$

Thus, to determine the magnitude and direction of the principal strains (i.e. ε_x, ε_y and θ), it is necessary to have three values of ε, measured in different directions. This is achieved in practice by using three strain gauges stuck on to the surface to be investigated and Figs. 12.20(a) and (b) show two common arrangements, referred to as *strain rosettes*.

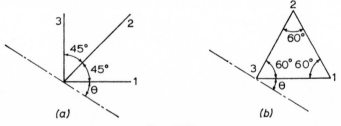

(a)   (b)

FIG. 12.20

Fig. 12.20(a) is a 45° rosette. If one of the principal planes is inclined at θ to the axis of gauge 1, then

$$\varepsilon_1 = m + n\cos 2\theta \qquad . \qquad . \qquad . \qquad . \qquad . \qquad (12.33)$$

$$\varepsilon_2 = m + n\cos 2(\theta + 45°) = m - n\sin 2\theta \qquad . \qquad (12.34)$$

and
$$\varepsilon_3 = m + n\cos 2(\theta + 90°) = m - n\cos 2\theta \qquad . \qquad (12.35)$$

Fig. 12.20(*b*) is a 120° rosette. If one of the principal planes is inclined at θ to the axis of gauge 1, then

$$\varepsilon_1 = m + n \cos 2\theta \quad . \quad . \quad . \quad . \quad . \quad . \quad . \quad (12.36)$$

$$\varepsilon_2 = m + n \cos 2(\theta + 120°) = m - \frac{n}{2} \cos 2\theta + \frac{\sqrt{3}n}{2} \sin 2\theta \quad (12.37)$$

and $\quad \varepsilon_3 = m + n \cos 2(\theta + 240°) = m - \frac{n}{2} \cos 2\theta - \frac{\sqrt{3}n}{2} \sin 2\theta \quad (12.38)$

In each case, the equations obtained are sufficient to determine *m*, *n* and θ; then $\varepsilon_x = m + n$ and $\varepsilon_y = m - n$.

1. *A cylindrical vessel, 300 mm external diameter, wall thickness 3 mm, is subjected to an axial tensile force of 100 kN and an internal pressure of 3·5 MN/m². Determine the normal and shear stresses on a plane making an angle of 30° with the axis of the cylinder.* (U. Lond.)

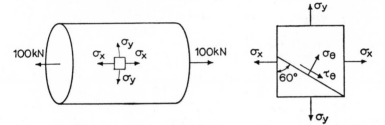

FIG. 12.21

From equations (1.7) and (1.9),

$$\sigma_c = \frac{pd}{2t} \quad \text{and} \quad \sigma_l = \frac{pd}{4t}, \text{ where } d \text{ is the internal diameter}$$

The longitudinal stress due to the axial load is given by

$$\sigma = \frac{P}{\pi Dt}, \text{ where } D \text{ is the mean diameter}$$

Thus, in Fig. 12.21,

$$\sigma_x = \frac{3 \cdot 5 \times 10^6 \times 0 \cdot 294}{4 \times 0 \cdot 003} + \frac{100 \times 10^3}{\pi \times 0 \cdot 297 \times 0 \cdot 003} \text{ N/m}^2 = 121 \cdot 5 \text{ MN/m}^2$$

and $\qquad \sigma_y = \dfrac{3 \cdot 5 \times 10^6 \times 0 \cdot 294}{2 \times 0 \cdot 003} \text{ N/m}^2 = 171 \cdot 5 \text{ MN/m}^2$

Therefore, from equations (12.3) and (12.4),

$$\sigma_\theta = \frac{121 \cdot 5 + 171 \cdot 5}{2} + \frac{121 \cdot 5 - 171 \cdot 5}{2} \cos 120° = \underline{159 \text{ MN/m}^2}$$

and $\qquad \tau_\theta = \dfrac{121 \cdot 5 - 171 \cdot 5}{2} \sin 120° = \underline{-21 \cdot 7 \text{ MN/m}^2}$

I

2. *At a point in the cross-section of a loaded beam, the major principal stress is 140 N/mm² tension and the maximum shear stress is 80 N/mm². Using either graphical or analytical methods, determine for this point, (a) the magnitude of the minor principal stress, (b) the magnitude of the direct stress on the plane of maximum shear stress, (c) the state of stress on a plane making an angle of 30° with the plane of the major principal tensile stress.* (I.C.E.)

$$\tau_{max} = \frac{\sigma_x - \sigma_y}{2}, \qquad \text{from equation (12.4)}$$

i.e. $\qquad 80 = \dfrac{140 - \sigma_y}{2} \quad \therefore \sigma_y = \underline{-20 \text{ N/mm}^2}$ (i.e. compressive)

For maximum shear, $\theta = 45°$, Fig. 12.22.

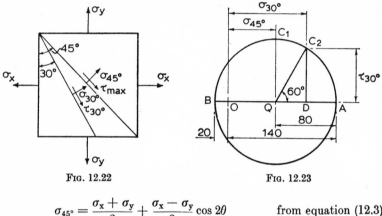

FIG. 12.22   FIG. 12.23

$$\sigma_{45°} = \frac{\sigma_x + \sigma_y}{2} + \frac{\sigma_x - \sigma_y}{2} \cos 2\theta \qquad \text{from equation (12.3)}$$

$$= \frac{140 - 20}{2} = \underline{60 \text{ N/mm}^2}$$

When $\qquad \theta = 30°$,

$$\sigma_{30°} = \frac{140 - 20}{2} + \frac{140 + 20}{2} \cos 60° = \underline{100 \text{ N/mm}^2}$$

$$\tau_{30°} = \frac{140 + 20}{2} \sin 60° = \underline{69 \cdot 3 \text{ N/mm}^2}$$

Graphical Solution

Set off OA = 140 N/mm², Fig. 12.23.

The maximum shear stress, $\dfrac{\sigma_x - \sigma_y}{2}$, is the radius of the circle,

i.e. $\qquad\qquad\qquad$ QA = 80 N/mm².

Then minor principal stress, $\sigma_y = OB$

$$= 20 \text{ N/mm}^2 \; (-\text{ve})$$

Set off $\qquad QC_1 = 2 \times 45° = 90°$

and $\qquad QC_2 = 2 \times 30° = 60°$

Then $\qquad \sigma_{45°} = OQ = 60 \text{ N/mm}^2$

$$\sigma_{30°} = OD = 100 \text{ N/mm}^2$$

and $\qquad \tau_{30°} = C_2D = 69\cdot3 \text{ N/mm}^2$

3. *At a point in a stressed material, the normal (tensile) and shear stresses on a certain plane XX are 95 N/mm² and 65 N/mm² respectively. The tensile stress on the plane of maximum shear is 55 N/mm².*

Find (a) the principal stresses, (b) the maximum shear stress, (c) the direction of the plane XX relative to the plane on which the major principal stress acts.

Illustrate your answer to (c) by a sketch. (U. Lond.)

From equation (12.3),

$$\sigma_\theta = \frac{\sigma_x + \sigma_y}{2} + \frac{\sigma_x - \sigma_y}{2} \cos 2\theta$$

and from equation (12.4)

$$\tau_\theta = \frac{\sigma_x - \sigma_y}{2} \sin 2\theta$$

Let $\qquad m = \dfrac{\sigma_x + \sigma_y}{2}$ and $n = \dfrac{\sigma_x - \sigma_y}{2}$

Then $\quad 95 = m + n \cos 2\theta$. (1)

$\qquad 65 = n \sin 2\theta$ . . (2)

and $\quad 55 = m + n \cos 2 \times 45°$

$$= m \quad . \quad . \quad . \quad (3)$$

$\therefore n \cos 2\theta = 40$

$\quad \therefore n = \sqrt{65^2 + 40^2} = 76\cdot3$

$\quad \therefore \sigma_x = m + n$

$$= \underline{131\cdot3 \text{ N/mm}^2}$$

and $\quad \sigma_y = m - n$

$$= \underline{-21\cdot3 \text{ N/mm}^2}$$

$\tan 2\theta = \dfrac{65}{40} \qquad = 1\cdot625$

$\therefore 2\theta = 58° 24' \; \therefore \theta = \underline{29° 12'}$

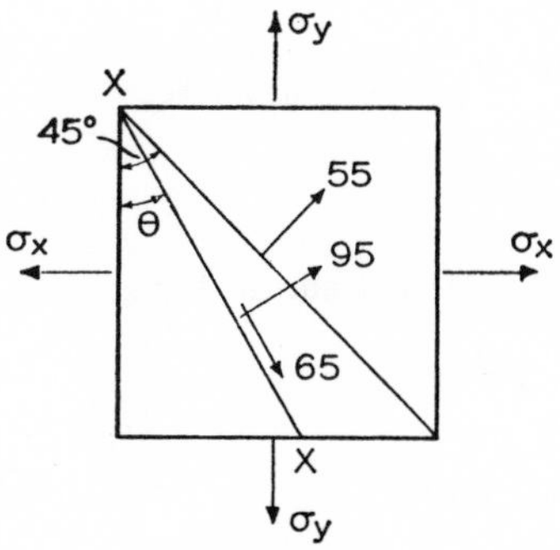

Fig. 12.24

The position of XX in relation to σ_x is shown in Fig. 12.24.

NOTE. If n is taken as the negative root, $\sigma_x = -21\cdot3$ and $\sigma_y = 131\cdot3$ N/mm². Sin 2θ and cos 2θ are then both negative, so that 2θ lies in the third quadrant. Thus $\theta = 119° 12'$ and Fig. 12.24 merely becomes turned anticlockwise through 90°.

4. *A thin cylindrical tube, 75 mm internal diameter and wall thickness 5 mm, is closed at the ends and subjected to an internal pressure of 5·5 MN/m². A torque of 1·6 kNm is also applied to the tube. Determine the maximum and minimum principal stresses and also the maximum shearing stress in the wall of the tube.* (U. Lond.)

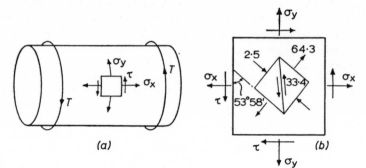

FIG. 12.25

Referring to Fig. 12.25,

$$\sigma_x = \frac{pd}{4t} = \frac{5\cdot5 \times 10^6 \times 0\cdot075}{4 \times 0\cdot005} \text{ N/m}^2 = 20\cdot6 \text{ MN/m}^2$$

$$\sigma_y = \frac{pd}{2t} = 41\cdot2 \text{ MN/m}^2$$

Since the tube is thin,

$$\text{mean shear stress} = \frac{\text{torque}}{\text{mean radius} \times \text{cross-sectional area}}$$

i.e
$$\tau = \frac{1\cdot6 \times 10^3}{0\cdot04 \times \pi \times 0\cdot08 \times 0\cdot005} = 31\cdot8 \text{ MN/m}^2$$

Therefore, from Art. 12.4

$$\sigma = \tfrac{1}{2}\{(\sigma_x + \sigma_y) \pm \sqrt{(\sigma_x - \sigma_y)^2 + 4\tau^2}\}$$
$$= \tfrac{1}{2}\{(20\cdot6 + 41\cdot2) \pm \sqrt{(20\cdot6 - 41\cdot2)^2 + 4 \times 31\cdot8^2}\}$$
$$= \underline{64\cdot3 \quad \text{and} \quad -2\cdot5 \text{ MN/m}^2}$$

$$2\theta = \tan^{-1}\frac{2\tau}{\sigma_x - \sigma_y} = \tan^{-1}\frac{2 \times 31\cdot8}{20\cdot6 - 41\cdot2} = 180° - 72° \, 4' \text{ and } 360° - 72° \, 4'$$

$$\therefore \theta = \underline{53° \, 58' \quad \text{and} \quad 143° \, 58'}$$

$$\tau_{max} = \frac{\sigma_1 - \sigma_2}{2} = \frac{64\cdot3 - (-2\cdot5)}{2}$$

$$= \underline{33\cdot4 \text{ MN/m}^2} \text{ acting on planes at 45° to the principal planes.}$$

The relation of the derived stresses to the applied stresses is shown in Fig. 12.25(*b*).

5. *A right-angled triangle ABC with the right-angle at C represents planes in an elastic material. There are shearing stresses of 45 N/mm² acting along the planes AC and CB towards C, and normal tensile stresses on AC and CB of 75 N/mm² and 60 N/mm² respectively. There is no stress on the plane perpendicular to planes AC and CB.*

Determine the positions of the plane AB when the resultant stress on AB has (a) the greatest magnitude, (b) the least magnitude, (c) the greatest component normal to AB, (d) the greatest tangential component along AB, (e) the least inclination to AB.

Analytical or graphical methods may be used; in the case of a graphical solution, indicate how the diagrams are constructed. State for each plane found, its angular position relative to AC and the magnitude of the stress referred to.

(U. Lond.)

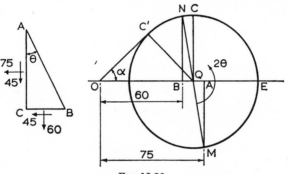

Fig. 12.26

From Art. 12.6, OA = 75 N/mm², OB = 60 N/mm², AM = BN = 45 N/mm², Fig. 12.26. The circle is then drawn with MN as diameter.

(a)   Maximum resultant stress = maximum principal stress,
$$OE = \underline{113 \cdot 2 \ N/mm^2}$$

Angle MQE = 80° 30′
$$\therefore \theta = \underline{40° \ 15'}$$

(b)   Minimum resultant stress = minimum principal stress,
$$OF = \underline{21 \cdot 9 \ N/mm^2}$$

Angle MQF = 260° 30′
$$\therefore \theta = \underline{130° \ 15'}$$

(c)   Greatest component stress on AB = maximum principal stress
$$= \underline{113 \cdot 2 \ N/mm^2}$$

(d)   Maximum shear stress = QC = $\underline{45 \cdot 6 \ N/mm^2}$

Angle MQC = 170° 30′
$$\therefore \theta = \underline{85° \ 15'}$$

(e) For the least inclination to AB, α is a maximum; this occurs when the resultant stress is tangential to the circle.

Resultant stress $= OC' = \underline{81{\cdot}4 \ N/mm^2}$.

Angle $MQC' = 213° \ \therefore \ \theta = \underline{106° \ 30'}$.

6. *At a point on the surface of a solid circular shaft of 150 mm diameter subjected to combined bending and torsion, the principal stresses are 120 MN/m^2 tension and 40 MN/m^2 compression. Find the bending moment and torque.*

If the maximum shearing stress in the material is limited to 100 MN/m^2, find by how much the torque can be increased, the bending moment remaining constant.   (U. Lond.)

From equation (12.21), $\dfrac{\pi}{32} d^3 \sigma = \tfrac{1}{2}\{M \pm \sqrt{M^2 + T^2}\}$

i.e. $\dfrac{\pi}{32} \times 0{\cdot}15^3 \times 120 \times 10^6 = \tfrac{1}{2}\{M + \sqrt{M^2 + T^2}\}$

and $-\dfrac{\pi}{32} \times 0{\cdot}15^3 \times 40 \times 10^6 = \tfrac{1}{2}\{M - \sqrt{M^2 + T^2}\}$

$$\therefore \ M = \underline{26{\cdot}5 \ kN \ m} \quad \text{and} \quad T = \underline{46 \ kN \ m}$$

From equation (12.23), $\dfrac{\pi}{16} d^3 \tau = \sqrt{M^2 + T^2}$

i.e. $\dfrac{\pi}{16} \times 0{\cdot}15^3 \times 100 \times 10^6 = \sqrt{(26{\cdot}5 \times 10^3)^2 + T^2} \ \text{N m}$

from which $T = 60{\cdot}8 \ kN \ m$

$$\therefore \ \text{increase in torque} = 60{\cdot}8 - 46 = \underline{14{\cdot}8 \ kN \ m}$$

7. *A propeller shaft of a ship is 0·45 m diameter and it supports a propeller of mass 15 t. The propeller can be considered as a load concentrated at the end of a cantilever of length 2 m. The propeller is driven at 100 rev/min when the speed of the ship is 32 km/h. If the engine develops 15 MW, calculate the principal stresses in the shaft and the maximum shear stress. It may be assumed that the propulsive efficiency of the propeller is 85 per cent.*   (I.Mech.E.)

At the bearing, Fig. 12.27(a),

$$M = 15 \times 10^3 \times 9{\cdot}81 \times 2 \ \text{N m} \qquad = 294{\cdot}3 \ kN \ m$$

$$T = \frac{\text{power}}{2\pi N/60} = \frac{15 \times 10^6 \times 60}{2\pi \times 100} \ \text{N m} = 1{\cdot}433 \ MN \ m$$

Engine power $= \dfrac{Pv}{\eta}$, where P is the propulsive force

$$\therefore \ P = \frac{15 \times 10^6 \times 0{\cdot}85 \times 3\ 600}{32 \times 10^3} \ \text{N} \qquad = 1{\cdot}435 \ MN$$

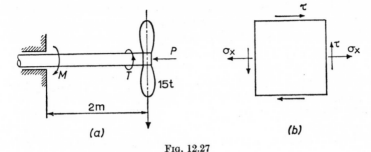

FIG. 12.27

Direct stress due to bending

$$= M \Big/ \frac{\pi d^3}{32}$$

$$= \frac{294 \cdot 3 \times 10^3 \times 32}{\pi \times 0 \cdot 45^3} \text{ N/m}^2 \qquad = 32 \cdot 9 \text{ MN/m}^2$$

Direct stress due to end thrust

$$= P \Big/ \frac{\pi}{4} d^2$$

$$= \frac{1 \cdot 435 \times 10^6 \times 4}{\pi \times 0 \cdot 45^2} \text{ N/m}^2 \qquad = 9 \cdot 02 \text{ MN/m}^2$$

∴ total direct stress,*

$$\sigma_x = 32 \cdot 9 + 9 \cdot 02 \qquad = 41 \cdot 92 \text{ MN/m}^2$$

Shear stress due to torque,

$$\tau = T \Big/ \frac{\pi}{16} d^3$$

$$= \frac{1 \cdot 433 \times 10^6 \times 16}{\pi \times 0 \cdot 45^3} \text{ N/m}^2 \qquad = 80 \text{ MN/m}^2$$

The stresses on an element on the upper surface of the shaft at the bearing are therefore as shown in Fig. 12.27(b), these being the greatest applied stresses in the shaft.

From equation (12.18),

$$\sigma = \tfrac{1}{2}\{\sigma_x \pm \sqrt{\sigma_x^2 + 4\tau^2}\}$$

$$= \tfrac{1}{2}\{41 \cdot 92 \pm \sqrt{41 \cdot 92^2 + 4 \times 80^2}\}$$

$$= \underline{103 \cdot 7 \quad \text{and} \quad -61 \cdot 8 \text{ MN/m}^2}$$

$$\tau_{\max} = \frac{\sigma_1 - \sigma_2}{2} = \frac{103 \cdot 7 - (-61 \cdot 8)}{2}$$

$$= \underline{82 \cdot 75 \text{ MN/m}^2}$$

* Note that these stresses act in the *same* direction and do *not* represent σ_x and σ_y.

8. *At a point in a piece of stressed material, the normal stress on a certain plane is 90 N/mm² tension and the shearing stress on this plane is 30 N/mm². On a plane inclined at 60° to the first-named plane, there is a tensile stress of 60 N/mm².*

Calculate (a) the principal stresses at the point, (b) the intensity of shearing stress on the plane having the 60 N/mm² normal stress, (c) the position of the principal planes relative to the given planes, and show the relative positions in a clear diagram.   (U. Lond.)

As in Example 3,

$$\sigma_\theta = m + n \cos 2\theta$$

and

$$\tau_\theta = n \sin 2\theta$$

where

$$m = \frac{\sigma_x + \sigma_y}{2} \quad \text{and} \quad n = \frac{\sigma_x - \sigma_y}{2}$$

$$\therefore\ 90 = m + n \cos 2\theta \quad . \quad . \quad . \quad . \quad . \quad (1)$$

$$30 = n \sin 2\theta \quad . \quad . \quad . \quad . \quad . \quad . \quad (2)$$

and

$$60 = m + n \cos 2(\theta + 60°)$$

$$= m - n\left(\frac{1}{2} \cos 2\theta + \frac{\sqrt{3}}{2} \sin 2\theta\right)$$

i.e.

$$120 = 2m - n \cos 2\theta - \sqrt{3}n \sin 2\theta . \quad . \quad . \quad (3)$$

From equations (1), (2) and (3),

$$m = 87{\cdot}32 \text{ N/mm}^2$$
$$n = 30{\cdot}12 \text{ N/mm}^2$$

and $\theta = 42° 27'$

from which

$$\sigma_x = \underline{117{\cdot}44 \text{ N/mm}^2}$$

and

$$\sigma_y = \underline{57{\cdot}14 \text{ N/mm}^2}$$

On the plane of the 60 N/mm² normal stress,

$$\tau = 30{\cdot}12 \sin 2(42° 27' + 60°)$$
$$= \underline{-12{\cdot}68 \text{ N/mm}^2}$$

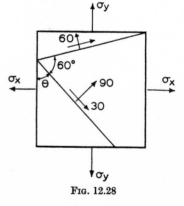

FIG. 12.28

The positions of the various planes are shown in Fig. 12.28. The negative sign for τ indicates that this stress is in the opposite direction to that shown in the diagram.

9. *At a point in a material under two-dimensional stress, the normal stresses, all tensile, on three planes are as follows:*

Plane	Inclination to plane A	Stress (N/mm²)
A	0°	97
B	45°	133
C	90°	27

Find (a) the shearing stresses on planes A, B and C, (b) the principal stresses and the inclination to plane A of the planes on which they act, (c) the maximum shearing stress, (d) the inclination to plane A of the plane on which the normal stress is zero.

Show by a sketch the relative positions of the various planes. (U. Lond.)

As in Example 3, $\sigma_\theta = m + n \cos 2\theta$

where $\qquad m = \dfrac{\sigma_x + \sigma_y}{2}$ and $n = \dfrac{\sigma_x - \sigma_y}{2}$

$$\therefore 97 = m + n \cos 2\theta \qquad . \qquad . \qquad . \qquad . \qquad . \qquad (1)$$

$$133 = m + n \cos 2(\theta + 45°) = m - n \sin 2\theta \quad . \quad (2)$$

and $\qquad 27 = m + n \cos 2(\theta + 90°) = m - n \cos 2\theta \quad . \quad (3)$

Adding (1) and (3), $2m = 124$

or $\qquad\qquad m = 62$

$$\therefore n \sin 2\theta = -71$$

and $\qquad n \cos 2\theta = 35$

$$\therefore n = \sqrt{71^2 + 35^2} = 79 \cdot 2, \text{ assuming the positive root*}$$
$$\therefore \sigma_x = 62 + 79 \cdot 2 \quad = 141 \cdot 2 \text{ N/mm}^2$$

and $\qquad\qquad \sigma_y = 62 - 79 \cdot 2 \quad = -17 \cdot 2 \text{ N/mm}^2$

$$\tan 2\theta = \frac{-71}{35} \qquad = -2 \cdot 028$$

Since n has been assumed positive, $\sin 2\theta$ is negative and $\cos 2\theta$ is positive, hence 2θ lies in the 4th quadrant.

$$\therefore 2\theta = 360 - 63° \, 46' = 296° \, 14'$$

or $\qquad\qquad \theta = \underline{148° \, 7'}$

$$\tau = n \sin 2\theta$$

When $\theta = 148° \, 7' \quad \tau = 79 \cdot 2 \sin 296° \, 14' = \underline{-71 \text{ N/mm}^2}$

When $\theta = 193° \, 7' \quad \tau = 79 \cdot 2 \sin 386° \, 14' = \underline{35 \text{ N/mm}^2}$

When $\theta = 238° \, 7', \quad \tau = 79 \cdot 2 \sin 476° \, 14' = \underline{71 \text{ N/mm}^2}$

* If n is assumed negative, σ_x and σ_y are interchanged. Sin 2θ becomes positive and cos 2θ negative, so that 2θ lies in the 2nd quadrant, giving $\theta = 58° \, 7'$. Thus the stresses on any given plane are unaffected and the notation merely becomes altered, σ_x being associated with θ and σ_y with $\theta \pm 90°$ in either case.

$$\tau_{\text{max}} = \underline{79 \cdot 2 \text{ N/mm}^2}$$

When $\sigma_\theta = 0$, $62 + 79 \cdot 2 \cos 2\theta = 0$

from which $\theta = \underline{90° \pm 19° \ 14'}$

The relative positions of the various planes are as shown in Fig. 12.29.

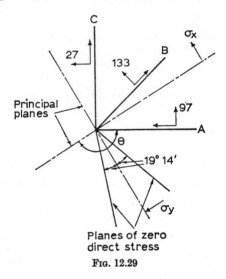

Fig. 12.29

10. *In order to determine the principal stresses at a point is a structural member, two strain gauges are fixed, their directions being at 30° to the known directions of the principal stresses. The measured strains in these two directions are $+455 \times 10^{-6}$ and -32×10^{-6} respectively. If $E = 200 \ GN/m^2$ and $v = 0 \cdot 3$, find the magnitudes of the principal stresses.* (U. Lond.)

From equation (12.29),

$$\varepsilon_\theta = \frac{\varepsilon_x + \varepsilon_y}{2} + \frac{\varepsilon_x - \varepsilon_y}{2} \cos 2\theta$$

$$= m + n \cos 2\theta$$

where $m = \dfrac{\varepsilon_x + \varepsilon_y}{2}$ and $n = \dfrac{\varepsilon_x - \varepsilon_y}{2}$

$\therefore +455 \times 10^{-6} = m + n \cos 60° \quad = m + \dfrac{n}{2}$

and $-32 \times 10^{-6} = m + n \cos 240° \quad = m - \dfrac{n}{2}$

$\therefore m = 211 \cdot 5 \times 10^{-6}$ and $n = 487 \times 10^{-6}$

$\therefore \varepsilon_x = 698 \cdot 5 \times 10^{-6}$ and $\varepsilon_y = -275 \cdot 5 \times 10^{-6}$

$$\therefore \sigma_x = \frac{E}{1 - v^2}(\varepsilon_x + v\varepsilon_y) \quad . \quad \text{from equation (12.27)}$$

$$= \frac{200 \times 10^9}{1 - 0.3^2}(698.5 - 0.3 \times 275.5) \times 10^{-6} \text{ N/m}^2$$

$$= 135.5 \text{ MN/m}^2$$

$$\sigma_y = \frac{E}{1 - v^2}(\varepsilon_y + v\varepsilon_x)$$

$$= \frac{200 \times 10^9}{1 - 0.3^2}(-275.5 + 0.3 \times 698.5) \times 10^{-6} \text{ N/m}^2$$

$$= -14.45 \text{ MN/m}^2 \text{ (i.e. compressive).}$$

The positions of the gauges relative to the principal planes are shown in Fig. 12.30.

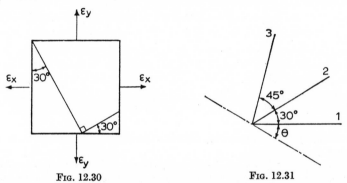

FIG. 12.30   FIG. 12.31

11. *In a strain rosette experiment, the three strain gauge measurements taken over a small area were:* $\varepsilon_{0°} = 400 \times 10^{-6}$, $\varepsilon_{30°} = 150 \times 10^{-6}$, $\varepsilon_{75°} = -40 \times 10^{-6}$.

What reading would have been recorded had a strain gauge been placed at 45° to the 0° line?

The positions of the gauges are shown in Fig. 12.31   .   .

As in Example 10, $\varepsilon_\theta = m + n \cos 2\theta$

where $m = \dfrac{\varepsilon_x + \varepsilon_y}{2}$ and $n = \dfrac{\varepsilon_x - \varepsilon_y}{2}$

$$\therefore 400 \times 10^{-6} = m + n \cos 2\theta \quad . \qquad . \qquad . \qquad (1)$$

$$150 \times 10^{-6} = m + n \cos 2(\theta + 30°)$$

$$= m + \frac{n}{2}(\cos 2\theta - \sqrt{3} \sin 2\theta) \quad . \qquad (2)$$

$$-40 \times 10^{-6} = m + n \cos 2(\theta + 75°)$$

$$= m - \frac{n}{2}(\sqrt{3} \cos 2\theta + \sin 2\theta) \quad . \qquad (3)$$

Multiplying equation (3) by $\sqrt{3}$ and subtracting from equation (2),

$$219 \cdot 25 \times 10^{-6} = -0 \cdot 732m + 2n \cos 2\theta \quad . \quad . \quad (4)$$

Subtracting equation (4) from equation (1) multiplied by 2,

$$580 \cdot 75 \times 10^{-6} = 2 \cdot 732m \quad \therefore \ m = 213 \times 10^{-6}$$

Therefore equations (2) and (3) reduce to

$$n(\cos 2\theta - \sqrt{3} \sin 2\theta) = -125 \times 10^{-6}$$

and $\ n(\sqrt{3} \cos 2\theta + \sin 2\theta) = 505 \times 10^{-6}$

Squaring both sides and adding,

$$n^2 \times 4 = 270{,}625 \times 10^{-12} \quad \therefore \ n = 260 \times 10^{-6}$$

Therefore equation (1) becomes

$$400 \times 10^{-6} = 213 \times 10^{-6} + 260 \times 10^{-6} \cos 2\theta$$

from which $\qquad\qquad 2\theta = 44°$

$$\therefore \ \varepsilon_{45°} = 213 \times 10^{-6} + 260 \times 10^{-6} \cos (44° + 90°)$$
$$= \underline{32 \times 10^{-6}}$$

12. *A closed-ended steel pressure vessel of 2·5 m diameter and a plate thickness of 20 mm has electric resistance strain gauges on the outer surface in the circumferential and axial directions. These gauges have a resistance of 200 ohms and a gauge factor of 2·09. When the pressure is raised to 10 MN/m², the change of resistance is 1·065 ohms for the circumferential gauge and 0·265 ohms for the axial gauge.*

Working from first principles, calculate the value of Young's modulus and Poisson's ratio. (I.Mech.E.)

From Art. 12. 10, gauge factor $= \dfrac{\mathrm{d}R}{R} \Big/ \dfrac{\mathrm{d}l}{l}$

$$\therefore \ \text{strain} = \frac{\mathrm{d}R}{R} \times \frac{1}{\text{gauge factor}}$$

$\therefore$ circumferential strain, $\varepsilon_c = \dfrac{1 \cdot 065}{200 \times 2 \cdot 09} = 0 \cdot 002\ 55$

and $\qquad$ longitudinal strain, $\varepsilon_l = \dfrac{0 \cdot 265}{200 \times 2 \cdot 09} = 0 \cdot 000\ 633$

From Art. 1.6, $\qquad \sigma_c = \dfrac{pd}{2t} = \dfrac{10 \times 10^6 \times 2 \cdot 5}{2 \times 0 \cdot 02} \ \text{N/m}^2 = 625 \ \text{MN/m}^2$

and $\qquad\qquad\qquad \sigma_l = \dfrac{\sigma_c}{2} = 312 \cdot 5 \ \text{MN/m}^2$

$$\therefore \ \varepsilon_c = \frac{\sigma_c - \nu\sigma_l}{E} = \frac{625 \times 10^6 - \nu \times 312 \cdot 5 \times 10^6}{E} \quad . \quad . \quad (1)$$

and $\qquad \varepsilon_l = \dfrac{\sigma_l - \nu\sigma_c}{E} = \dfrac{312 \cdot 5 \times 10^6 - \nu \times 625 \times 10^6}{E} \quad . \quad . \quad (2)$

Therefore, from equations (1) and (2), $E = \underline{210 \ \text{GN/m}^2}$ and $\ \nu = \underline{0 \cdot 287}$

13. A cylindrical boiler shell 1·5 m diameter is made of plates 10 mm thick. Find the normal, shear and resultant stresses on a plane inclined at 60° to a line on the surface parallel with the boiler axis, when the internal pressure is 1·5 MN/m². Derive any formulae used. (*U. Lond.*)

(*Ans.:* 70·31 MN/m²; 24·35 MN/m²; 74·4 MN/m²)

14. The principal stresses at a point in a material are 30 N/mm² tension and 50 N/mm² tension. Working from first principles, determine, for a plane inclined at 40° to the plane on which the latter stress acts: (*a*) the magnitude and angle of obliquity of the resultant stress; (*b*) the normal and tangential component stresses. (*U. Lond.*)

(*Ans.:* 42·8 N/mm² at 13° 18′ to normal stress; 41·73 N/mm²; 9·85 N/mm²)

15. The principal stresses at a point in a bar under two-dimensional stress are 80 MN/m² tension and 50 MN/m² compression. Calculate from first principles the resultant stress on a plane inclined at 30° to the line of action of the tensile stress and show its direction by means of a sketch. (*U. Lond.*)

(*Ans.:* 59 MN/m² at 72° 45′ to normal)

16. Draw and describe Mohr's Circle of Stress and prove that it may be used to represent the state of stress at a point within a stressed material. Illustrate your answer by sketches.

If, at a point within a material, the minimum and maximum principal stresses are 20 N/mm² and 60 N/mm² respectively (both tension), determine the shearing stress and normal stress on a plane passing through the point and making an angle of $\tan^{-1} 0·25$ with the plane on which the maximum principal stress acts. (*U. Lond.*)

(*Ans.:* 9·4 N/mm²; 57·7 N/mm²)

17. Direct stresses of 80 MN/m² tension and 60 MN/m² compression are applied to an elastic material at a certain point, on planes at right angles to one another. The greater principal stress in the material is limited to 100 MN/m² tension. To what shearing stress may the material be subjected on the given planes and what will then be the maximum shearing stress at the point? Work from first principles. (*U. Lond.*)

(*Ans.:* 56·56 MN/m²; 90 MN/m²)

18. In a piece of stressed material there are two planes perpendicular to one another on which the direct stresses are respectively 80 N/mm² tension and 45 N/mm² compression. In addition there is a shearing stress of 50 N/mm² on these planes. Working entirely from first principles, calculate the principal stresses and draw a clear diagram to show the principal planes relative to the given planes. What is the maximum shearing stress and where does it act? (*U. Lond.*)

(*Ans.* +97·5 N/mm²; −62·5 N/mm²; 19° 18′ and 109° 18′ to plane of 45 N/mm²
stress; 80 N/mm² at 45° to principal stresses)

19. In a piece of material a tensile stress σ_1 and a shearing stress τ act on a given plane. Show that the principal stresses are always of opposite sign.

If an additional tensile stress σ_2 acts on a plane perpendicular to that on which σ_1 acts and all the stresses are co-planar, find the condition that both principal stresses may be of the same sign. (*U. Lond.*) (*Ans.:* $\sigma_1\sigma_2 > \tau^2$)

20. On a plane PQ passing through a point in a piece of steel subjected to plane stress there is a tensile stress of 60 MN/m² and a shearing stress of 40 MN/m². On a plane at 45° to PQ there is a tensile stress of 120 MN/m² and an undetermined shearing stress.

Working from first principles or proving any formula used, find: (*a*) the values of the principal stresses at the point; (*b*) the value of the maximum shearing stress; (c) the position of the principal planes relative to PQ (illustrating with a diagram); (d) the values of the principal strains. $v = 0.3$ and $E = 200 \text{ GN/m}^2$. (*U. Lond.*)

(*Ans.*: 267·6 MN/m²; 52·4 MN/m²; 107·6 MN/m²; 79° 6' and 10° 54';
1·26 × 10⁻³; 0·14 × 10⁻³)

21. On a certain plane in a piece of stressed material there is a tensile stress of 100 N/mm² and a shearing stress of 55 N/mm². On a plane making 30° (measured anti-clockwise) to this plane there is a tensile stress of 20 N/mm², and an undetermined shearing stress. Find the position of the principal planes and the magnitude of the principal stresses. (*U. Lond.*)

(*Ans.*: 69° 54' and 159° 54'; +120·3 N/mm²; −49·7 N/mm²)

22. A thin cylindrical tube with closed ends has an internal diameter of 50 mm and a wall thickness of 2·5 mm. The tube is axially loaded in tension with a load of 10 kN and is subjected to an axial torque of 500 N m while under an internal pressure of 6 MN/m². Determine the maximum and minimum principal stresses on the outer surface of the tube and the maximum shear stress. Indicate on a diagram of the tube the directions in which these stresses act. (*U. Lond.*)

(*Ans.*: 103·3 MN/m²; 10·98 MN/m²; 57·13 MN/m²; 43° 14' to axis)

23. If a shaft having a diameter of 100 mm is subjected to a bending moment of 6·5 kN m in addition to the torque which it transmits, find the maximum torque allowable if the direct stress in the shaft is not to exceed 75 MN/m² and the shearing stress is not to exceed 50 MN/m². State clearly which of the two limiting stresses is reached and determine the maximum value of the other stress. (*U. Lond.*)   (*Ans.*: 5·072 kN m (max. direct stress); 41·9 MN/m²)

24. A hollow shaft of 200 mm outside diameter and 125 mm bore is subjected simultaneously to a bending moment of 43 kN m and a torque of 65 kN m. Calculate the maximum bending stress and the maximum torsional shearing stress. Hence find directly, without determining the principal stresses, the maximum shearing stress in the shaft. (*U. Lond.*)

(*Ans.*: 64·6 MN/m²; 48·8 MN/m²; 58·6 MN/m²)

25. A flywheel of mass 500 kg is mounted on a shaft 80 mm in diameter and midway between bearings 0·6 m apart, in which the shaft may be assumed to be directionally free. If the shaft is transmitting 30 kW at 360 rev/min, calculate the principal stresses and the maximum shearing stresses in the shaft at the ends of a vertical and a horizontal diameter in a plane close to that of the flywheel. (*U. Lond.*)

(*Ans.*: 18·1 MN/m²; 10·78 MN/m²; 7·9 MN/m²; 7·9 MN/m² (not allowing for direct shear stress, which amounts to 0·65 MN/m²))

26. Find the dimensions of a hollow steel shaft, internal diameter = 0·6 × external diameter, to transmit 150 kW at a speed of 250 rev/min if the shearing stress is not to exceed 70 MN/m².

If a bending moment of 2·7 kN m is now applied to the shaft, find the speed at which it must be driven to transmit the same power for the same value of the maximum shearing stress. (*U. Lond.*) (*Ans.*: 78·2 mm; 46·9 mm; 283 rev/min)

27. In a circular shaft subjected to an axial twisting moment T and a bending moment M, show that when $M = 1.2T$, the ratio of the maximum shearing stress to the greater principal stress is approximately 0·566. (*U. Lond.*)

28. A shaft of solid circular cross-section is subjected simultaneously to a torque T and a pure bending moment M. At a point on the circumference of the shaft the maximum principal stress is numerically 4 times the minimum principal stress.

Determine the ratio $M : T$ and the angle between the plane of the maximum principal stress and the plane of the bending stress. *(I.C.E.)*

$(Ans.: \frac{3}{4}; 26° 30')$

29. A hollow steel shaft 100 mm external diameter and 50 mm internal diameter transmits 600 kW at 500 rev/min and is subjected to an end thrust of 50 kN. Find what bending moment may be safely applied to the shaft if the greater principal stress is not to exceed 100 MN/m².

What will then be the value of the smaller principal stress? *(U. Lond.)*

$(Ans.: 4.85 \text{ kN m}; 38.85 \text{ MN/m}^2 \text{ tension})$

30. A hollow steel shaft 90 mm external diameter and 20 mm thick transmits 200 kW at 250 rev/min and is subjected to an axial thrust of 50 kN in addition to a bending moment M. Determine the value of M if the greater principal stress is limited to 100 MN/m². What is then the value of the smaller principal stress? *(U. Lond.)*

$(Ans.: 3.48 \text{ kN m}; 34.8 \text{ MN/m}^2 \text{ tension})$

31. A solid shaft 120 mm diameter transmits 600 kW at 300 rev/min. It is also subjected to a bending moment of 10 kN m and to an end thrust. If the maximum principal stress is limited to 100 MN/m², determine the permissible end thrust.

Determine the position of the plane in which the principal stress acts and draw a diagram showing the position of the plane relative to the torque and the plane of the bending moment applied to the shaft. *(U. Lond.)*

$(Ans.: 107 \text{ kN}; 60° 38' \text{ to axis})$

32. A shaft of 200 mm diameter transmits 2 MW at 250 rev/min and is subjected to a bending moment of 50 kN m. Calculate the maximum permissible end thrust on the shaft if the maximum shearing stress must not exceed 80 MN/m². *(U. Lond.)*

$(Ans.: 2 \text{ MN})$

33. Determine the principal stresses for a piece of material, subjected to a pure shearing stress plus a simple direct stress.

A hollow circular shaft 200 mm external diameter and 100 mm internal diameter is subjected to a direct compression load of 750 kN, a bending moment of 45 kN m and a twisting moment of 65 kN m. Calculate the maximum principal stress and the maximum shearing stress. *(U. Lond.)*

$(Ans.: 110.7 \text{ MN/m}^2; 64.2 \text{ MN/m}^2)$

34. A metal cylinder 450 mm long, 230 mm outside diameter and 215 mm inside diameter, is subjected to internal pressure and at the same time to an axial torque of 40 kN m. Find the greatest internal pressure which can be applied if the maximum shearing stress is not to exceed 90 MN/m². Treat as a thin cylinder. *(U. Lond.)*

$(Ans.: 16.3 \text{ MN/m}^2)$

35. A thin tube 50 mm diameter and 1.5 mm thick has an axial pull of 20 kN and an axial torque of 250 N m applied to it. Working from first principles, find the magnitude and direction of the principal stresses at any point in the external surface. *(U. Lond.)*

$(Ans.: +102.4 \text{ MN/m}^2; -17.54 \text{ MN/m}^2; 22° 30' \text{ and } 112° 30' \text{ to axis})$

36. A timber beam, 300 mm deep by 150 mm wide, is simply supported on a span of 4 m and carries a point load of 10 kN at the centre of the span. At a point 75 mm above the underside of the beam and at a distance of 1 m from the left-hand support the grain of the timber has a slope of 1 vertical to 3 horizontal, upwards to the right. Determine the shearing stress acting along the grain. *(U. Lond.)*

$(Ans.: 0.433 \text{ MN/m}^2)$

37. A beam of rectangular section 50 mm wide and 150 mm deep is subjected at a certain section, to a bending moment which produces a maximum bending stress of 120 MN/m², and a shearing force which produces a maximum shearing stress of 48 MN/m². The bending moment produces compressive stress above the neutral axis. Find the value of the tensile principal stress at the neutral axis and at distances of 25 mm, 50 mm and 75 mm above and below the neutral axis.

Plot on square paper a graph showing how the tensile principal stress varies across the section. (*U. Lond.*) (*Ans.:* 0, 8·1, 27·2, 48, 67·2, 88·1, 120 MN/m²)

38. Prove that, if ε_x and ε_y are the strains in the directions of the principal stresses, the strain in a direction at an angle θ with that of ε_x is

$$\frac{\varepsilon_x + \varepsilon_y}{2} + \frac{\varepsilon_x - \varepsilon_y}{2} \cos 2\theta$$

The principal stresses at a point in a material are 160 and 40 MN/m², both tensile. If $E = 200$ GN/m² and $\nu = 0.28$, find the strain in a direction inclined at 30° to that of the greater principal stress.

Also find in what direction the strain is zero. (*U. Lond.*)

(*Ans.:* 0.552×10^{-3}; 79° 50′ to ε_x)

39. Prove that, in a two-dimensional stress system, if ε_x and ε_y are the strains in two perpendicular directions, the normal stresses in these directions are given by:

$$\sigma_x = \frac{E}{1 - \nu^2}(\varepsilon_x + \nu\varepsilon_y) \qquad \sigma_y = \frac{E}{1 - \nu^2}(\varepsilon_y + \nu\varepsilon_x)$$

By means of strain gauges the strains in two perpendicular directions at 30° to the directions of the principal stresses are found to be 425×10^{-6} and 82×10^{-6} respectively, both tensile. Find the normal stresses in the direction of the measured strains, and also the principal stresses. $E = 200$ GN/m²; $\nu = 0.3$. (*U. Lond.*)

(*Ans.:* 98·8 and 46 MN/m²; 125·2 and 19·6 MN/m²)

40. In a two-dimensional strain system the following readings were taken in a rectangular strain rosette: $\varepsilon_{0°} = 0.4 \times 10^{-3}$; $\varepsilon_{45°} = 0.4 \times 10^{-3}$; $\varepsilon_{90°} = 0.1 \times 10^{-3}$.

Determine the magnitudes and the directions of the principal strains.

If $E = 200$ GN/m² and $\nu = 0.3$, find the principal stresses. (*U. Lond.*)

(*Ans.:* $0.462\ 1 \times 10^{-3}$, $0.037\ 9 \times 10^{-3}$; 67° 30′ and 157° 30′ to ε_0; 104 and 38·85 MN/m²)

41. A rosette of three strain gauges on the surface of a metal plate under stress gave the following strain readings: No. 1 at 0°, +0·000 592; No. 2 at 45°, +0·000 308; No. 3 at 90°, −0·000 432, the angles being measured anti-clockwise from gauge No. 1. Determine the magnitude of the principal strains and their directions relative to the axis of gauge No. 1.

If $E = 200$ GN/m² and $\nu = \frac{1}{3}$, find the principal stresses.

Prove any formula used. (*U. Lond.*)

(*Ans.:* +0·000 64, −0·000 48; 168°, 78°; +109 MN/m², −63·3 MN/m²)

42. A rosette of strain gauges is fixed to a structural member. When the member is loaded in a certain way readings are obtained as follows:

Gauge No.	Direction relative to Gauge No. 1	Strain
1	0°	$+425 \times 10^{-6}$
2	45°	$+542 \times 10^{-6}$
3	90°	$+ 82 \times 10^{-6}$

If $E = 200$ GN/m² and $\nu = 0.3$, find the magnitude of the principal stresses and their directions relative to the axis of gauge No. 1. (*U. Lond.*)

(*Ans.:* 124 MN/m², 20·8 MN/m²; 150° 23′, 60° 23′)

CHAPTER 13

ELASTIC CONSTANTS; VOLUMETRIC STRAIN

13.1 Relation between E, G and ν. Fig. 13.1(a) shows a square element of a material which is subjected to pure shear stress τ and Fig. 13.1(b) shows the distorted shape which the element will assume.

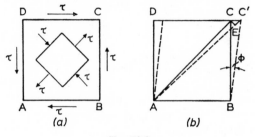

FIG. 13.1

As shown in Art. 12.3, the applied shear stress induces equal tensile and compressive stresses on planes at 45° to the planes of shear, so that

$$\text{strain on diagonal AC} = \frac{\tau}{E} + \nu\frac{\tau}{E} = \frac{\tau}{E}(1 + \nu)$$

Also

$$\text{strain on diagonal AC} = \frac{EC'}{AC}$$

$$= \frac{CC'}{\sqrt{2}} \times \frac{1}{\sqrt{2}BC} = \frac{CC'}{2CD}$$

But

$$\frac{CC'}{CD} = \phi = \frac{\tau}{G}$$

$$\therefore \frac{\tau}{E}(1 + \nu) = \frac{\tau}{2G}$$

from which

$$E = 2G(1 + \nu) \qquad . \qquad . \qquad . \quad (13.1)$$

13.2 Three-dimensional strain. Fig. 13.2 shows an element of a material which is subjected to three principal stresses, σ_x, σ_y and σ_z.

Strain on side x,

$$\varepsilon_x = \frac{\sigma_x}{E} - \nu\frac{\sigma_y}{E} - \nu\frac{\sigma_z}{E}$$

$$= \frac{1}{E}\{\sigma_x - \nu(\sigma_y + \sigma_z)\} \qquad . \qquad . \quad (13.2)$$

Similarly, $$\varepsilon_y = \frac{1}{E}\{\sigma_y - \nu(\sigma_z + \sigma_x)\} \qquad . \qquad . \qquad . \quad (13.3)$$

and $$\varepsilon_z = \frac{1}{E}\{\sigma_z - \nu(\sigma_x + \sigma_y)\} \qquad . \qquad . \qquad . \quad (13.4)$$

13.3 Volumetric strain. The volumetric strain is the ratio

$$\frac{\text{change in volume}}{\text{original volume}},$$

i.e. $$\varepsilon_v = \frac{\delta v}{v} . \qquad . \quad (13.5)$$

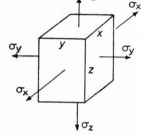

Fig. 13.2

Referring to Fig. 13.2,

new length of side $x = x(1 + \varepsilon_x)$
new length of side $y = y(1 + \varepsilon_y)$
and new length of side $z = z(1 + \varepsilon_z)$

$\therefore$ new volume $= xyz(1 + \varepsilon_x)(1 + \varepsilon_y)(1 + \varepsilon_z)$
$= xyz(1 + \varepsilon_x + \varepsilon_y + \varepsilon_z)$,

neglecting products of strains,

$$\therefore \varepsilon_v = \frac{xyz(1 + \varepsilon_x + \varepsilon_y + \varepsilon_z) - xyz}{xyz}$$

$$= \varepsilon_x + \varepsilon_y + \varepsilon_z . \qquad . \qquad . \qquad . \quad (13.6)$$

i.e.   volumetric strain = sum of perpendicular linear strains

Alternatively, $v = xyz$

$$\therefore \log v = \log x + \log y + \log z$$

$$\therefore \frac{dv}{v} = \frac{dx}{x} + \frac{dy}{y} + \frac{dz}{z}$$

i.e. $$\varepsilon_v = \varepsilon_x + \varepsilon_y + \varepsilon_z$$

13.4 Bulk modulus. If a material is subjected to a stress σ in all directions (e.g. hydrostatic pressure), then

$$\text{bulk modulus} = \frac{\text{stress}}{\text{volumetric strain}}$$

i.e. $$K = \frac{\sigma}{\varepsilon_v} \qquad . \qquad . \qquad . \qquad . \quad (13.7)$$

13.5 Relation between E, K and ν. If, in Fig. 13.2, $\sigma_x = \sigma_y = \sigma_z = \sigma$,

then strain in each direction $= \dfrac{\sigma}{E}(1 - 2\nu)$

Therefore, from equation (13.6), $\varepsilon_v = \dfrac{3\sigma}{E}(1 - 2\nu) = \dfrac{\sigma}{K}$

$$\therefore E = 3K(1 - 2\nu) \qquad . \qquad . \qquad . \quad (13.8)$$

13.6 Relation between E, G and K.

From equation (13.1) $E = 2G(1 + \nu)$ $\therefore \nu = \dfrac{E}{2G} - 1$

From equation (13.8), $E = 3K(1 - 2\nu)$ $\therefore \nu = \dfrac{1}{2} - \dfrac{E}{6K}$

Equating the expressions for ν,

$$E\left(\frac{1}{G} + \frac{1}{3K}\right) = 3$$

from which $E = \dfrac{9GK}{G + 3K}$.   .   .   .   . (13.9)

13.7 Volumetric strain due to unequal stresses.

In the general case of unequal stresses, the strain in each of the co-ordinate directions can be determined from equations (13.2), (13.3) and (13.4) and the volumetric strain is then obtained from equation (13.6). In the case of a solid body, however, the volumetric strain can be conveniently expressed directly in terms of the applied stresses.   Thus

$$\varepsilon_v = \varepsilon_x + \varepsilon_y + \varepsilon_z$$
$$= \frac{1}{E}\{\sigma_x - \nu(\sigma_y + \sigma_z)\} + \frac{1}{E}\{\sigma_y - \nu(\sigma_z + \sigma_x)\} + \frac{1}{E}\{\sigma_z - \nu(\sigma_x + \sigma_y)\}$$
$$= (\sigma_x + \sigma_y + \sigma_z) \times \frac{1 - 2\nu}{E}$$
$$= \frac{\sigma_x + \sigma_y + \sigma_z}{3K} \qquad . \qquad . \qquad . \qquad . \qquad . \qquad . \qquad (13.10)$$

This expression is *not* applicable to the change in cubic content of a hollow vessel (see Examples 7, 8 and 9).

1. *A piece of C.I., 150 mm long and 25 mm square, is compressed by an axial load of 90 kN. Find the alteration in length if all the lateral strain is prevented by the application of uniform lateral pressure on the four sides. Find also the modified modulus of elasticity.* $E = 115\ GN/m^2$ *and* $\nu = \frac{1}{4}$.

Let the axial stress be σ and the lateral pressure be p, Fig. 13.3.

Then $\sigma = \dfrac{90 \times 10^3}{0 \cdot 025^2}\ \text{N/m}^2 = 144\ \text{MN/m}^2$

Lateral strain $= \dfrac{p}{E} - \nu\dfrac{p}{E} - \nu\dfrac{\sigma}{E} = 0$

i.e. $p(1 - \tfrac{1}{4}) = \tfrac{1}{4} \times 144$
$$\therefore p = 48\ \text{MN/m}^2$$

$\therefore$ longitudinal strain $= \dfrac{\sigma}{E} - 2\nu\dfrac{p}{E}$

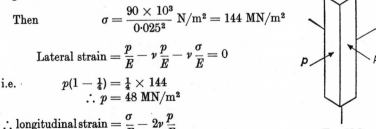

Fig. 13.3

$$= \frac{144 \times 10^6 - \frac{1}{2} \times 48 \times 10^6}{115 \times 10^9}$$

$$= 0.001\ 044$$

$$\therefore \text{ decrease in length} = 150 \times 0.001\ 044$$

$$= \underline{0.156\ 6 \text{ mm}}$$

Modified modulus of elasticity $= \dfrac{\text{axial stress}}{\text{axial strain}}$

when strains in directions perpendicular to the axis are prevented

$$= \frac{144 \times 10^6}{0.001\ 044} \text{ N/m}^2 = 138 \text{ GN/m}^2$$

2. *A steel bar 100 mm long and 20 mm diameter is subjected to an axial compressive stress of 60 MN/m² and a sleeve, fitted over the bar, reduces the lateral expansion to one half the unrestricted value.*

Determine (a) the change in diameter of the bar, (b) the change in length of the bar, (c) the change in volume of the bar. E = 200 GN/m² and ν = ¼.

Let the axial stress be σ and the lateral pressure be p, Fig. 13.4.

Regarding compressive strain as positive,

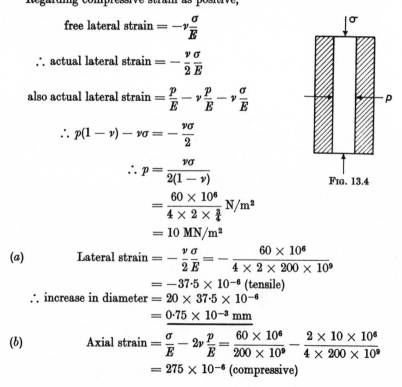

free lateral strain $= -\nu\dfrac{\sigma}{E}$

$\therefore$ actual lateral strain $= -\dfrac{\nu}{2}\dfrac{\sigma}{E}$

also actual lateral strain $= \dfrac{p}{E} - \nu\dfrac{p}{E} - \nu\dfrac{\sigma}{E}$

$\therefore p(1 - \nu) - \nu\sigma = -\dfrac{\nu\sigma}{2}$

$\therefore p = \dfrac{\nu\sigma}{2(1 - \nu)}$

$$= \frac{60 \times 10^6}{4 \times 2 \times \frac{3}{4}} \text{ N/m}^2$$

$$= 10 \text{ MN/m}^2$$

Fig. 13.4

(a)   Lateral strain $= -\dfrac{\nu}{2}\dfrac{\sigma}{E} = -\dfrac{60 \times 10^6}{4 \times 2 \times 200 \times 10^9}$

$$= -37.5 \times 10^{-6} \text{ (tensile)}$$

$\therefore$ increase in diameter $= 20 \times 37.5 \times 10^{-6}$

$$= \underline{0.75 \times 10^{-3} \text{ mm}}$$

(b)   Axial strain $= \dfrac{\sigma}{E} - 2\nu\dfrac{p}{E} = \dfrac{60 \times 10^6}{200 \times 10^9} - \dfrac{2 \times 10 \times 10^6}{4 \times 200 \times 10^9}$

$$= 275 \times 10^{-6} \text{ (compressive)}$$

$\therefore$ decrease in length $= 100 \times 275 \times 10^{-6}$

$$= \underline{27 \cdot 5 \times 10^{-3} \text{ mm}}$$

(c)   Volumetric strain $= \varepsilon_a + 2\varepsilon_d = 275 \times 10^{-6} - 2 \times 37 \cdot 5 \times 10^{-6}$

$$= 200 \times 10^{-6}$$

$\therefore$ decrease in volume $= \dfrac{\pi}{4} \times 20^2 \times 100 \times 200 \times 10^{-6}$

$$= \underline{6 \cdot 284 \text{ mm}^3}$$

Alternatively, $K = \dfrac{E}{3(1 - 2\nu)} = \dfrac{200}{3(1 - 2 \times \frac{1}{4})} = \dfrac{400}{3} \text{ GN/m}^2$

$\therefore \varepsilon_v = \dfrac{\sigma + p + p}{3K}$.   .   from equation (13.10)

$$= \dfrac{60 \times 10^6 + 2 \times 10 \times 10^6}{3 \times \dfrac{400}{3} \times 10^9}$$

$$= 200 \times 10^{-6}, \text{ as before}$$

3. *A mild steel rod ABC of circular section transmits an axial pull. The total length is 1·45 m, AB being 0·8 m long and 25 mm diameter, and BC 0·65 m long and 20 mm diameter. If the total change in length is 0·75 mm, determine for the separate parts AB and BC, the changes in (a) length, (b) diameter, and (c) volume. Take $\nu = 0 \cdot 3$.*   (U. Lond.)

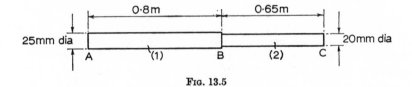

Fig. 13.5

Let x_1 and x_2 be the extensions of parts AB and BC respectively, Fig. 13.5.

Then $x_1 + x_2 = 0 \cdot 75 \text{ mm}$.   .   .   .   .   .   (1)

and $\dfrac{x_1}{x_2} = \dfrac{\dfrac{Pl_1}{a_1 E}}{\dfrac{Pl_2}{a_2 E}} = \dfrac{a_2 l_1}{a_1 l_2}$, where P is the axial load

$$= \dfrac{20^2 \times 0 \cdot 80}{25^2 \times 0 \cdot 65} = 0 \cdot 787 \quad . \quad . \quad . \quad (2)$$

Hence, from equations (1) and (2),

$$x_1 = \underline{0 \cdot 33 \text{ mm}} \quad \text{and} \quad x_2 = \underline{0 \cdot 42 \text{ mm}}$$

$$\varepsilon_1 = \frac{0 \cdot 000\,33}{0 \cdot 80} = 0 \cdot 000\,412\,5$$

and
$$\varepsilon_2 = \frac{0 \cdot 000\,42}{0 \cdot 65} = 0 \cdot 000\,646$$

$\therefore$ reduction in diameter of AB $= 0 \cdot 025 \times 0 \cdot 3 \times 0 \cdot 000\,412\,5$ m
$$= \underline{3 \cdot 1 \ \mu m}$$

and reduction in diameter of BC $= 0 \cdot 02 \times 0 \cdot 3 \times 0 \cdot 000\,646$ m
$$= \underline{3 \cdot 88 \ \mu m}$$

Volumetric strain on AB $= 0 \cdot 000\,412\,5(1 - 2 \times 0 \cdot 3)$
$$= 0 \cdot 000\,165$$

$\therefore$ increase in volume of AB $= \dfrac{\pi}{4} \times 0 \cdot 025^2 \times 0 \cdot 80 \times 0 \cdot 000\,165$ m^3

$$= \underline{64 \cdot 8 \text{ mm}^3}$$

Volumetric strain on BC $= 0 \cdot 000\,646(1 - 2 \times 0 \cdot 3)$
$$= 0 \cdot 000\,259$$

$\therefore$ increase in volume of BC $= \dfrac{\pi}{4} \times 0 \cdot 02^2 \times 0 \cdot 65 \times 0 \cdot 000\,259$ m^3

$$= \underline{53 \cdot 0 \text{ mm}^3}$$

4. *A 50 mm diameter steel bar is completely prevented from increasing in length and its temperature is raised by t deg C. Show that the lateral expansion of the bar depends on the values of Poisson's ratio v, and the coefficient of linear expansion α, but is independent of the modulus of elasticity E.*

The bar is found to increase in diameter by 0·043 mm under the above conditions when it is heated through 60 deg C. The force required to prevent length increase is found to be 270 kN. When the bar is free to expand, it is found to increase in length by 0·132 mm over a 0·2 m gauge length. Determine the values of E, v, α and G, the modulus of rigidity. (U. Lond.)

The axial force preventing increase in length causes an axial strain equal to the natural extension per unit length due to the increase in temperature,

i.e.   axial strain $= -\alpha t$ (compressive)

$\therefore$ lateral strain due to axial force $= v\alpha t$ (tensile)

$\therefore$ total lateral expansion $= 0 \cdot 05(\alpha t + v\alpha t)$ m

$$= \underline{0 \cdot 05\alpha t(1 + v)},$$

which is independent of E

$$0 \cdot 05\alpha t(1 + v) = 0 \cdot 043 \times 10^{-3}$$

$$\therefore \alpha(1 + v) = \frac{0 \cdot 043 \times 10^{-3}}{0 \cdot 05 \times 60} = 0 \cdot 014\,33 \times 10^{-3} \quad (1)$$

Axial strain, $\alpha t = \dfrac{\sigma}{E} = \dfrac{P}{aE}$, where P is the axial force

$$\therefore P = \alpha t a E$$

i.e.
$$270 \times 10^3 = \alpha \times 60 \times \frac{\pi}{4} \times 0.05^2 \times E$$

$$= \frac{3}{80}\pi\alpha E \qquad . \qquad . \qquad . \qquad . \qquad (2)$$

Free extension $= l\alpha t$

i.e.
$$0.132 \times 10^{-3} = 0.2 \times \alpha \times 60$$

$$\therefore \alpha = \underline{0.000\ 011/\text{deg C}}$$

Substituting in equation (1), $\quad \nu = \underline{0.3}$

Substituting in equation (2), $\quad E = \underline{208\ \text{GN/m}^2}$

$$E = 2G(1 + \nu)\ . \qquad \text{from equation (13.1)}$$

$$\therefore G = \frac{208}{2 \times 1.3} = \underline{80\ \text{GN/m}^2}$$

5. *A close-coiled spring made of circular wire has a mean coil diameter of 80 mm. When subjected to an axial load, the stiffness is found to be 3 kN/m and when a pure couple is applied about the axis of the spring, the torsional stiffness is 6·25 Nm/rad. Determine Poisson's ratio for the material of the spring.* (I.Mech.E.)

From equation (9.2), $\qquad \delta = \dfrac{8WD^3n}{Gd^4}$

$$\therefore \text{axial stiffness} = \frac{W}{\delta} = \frac{Gd^4}{8D^3n}$$

i.e.
$$3 \times 10^3 = \frac{Gd^4}{8 \times 0.08^3 n}$$

$$\therefore \frac{Gd^4}{n} = 12.3\ \text{N m}^2$$

From equation (9.5), $\qquad \phi = \dfrac{64MDn}{Ed^4}$

$$\therefore \text{torsional stiffness} = \frac{M}{\phi} = \frac{Ed^4}{64Dn}$$

i.e.
$$6.25 = \frac{Ed^4}{64 \times 0.08n}$$

$$\therefore \frac{Ed^4}{n} = 32\ \text{N m}^2$$

$$\therefore \frac{E}{G} = \frac{32}{12.3} = 2(1 + \nu)\ . \qquad \text{from equation (13.1)}$$

from which
$$\nu = \underline{0.3}$$

6. *A solid cylindrical test piece, 75 mm long and 50 mm diameter, is enclosed within a hollow pressure vessel. With the test piece in the vessel, 20×10^3 mm³ of oil are required just to fill the pressure vessel. Measurement shows that a further 50 mm³ of oil have to be pumped into the vessel to raise the oil pressure to 7 MN/m².*

The experiment is repeated using the same pressure vessel and oil, but without the test piece inside the vessel. This time, after initially filling the pressure vessel, a further 364 mm³ of oil are needed to raise the pressure to 7 MN/m².

The test piece is made of aluminium, for which Young's modulus and Poisson's ratio are 70 GN/m² and 0·30 respectively. Find the bulk modulus of the oil. (U. Lond.)

$$\text{Volume of test piece} = \frac{\pi}{4} \times 50^2 \times 75 = 147 \cdot 4 \times 10^3 \text{ mm}^3$$

$$\therefore \text{ volume of vessel} = (147 \cdot 4 + 20) \times 10^3 = 167 \cdot 4 \times 10^3 \text{ mm}^3$$

$$\text{For aluminium, } K = \frac{E}{3(1 - 2v)} \qquad . \qquad . \qquad \text{from equation (13.8)}$$

$$= \frac{70}{3(1 - 2 \times 0 \cdot 3)} = 58 \cdot 3 \text{ GN/m}^2$$

Let the expansion of the pressure vessel be δv. Then, at 7 MN/m² with the test piece inside the vessel, the additional volume pumped in is absorbed in expanding the vessel, compressing the oil and compressing the test piece,

i.e.
$$50 = \delta v + \frac{7 \times 10^6 \times 20 \times 10^3}{K_{\text{oil}}} + \frac{7 \times 10^6 \times 147 \cdot 4 \times 10^3}{K_{\text{al}}}$$

At 7 MN/m² without the test piece inside the vessel,

$$364 = \delta v + \frac{7 \times 10^6 \times 167 \cdot 4 \times 10^3}{K_{\text{oil}}}$$

$$\therefore 364 - 50 = \frac{7 \times 147 \cdot 4 \times 10^9}{K_{\text{oil}}} + \frac{7 \times 147 \cdot 4 \times 10^9}{K_{\text{al}}}$$

i.e. $0 \cdot 304 \times 10^{-9} = \left(\frac{1}{K_{\text{oil}}} - \frac{1}{58 \cdot 3 \times 10^9} \right)$

from which $K_{\text{oil}} = \underline{3 \cdot 11 \text{ GN/m}^2}$

7. *A closed cylindrical vessel with plane ends is made of steel plate 3 mm thick, the internal dimensions being length 0·6 m and diameter 0·25 m. Determine first the longitudinal and hoop stresses in the cylindrical shell due to an internal pressure of 2·8 MN/m², ignoring any stiffening effects due to the ends, and then calculate the increases in (a) length, (b) diameter and (c) volume of the vessel.*

For steel, take $E = 200$ GN/m² and Poisson's ratio $= 0.286$.

(U. Lond.)

From Art. 1.4,

longitudinal stress, $\sigma_l = \dfrac{pd}{4t}$

$$= \frac{2.8 \times 10^6 \times 0.25}{4 \times 0.003} = \underline{58.3 \text{ MN/m}^2}$$

and

circumferential stress, $\sigma_c = 2\sigma_l = \underline{116.6 \text{ MN/m}^2}$

Longitudinal strain, $\varepsilon_l = \dfrac{\sigma_l}{E} - \nu\dfrac{\sigma_c}{E}$ *

$$= \frac{58.3 \times 10^6}{200 \times 10^9}(1 - 2 \times 0.286) = 0.000\,125$$

$\therefore$ increase in length $= 0.6 \times 0.000\,125$ m $= \underline{0.075 \text{ mm}}$

Circumferential strain, $\varepsilon_c = \dfrac{\sigma_c}{E} - \nu\dfrac{\sigma_l}{E}$

$$= \frac{58.3 \times 10^6}{200 \times 10^9}(2 - 0.286) = 0.000\,5$$

The strain on the diameter, ε_d, is the same as the strain on the circumference, so that

increase in diameter $= 0.25 \times 0.000\,5$ m $= \underline{0.125 \text{ mm}}$

Volumetric strain, $\varepsilon_v = \varepsilon_l + 2\varepsilon_d$†   .   . from equation (13.6)
$= 0.000\,125 + 2 \times 0.000\,5$
$= 0.001\,125$

$\therefore$ increase in volume $= \dfrac{\pi}{4} \times 0.25^2 \times 0.6 \times 0.001\,125$ m³

$$= \underline{33.2 \times 10^3 \text{ mm}^3}$$

---

* In *thin* cylinders, the radial stress is negligible in comparison with the circumferential and longitudinal stresses.

† Alternatively, $\qquad v = \dfrac{\pi}{4}d^2 l$

$$\therefore \log v = \log\frac{\pi}{4} + 2\log d + \log l$$

$$\therefore \frac{dv}{v} = 2\frac{dd}{d} + \frac{dl}{l}$$

i.e. $\qquad\qquad\qquad \varepsilon_v = 2\varepsilon_d + \varepsilon_l$

8. *A spherical vessel of 1·5 m diameter is made from 10 mm thick steel plate, and it is to be subjected to a hydraulic test. Determine the additional volume of water which it is necessary to pump into the vessel when the vessel is initially just filled with water, in order to raise the pressure to the proof pressure of 10 MN/m². The bulk modulus of water is 2 GN/m². E = 200 GN/m² and ν = 0·286.*   (I.Mech.E.)

From Art. 1.5,

$$\text{circumferential stress, } \sigma_c = \frac{pd}{4t}$$

$$= \frac{10 \times 10^6 \times 1\cdot5}{4 \times 0\cdot01} = 375 \times 10^6 \text{ N/m}^2$$

$$\therefore \text{ circumferential strain, } \varepsilon_c = \frac{\sigma_c}{E} - \nu\frac{\sigma_c}{E}^*$$

$$= \frac{375 \times 10^6}{200 \times 10^9}(1 - 0\cdot286) = 0\cdot001\ 34$$

The diametral strain, ε_d, is the same as the circumferential strain, so that the strain on the cubic content of the vessel = $3\varepsilon_d$

$$= 0\cdot004\ 02$$

$$\therefore \text{ increase in capacity of vessel} = v \times 0\cdot004\ 02$$

$$\text{Volumetric strain on water} = \frac{p}{K}$$

$$= \frac{10 \times 10^6}{2 \times 10^9} = 0\cdot005$$

$$\therefore \text{ compression of water initially in vessel} = v \times 0\cdot005$$

$$\therefore \text{ additional volume of water pumped in} = v(0\cdot004\ 02 + 0\cdot005)$$

$$= \frac{4}{3}\pi \times 0\cdot75^3 \times 0\cdot009\ 02$$

$$= \underline{0\cdot016 \text{ m}^3}$$

9. *The ends of a thin cylinder 150 mm internal diameter and wall thickness 2·5 mm are closed by rigid plates and it is then filled with a liquid. When an axial compressive force of 28 kN is applied to the cylinder, the pressure of the liquid rises by 60 kN/m². Find the bulk modulus of the liquid. E = 200 GN/m² and ν = 0·3.*

Let P be the axial force and p the resulting pressure rise, Fig. 13.6.

---

* As in Example 7, the effect of the radial stress is negligible.

Then

longitudinal stress, $\sigma_l = \dfrac{P}{\pi D t} - \dfrac{pd}{4t}$

$$= \frac{28 \times 10^3}{\pi \times 0.152\,5 \times 0.002\,5} - \frac{60 \times 10^3 \times 0.15}{4 \times 0.002\,5}$$

$$= 21.7 \times 10^6 \text{ N/m}^2 \text{ (compressive)}$$

Circumferential stress, $\sigma_c = \dfrac{pd}{2t}$

$$= \frac{60 \times 10^3 \times 0.15}{2 \times 0.002\,5}$$

$$= 1.8 \times 10^6 \text{ N/m}^2 \text{ (tensile)}$$

$\therefore$ longitudinal strain, $\varepsilon_l = \dfrac{21.7 \times 10^6 + 0.3 \times 1.8 \times 10^6}{200 \times 10^9}$

$$= 111.2 \times 10^{-6} \text{ (compressive)}$$

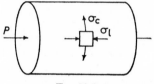

Fig. 13.6

and

circumferential strain, $\varepsilon_c = \dfrac{1.8 \times 10^6 + 0.3 \times 21.7 \times 10^6}{200 \times 10^9}$

$$= 41.5 \times 10^{-6} \text{ (tensile)}$$

This is also the diametral strain, ε_d, so that volumetric strain on cylinder

$$= \varepsilon_l - 2\varepsilon_d$$

$$= (111.2 - 2 \times 41.5) \times 10^{-6}$$

$$= 28.2 \times 10^{-6}$$

Volumetric strain on liquid $= \dfrac{p}{K} = \dfrac{60 \times 10^3}{K}$

Since no liquid is pumped in or escapes,

strain on cylinder capacity = strain on liquid contents

i.e.

$$28.2 \times 10^{-6} = \frac{60 \times 10^3}{K}$$

$$\therefore K = \underline{2.13 \text{ GN/m}^2}$$

10. Derive expressions for Poisson's ratio (ν) and bulk modulus (K) in terms of the moduli of elasticity (E) and rigidity (G).

A steel bar 25 mm diameter carries a tensile load of 50 kN. Calculate the bulk modulus and the reduction in diameter of the bar if E is 200 GN/m² and G is 80 GN/m². *(U. Lond.)*   *(Ans.:* 133·3 GN/m²; 0·003 18 mm)

11. A uniform bar 9 m long carries in tension an axial load of 200 kN. Determine the increase in volume of the bar if the modulus of rigidity and Poisson's ratio are 80 GN/m² and 0·25 respectively. *(U. Lond.)*   *(Ans. :* 4·5 × 10³ mm³)

12. An axial compressive load of 500 kN is applied to a metal bar of square section 50 mm × 50 mm. The contraction on a 200 mm gauge length is found to be 0·55 mm and the increase in thickness 0·045 mm. Find the value of Young's modulus and Poisson's ratio.

If in addition to the axial load of 500 kN a uniform lateral pressure of 80 MN/m² is applied to the two opposite sides of the bar in both directions, find the contraction on the 200 mm gauge length and the change in thickness. *(U. Lond.)*
          (Ans.: 72·7 GN/m²; 0·327; 0·406 mm; 0·007 9 mm)

13. A cylinder of metal under axial compression is restrained so that lateral expansion is half the unrestrained value. Calculate the ratio of the axial strain in this cylinder to its axial strain if free to expand laterally. Poisson's ratio = 0·25 *(U. Lond.)*   *(Ans.:* 11 : 12)

14. Establish the expression for bulk modulus in terms of Young's modulus and Poisson's ratio.

A solid steel sphere of 400 mm diameter is subjected to a uniform hydraulic pressure $p = 3·5$ MN/m². Determine the decrease in the volume of the sphere if Poisson's ratio and Young's modulus are 0·3 and 200 GN/m² respectively. *(U. Lond.)*   *(Ans.:* 703·5 mm³)

15. For an elastic material, express Poisson's ratio in terms of the bulk modulus and the modulus of rigidity, and prove the derivation of the expression.

Determine the percentage change in volume of a steel bar 80 mm square in section and 1·2 m long when subjected to an axial compressive load of 20 kN. What change in volume would a 100 mm cube of steel suffer at a depth of 5 km in sea-water? Specific gravity of sea water = 1·025. $E = 200$ GN/m²; $G = 80$ GN/m². *(U. Lond.)*   *(Ans.:* 0·000 781; 377 mm³)

16. A piece of material is subjected to three mutually perpendicular tensile stresses and the strains in the three directions are in the ratio 3 : 4 : 5. If the value of Poisson's ratio is 0·286 find the ratio of the stresses and their value when the greatest stress in 100 MN/m². *(U. Lond.)*
          (Ans.: 1 : 1·09 : 1·185; 84·4 MN/m²; 92·2 MN/m²)

17. In tests on a sample of steel bar of 25 mm diameter, it is found that a tensile load of 50 kN results in an extension of 0·099 4 mm on a gauge length of 200 mm, and that a torque of 200 N m produces an angle of twist of 0·925° in a length of 250 mm. Deduce the value of Poisson's ratio for the steel, and prove the formula which you use. *(U. Lond.)*   *(Ans.:* 0·27)

18. Prove that $E = 2G(1 + \nu)$.

During a torsion test on a brass rod of 40 mm diameter, a twist of 0·8° was recorded over a 250 mm gauge length when a torque of 500 N m was applied. A tensile test on the rod showed that the stretch over the same gauge length for a pull of 60 kN was 0·125 mm. Calculate: (a) the maximum stress in the rod during each test, (b) the modulus of elasticity, (c) the modulus of rigidity, and (d) Poisson's ratio. *(U. Lond.)*
          (Ans.: 39·75 MN/m²; 47·7 MN/m²; 95·4 GN/m²; 35·6 GN/m²; 0·34)

19. Derive an expression showing the relationship between percentage volume change, Poisson's ratio, elastic modulus and stress for a short column, loaded axially.

A circular shaft 100 mm in diameter and 1 m long is loaded axially with a compressive load of 1 MN and is found to be reduced in volume by 0·27 per cent. If $E = 200$ GN/m², determine the angle of twist of one end of a shaft relative to the other if it is subjected to a torque of 15 kN m. (*U. Lond.*)

(*Ans.:* 1·13°)

20. Deduce the relation between the modulus of elasticity, the modulus of rigidity and Poisson's ratio.

A hollow shaft of 75 mm external diameter and 50 mm internal diameter twists through an angle of 0·52° in a length of 1 m when subjected to an axial twisting moment of 1 kN m. Estimate the deflection at the centre of the shaft due to its own weight when placed in a horizontal position on supports 1 m apart. Weight of shaft = 200 N/m and Poisson's ratio = 0·3. (*U. Lond.*)   (*Ans.:* 0·0181 mm)

21. Two specimens, each 20 mm diameter, were machined from the same sample of metal. One specimen was tested in tension, showing an average extension of $3 \cdot 1 \times 10^{-9}$ m/N of axial pull, measured on a 200 mm gauge length. The second specimen was subjected to an axial torque, applied about the longitudinal axis, and was found to twist through 0·009 12° in a 200 mm gauge length for every N m of applied torque. Calculate the modulus of elasticity, the modulus of rigidity and Poisson's ratio for the metal. (*I.C.E.*)

(*Ans.:* 205 GN/m²; 80 GN/m²; 0·28)

22. Establish a relationship between the modulus of elasticity, modulus of rigidity and Poisson's ratio for an elastic material.

A close-coiled helical spring of circular wire and mean diameter 100 mm was found to extend 42·6 mm under an axial load of 50 N. The same spring, when firmly fixed at one end, was found to rotate through 90° under a torque of 6 N m applied in a plane at right angles to the axis of the spring. Calculate the value of Poisson's ratio for the material of the spring. (*U. Lond.*)   (*Ans.:* 0·3)

23. A closely coiled helical spring of circular wire has a mean diameter of coils = D. It is found to extend a length δ when loaded by an axial load W. When subjected to an axial torque T, the angle of twist, in radians, is observed to be θ.

Working from first principles, prove that Poisson's ratio for the material is

$$\frac{4T\delta}{D^2W\theta} - 1. \quad (U.\ Lond.)$$

24. The ends of a long thin-walled cylindrical tube are closed by rigid flat plates. The vessel is then subjected to internal fluid pressure under the following conditions: (*a*) free movement of the ends being allowed; (*b*) the ends being rigidly stayed together. Show that, if Poisson's ratio = 0·25, the resulting increase in the volume of the vessel will be the same in both cases. (*U. Lond.*)

25. A spherical steel vessel having an inside diameter of 0·75 m and a wall thickness of 11 mm is filled with water at a gauge pressure of 5·8 MN/m². The pressure is lowered by allowing some of the water to escape, and to reduce the pressure to atmospheric, the volume of the water released is 0·000 885 m³. Find the bulk modulus of the water. E for steel = 200 GN/m² and Poisson's ratio = 0·286. (*U. Lond.*)   (*Ans.:* 2·1 GN/m²)

26. The dimensions of a steel cylinder are: length 1·8 m, internal diameter 0·3 m, thickness of walls 12 mm. The cylinder is initially filled with water at atmospheric pressure. Treating it as a thin cylinder, find the increase in volume when the water is pumped in so as to raise the internal pressure to 7 MN/m². If the quantity of water which has to be pumped in to produce this pressure is 0·000 53 m³, find the value of the bulk modulus of the water. Neglect the deformation of the ends. Take $E = 200$ GN/m² and $v = 0·25$.   (*U. Lond.*)

(*Ans.:* 0·000 111 5 m³; 2·13 GN/m²)

27. A copper tube of 50 mm internal diameter, 1·2 m long and 1·25 mm thick, has closed ends and is filled with water under pressure. Neglecting any distortion of the end plates, determine the alteration of pressure when an additional volume of 3×10^{-6} m³ of water is pumped into the tube. Modulus of elasticity for copper = 100 GN/m². Poisson's ratio = 0·3. Bulk modulus for water = 2 GN/m². (*U. Lond.*)   (*Ans.:* 1·445 MN/m²)

28. A copper cylinder, 0·9 m long, 0·4 m external diameter and 6 mm thick, with flat ends, is initially full of oil at atmospheric pressure. Calculate the volume of oil which must be pumped into the cylinder in order to raise the pressure to 5 MN/m² above atmospheric pressure. For copper, assume $E = 100$ GN/m² and Poisson's ratio = $\frac{1}{3}$. Take the bulk modulus of the oil as 2·6 GN/m². Neglect deformation of the end plates.   (*U. Lond.*)   (*Ans.:* 521 × 10³ mm³)

29. The internal diameter of a thin straight metal tube full of water is 300 mm and its thickness 3 mm. The ends are closed with rigid end plates and an axial compressive load L is applied to it. If the rise in pressure of the water is observed to be 51 kN/m², find the load L. Neglect bending in the tube due to end effects. For the metal, $E = 140$ GN/m² and Poisson's ratio = 0·35. Bulk modulus for water = 2·05 GN/m².   (*U. Lond.*)   (*Ans.:* 10·6 kN)

30. A thin cylinder of 150 mm internal diameter and wall thickness 2·5 mm has its ends closed by rigid plates and is then filled with water. When an external axial pull of 18 kN is applied to the ends, the water pressure, read by a gauge, is observed to fall by 48 kN/m². Neglecting any end effects due to the plates, determine the value of Poisson's ratio for the metal. E for the metal = 140 GN/m²; bulk modulus of water = 2·2 GN/m².   (*U. Lond.*)   (*Ans.:* 0·311)

31. A steel tube having outside and inside diameters of 45 mm and 38 mm is firmly plugged at both ends leaving an internal length of 250 mm between the flat ends of the plugs. The plugs are designed so that water can be admitted to the inner space and also so that an axial pull can be applied to the tube. If the tube is subjected to an axial pull of 40 kN and in addition is filled with water at a gauge pressure of 1·7 MN/m², find the volume of water which will escape from the tube if the axial load is removed and the inner space opened to the atmosphere. K for water = 2·1 GN/m², $E = 200$ GN/m², Poisson's ratio = 0·286. (*U. Lond.*)   (*Ans.:* 308 mm³)

CHAPTER 14

THICK CYLINDERS

14.1 Lamé's Theory. In Art. 1.6, a formula is derived for the circumferential stress in a thin cylinder, based on the assumption that this is uniformly distributed across the thickness of the metal. Also, in calculating the volumetric strain on the contents of a thin cylinder under pressure (Examples 7 and 9, Chapter 13), it is assumed that the radial stress is negligible in relation to the circumferential and longitudinal stresses. When the thickness of the cylinder is appreciable in relation to the diameter, however, these assumptions are no longer justified and the variation in radial and circumferential stresses across the thickness is obtained from *Lamé's Theory*.

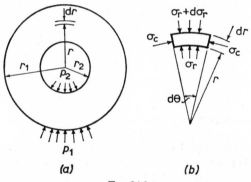

FIG. 14.1

Fig. 14.1(a) shows a thick cylinder, of external and internal radii r_1 and r_2 respectively, with external and internal pressures p_1 and p_2, and Fig. 14.1(b) shows the stresses acting on an element of radius r and thickness dr, subtending an angle $d\theta$ at the centre. The radial and circumferential stresses, σ_r and σ_c, have both been assumed to be compressive, which is considered *positive*.

If the radial stress varies from σ_r to $\sigma_r + d\sigma_r$ over the thickness dr, then, resolving forces on the element radially over a unit length of cylinder,

$$(\sigma_r + d\sigma_r)(r + dr)\,d\theta = \sigma_r r\,d\theta + 2\sigma_c\,dr\,\frac{d\theta}{2}$$

i.e.
$$r\,d\sigma_r + \sigma_r\,dr = \sigma_c\,dr^*$$

or
$$\sigma_r + r\frac{d\sigma_r}{dr} = \sigma_c \qquad . \qquad . \qquad . \qquad . \qquad . \quad (14.1)$$

* If allowance is made for the variation in σ_c over the radial thickness dr, the further term obtained is of the second order of small quantities.

If the longitudinal stress and strain are denoted by σ_l and ε_l respectively,

then
$$\varepsilon_l = \frac{\sigma_l}{E} - \nu\left(\frac{\sigma_r + \sigma_c}{E}\right)$$

It is assumed that ε_l is constant across the thickness, i.e. that a plane cross-section of the cylinder remains plane after the application of pressure, and that σ_l is also uniform across the thickness, both assumptions being reasonable on planes remote from the ends of the cylinder.

It therefore follows from these assumptions that $\sigma_r + \sigma_c$ is a constant, which will be denoted by $2a$.

Thus
$$\sigma_c = 2a - \sigma_r \quad . \qquad . \qquad . \quad (14.2)$$

Substituting in equation (14.1),
$$\sigma_r + r\frac{d\sigma_r}{dr} = 2a - \sigma_r$$

or
$$2\sigma_r r + r^2\frac{d\sigma_r}{dr} - 2ar = 0 \quad \text{multiplying through by } r$$

i.e.
$$\frac{d}{dr}(\sigma_r r^2 - ar^2) = 0$$

$$\therefore \sigma_r r^2 - ar^2 = b$$

or
$$\sigma_r = a + \frac{b}{r^2} \quad . \qquad . \qquad . \quad (14.3)$$

Therefore, from equation (14.2),
$$\sigma_c = a - \frac{b}{r^2} \quad . \qquad . \qquad . \quad (14.4)$$

Equations (14.3) and (14.4) are known as *Lamé's Equations*; in any given application, there will always be two conditions sufficient to solve for the constants a and b and radial and circumferential stresses at any radius r can then be evaluated.

Thus, in the common case of a cylinder with internal pressure only, Fig. 14.2,

$$\sigma_r = p \quad \text{when } r = r_2$$
and
$$\sigma_r = 0 \quad \text{when } r = r_1$$

$$\therefore p = a + \frac{b}{r_2^2}$$

and
$$0 = a + \frac{b}{r_1^2}$$

from which $a = -p\dfrac{r_2^2}{r_1^2 - r_2^2}$

and $b = p\dfrac{r_1^2 r_2^2}{r_1^2 - r_2^2}$

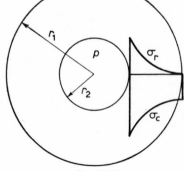

Fig. 14.2

$$\therefore \sigma_r = a + \frac{b}{r^2}$$

$$= -p \frac{r_2^2}{r_1^2 - r_2^2}\left(1 - \frac{r_1^2}{r^2}\right) \quad . \quad . \quad . \quad (14.5)$$

and

$$\sigma_c = a - \frac{b}{r^2}$$

$$= -p \frac{r_2^2}{r_1^2 - r_2^2}\left(1 + \frac{r_1^2}{r^2}\right) \quad . \quad . \quad . \quad (14.6)$$

The maximum radial and circumferential stresses occur at $r = r_2$, when $\sigma_r = p$

and $\qquad \sigma_c = -p \dfrac{r_1^2 + r_2^2}{r_1^2 - r_2^2}$, the negative sign indicating tension. . (14.7)

The variations in σ_r and σ_c across the thickness are shown in Fig. 14.2.

14.2 Comparison with thin-cylinder theory. From equation (14.7)

$$\sigma_c = p \frac{r_1^2 + r_2^2}{r_1^2 - r_2^2} \text{ (numerically)}$$

$$= p \frac{d^2 + 2dt + 2t^2}{2t(d + t)} \quad \text{where } t = r_1 - r_2 \quad \text{and} \quad d = 2r_2$$

i.e. $\qquad \dfrac{\sigma_c}{p} = \dfrac{1}{2k(1 + k)} + 1 \qquad \text{where } k = \dfrac{t}{d}$

Assuming that σ_c is constant across the thickness, as in Art. 1.4,

$$\sigma_c = \frac{pd}{2t}$$

or

$$\frac{\sigma_c}{p} = \frac{1}{2k}$$

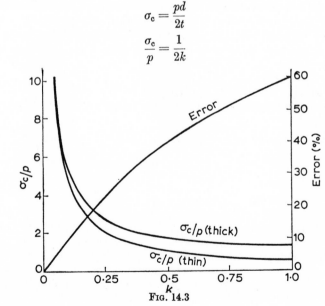

FIG. 14.3

K

The relation between σ_c/p and k from both theories is shown in Fig. 14.3 and also the error in using the thin cylinder theory, assuming Lamé's Theory to be correct. The error is 5 per cent when $k = 0.05$ (i.e. when $t = d/20$) but this falls to 0·2 per cent if the mean diameter is used in place of the internal diameter in the thin cylinder theory.

14.3 Longitudinal and shear stresses. It is assumed in Lamé's Theory that the longitudinal stress, σ_l, is uniform across a cross-section and its value is obtained by considering the equilibrium of the forces exerted on the end of the cylinder.

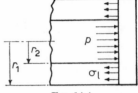

FIG. 14.4

Thus, in the case of a cylinder with internal pressure only, Fig. 14.4,

$$p \times \pi r_2^2 = \sigma_l \times \pi(r_1^2 - r_2^2)$$

$$\therefore \sigma_l = p\,\frac{r_2^2}{r_1^2 - r_2^2} \qquad . \qquad . \qquad . \qquad . \qquad . \qquad . \qquad (14.8)$$

To agree with the sign convention adopted for σ_r and σ_c, this should be negative since it is tensile and it will be seen from Art. 14.1 that it then corresponds with the value of a in Lamé's equations as applied to this case.*

In the absence of any external shearing force or torque, σ_r, σ_c and σ_l are principal stresses and hence the maximum shear stress at any point is half the difference of the maximum and minimum principal stresses (see Art 12.2). Remembering that σ_r is compressive, while σ_c and σ_l are usually tensile, the maximum shear stress at any point is given by

$$\tau = \frac{\sigma_r - \sigma_c}{2} \quad \text{since } \sigma_c > \sigma_l$$

$$= \frac{1}{2}\left\{\left(a + \frac{b}{r^2}\right) - \left(a - \frac{b}{r^2}\right)\right\} = \frac{b}{r^2} \qquad . \qquad . \qquad (14.9)$$

Thus the maximum shear stress in the cylinder will occur at the inside surface, where $r = r_2$.

14.4 The Lamé Line. Equations (14.3) and (14.4) can be written

$$\sigma_r = a + b\left(\frac{1}{r^2}\right)$$

and

$$\sigma_c = a + b\left(-\frac{1}{r^2}\right)$$

If, therefore, σ_r is plotted against $1/r^2$ and σ_c is plotted against $-1/r^2$, the two equations will be represented by the same straight line since they both have the same constant a and the same slope b. The two conditions

---

* It can be shown similarly that in the case of internal and external pressure, the longitudinal stress is again equal to the corresponding value of a if the external pressure is also assumed to act on the outside of the end plate.

which are used to solve for the constants a and b in the analytical solution are used to determine the position of the line, from which any desired values of σ_r and σ_c can then be read off.

Thus, for the simple case considered in Art. 14.1, the Lamé line is as shown in Fig. 14.5, σ_r being equal to p at $1/r_2^2$ and zero at $1/r_1^2$. The maximum value of σ_c is then evidently at $-1/r_2^2$ and is given by

$$\frac{\sigma_c}{p} = \frac{\dfrac{1}{r_1^2} + \dfrac{1}{r_2^2}}{\dfrac{1}{r_2^2} - \dfrac{1}{r_1^2}} \qquad \text{from similar triangles}$$

$$= \frac{r_1^2 + r_2^2}{r_1^2 - r_2^2}. \qquad . \quad \text{as in equation (14.7)}$$

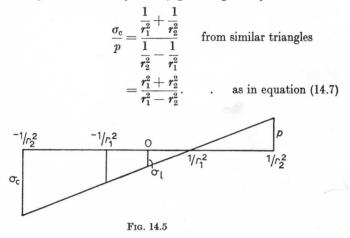

FIG. 14.5

The intercept at $1/r = 0$ represents the value of the constant a and from Art. 14.3, this is the longitudinal stress, σ_l.

14.5 Compound cylinders. A compound cylinder consists of two concentric cylinders, as shown in Fig. 14.6, the outer cylinder being shrunk on to the inner cylinder so that the latter is initially in compression before the application of internal pressure.

The final stresses are then the resultants of those due to pre-stressing and those due to the internal pressure.

If the radius of the common surface is r_0 and the pressure at this surface *before the application of the internal pressure* is p_0, then the initial stresses are determined by considering the two cylinders separately, the boundary conditions for the outer cylinder being $\sigma_r = p_0$ when $r = r_0$ and $\sigma_r = 0$ when $r = r_1$ and for the inner cylinder, $\sigma_r = p_0$ when $r = r_0$ and $\sigma_r = 0$ when $r = r_2$. The stresses due to internal pressure are obtained by considering the cylinder to be homogeneous, with $\sigma_r = p$ at $r = r_2$ and $\sigma_r = 0$ at $r = r_1$.

The various stresses are then combined algebraically, as shown in Fig. 14.7, from which it is

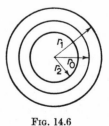

FIG. 14.6

evident that the maximum resultant circumferential stress is less than for a homogeneous cylinder of the same cross-section with the same internal pressure. Alternatively, for the same maximum stress, a thinner cylinder can be used if it is pre-stressed, the optimum conditions being when the resultant circumferential stress is the same at the inner surface of each cylinder.

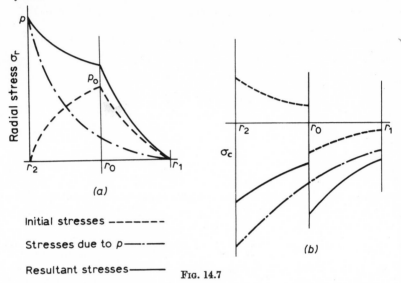

Initial stresses ‑‑‑‑‑‑‑‑

Stresses due to p ‑‑·‑‑

Resultant stresses‑‑‑‑‑

FIG. 14.7

14.6   Solid shaft subjected to external pressure. If a solid shaft of radius r_1 is subjected to an external pressure p, then

$$p = a + \frac{b}{r_1^2}$$

Since σ_r and σ_c are not infinite at $r = 0$, it follows that $b = 0$, so that $\sigma_r = \sigma_c = a = p$ at all radii.

14.7   Shrinkage allowance. In order to produce the desired initial pressure p_0 at the common surface of a compound cylinder, it is necessary for the inside diameter of the outer cylinder to be slightly smaller than the outside diameter of the inner cylinder. The outer cylinder is then heated until it will slide over the inner cylinder, whence, on cooling, it exerts the required pressure at the common surface. The initial difference in diameters at this surface is termed the *shrinkage allowance*.

For the inner cylinder, let the circumferential stress at the outer surface due to p_0 be σ_c'.

Then circumferential strain at outer surface

$$= \frac{\sigma_c'}{E} - \nu \frac{p_0}{E}$$

$\therefore$ decrease in diameter $= \dfrac{2r_0}{E}(\sigma_c' - \nu p_0)$

For the outer cylinder, let the circumferential stress at the inner surface due to p_0 be σ_c''.
Then circumferential strain at inner surface

$$= \frac{\sigma_c''}{E} - \nu \frac{p_0}{E}$$

$\therefore$ decrease* in diameter $= \dfrac{2r_0}{E}(\sigma_c'' - \nu p_0)$

$\therefore$ initial difference in diameter $= \dfrac{2r_0}{E}\{(\sigma_c' - \nu p_0) - (\sigma_c'' - \nu p_0)\}$

$$= \frac{2r_0}{E}(\sigma_c' - \sigma_c'') \quad . \qquad . \qquad (14.10)$$

If the materials of the two cylinders are different, with moduli of elasticity E_1 and E_2 and Poisson's ratio ν_1 and ν_2 respectively for the inner and outer cylinders,

then $\qquad$ shrinkage allowance $= 2r_0 \left\{ \dfrac{\sigma_c' - \nu_1 p_0}{E_1} - \dfrac{\sigma_c'' - \nu_2 p_0}{E_2} \right\}$ $\qquad$ (14.11)

1. *Find the ratio of thickness to internal diameter for a tube subjected to internal pressure when the ratio of the internal pressure to the greatest circumferential stress is* 0·5.

Find the alteration in thickness of metal in such a tube, 0·2 *m internal diameter, when the internal pressure is* 75 *MN/m².* $E = 200$ *GN/m² and* $\nu = 0.3$. (U. Lond.)

From equation (14.7), $\qquad \sigma_c = -p\dfrac{r_1^2 + r_2^2}{r_1^2 - r_2^2}$

But $\qquad p = -\dfrac{\sigma_c}{2} \qquad \therefore \dfrac{r_1^2 + r_2^2}{r_1^2 - r_2^2} = 2$

from which $\qquad\qquad r_1 = \sqrt{3}\,r_2$

$$\therefore t = r_1 - r_2 = (\sqrt{3} - 1)r_2$$

so that $\qquad\qquad \dfrac{t}{d_2} = \dfrac{\sqrt{3} - 1}{2} = \underline{0.366}$

---

* It is assumed that all stresses are compressive but in fact σ_c will be tensile and the inner surface will therefore *increase* in diameter. This will, however, be corrected automatically by the negative sign which will arise in the calculation of σ_c'' and the shrinkage allowance thus involves the *numerical sum* of the circumferential stresses.

Alternatively, set off $-\sigma_c$ at $-1/r_2^2$ and $\sigma_r = \sigma_c/2$ at $+1/r_2^2$, Fig. 14.8. Then $\sigma_r = 0$ at $1/r_1^2$.

From similar triangles,
$$\frac{\dfrac{1}{r_2^2} + \dfrac{1}{r_1^2}}{\dfrac{1}{r_2^2} - \dfrac{1}{r_1^2}} = 2$$

from which
$$r_1 = \sqrt{3 r_2}, \quad \text{as before}$$

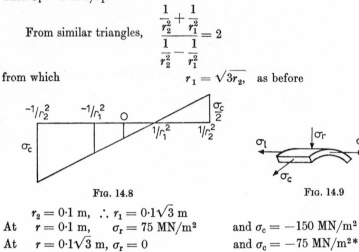

FIG. 14.8   FIG. 14.9

$r_2 = 0{\cdot}1$ m, $\therefore$ $r_1 = 0{\cdot}1\sqrt{3}$ m

At $r = 0{\cdot}1$ m, $\sigma_r = 75$ MN/m^2 and $\sigma_c = -150$ MN/m^2

At $r = 0{\cdot}1\sqrt{3}$ m, $\sigma_r = 0$ and $\sigma_c = -75$ MN/m^2*

$$\sigma_l = -p\,\frac{r_2^2}{r_1^2 - r_2^2}$$

$$= -75 \times \frac{0{\cdot}1^2}{(0{\cdot}1\sqrt{3})^2 - 0{\cdot}1^2} = -37{\cdot}5 \text{ MN/m}^2$$

The system of stresses applied to an element of the cylinder is shown in Fig. 14.9.

Tensile circumferential strain at internal surface

$$= \frac{\sigma_c}{E} + \nu\frac{\sigma_r}{E} - \nu\frac{\sigma_l}{E}$$

$$= \frac{(150 + 0{\cdot}3 \times 75 - 0{\cdot}3 \times 37{\cdot}5) \times 10^6}{200 \times 10^9}$$

$$= 0{\cdot}806\ 3 \times 10^{-3}$$

$\therefore$ increase in internal radius $= 0{\cdot}1 \times 0{\cdot}806\ 3 \times 10^{-3}$
$$= 0{\cdot}080\ 63 \times 10^{-3} \text{ m}$$

Tensile circumferential strain at external surface

$$= \frac{(75 + 0{\cdot}3 \times 0 - 0{\cdot}3 \times 37{\cdot}5) \times 10^6}{200 \times 10^9}$$

$$= 0{\cdot}318\ 8 \times 10^{-3}$$

$\therefore$ increase in external radius $= 0{\cdot}1\sqrt{3} \times 0{\cdot}318\ 8 \times 10^{-3}$
$$= 0{\cdot}055\ 3 \times 10^{-3} \text{ m}$$

* It is convenient to remember that $\sigma_l + \sigma_c$ is constant (see equation 14.2).

$\therefore$ decrease in thickness $= (0.080\ 63 - 0.055\ 3) \times 10^{-3}$ m
$$= \underline{0.025\ 3\ \text{mm}}$$

2. *A thick-walled cylinder, 0·2 m internal diameter, is to contain fluid at a pressure of 50 MN/m². Find the necessary thickness if the maximum shearing stress is not to exceed 100 MN/m². What will then be the greatest and least values of the hoop stress in the material?*

If the inner surface becomes corroded and the cylinder has to be re-bored, by how much can the inside diameter be increased without raising by more than 5 per cent the maximum shearing stress induced by the same internal pressure?

(U. Lond.)

From equation (14.9), $\qquad \tau = \dfrac{\sigma_r - \sigma_c}{2} = \dfrac{b}{r^2},$

so that τ_{max} occurs when $r = 0.1$ m,

i.e. $\qquad\qquad\qquad 100 = \dfrac{b}{0.1^2} \qquad \therefore b = 1$

Also, at $r = 0.1$ m, $\qquad \sigma_r = 50$ MN/m²

$$\therefore 50 = a + \frac{1}{0.1^2} \quad \therefore a = -50$$

At $r = r_1$, $\sigma_r = 0$, $\qquad \therefore 0 = -50 + \dfrac{1}{r_1^2} \quad \therefore r_1 = 0.141\ 4$ m

$$\therefore \text{thickness} = \underline{0.041\ 4\ \text{m}}$$

At $r = 0.1$ m, $\qquad \sigma_c = -50 - \dfrac{1}{0.1^2} \qquad = \underline{-150\ \text{MN/m}^2}$

At $r = 0.141\ 4$ m, $\qquad \sigma_c = -50 - \dfrac{1}{0.141\ 4^2} = \underline{-100\ \text{MN/m}^2}$

Alternatively, $\sigma_r + \sigma_c$ is constant, so that
$$\sigma_c \text{ at outer surface} = (50 - 150) - 0 = -100\ \text{MN/m}^2$$
When cylinder is re-bored,

$$\tau_{\text{max}} = 105\ \text{MN/m}^2 \qquad = \frac{b}{r_2^2}$$

Also at $r = r_2$, $\qquad \sigma_r = 50$ MN/m² $\qquad = a + \dfrac{b}{r_2^2} = a + 105$

$$\therefore a = -55$$
At $r = 0.141\ 4$ m, $\qquad \sigma_r = 0$

$$\therefore 0 = -55 + \frac{b}{0.141\ 4^2}$$

$$\therefore b = 1.1$$

$$\therefore r_2 = \sqrt{\frac{1.1}{105}} = 0.102\ 3\ \text{m}$$

$\therefore$ increase in diameter $= 0.004\ 6$ m $= \underline{4.6\ \text{mm}}$

3. *In a closed-ended cylinder with a diameter ratio of 2·5, the axial and circumferential strains at the outer surface were found to be* $0·918 \times 10^{-4}$ *and* $3·69 \times 10^{-4}$ *when the pressure was* $230 \ MN/m^2$. *Determine the values of the moduli of elasticity and rigidity and Poisson's ratio.*

At $r = r_2$, $\sigma_r = 230 \ \text{MN/m}^2$,

$$\therefore 230 = a + \frac{b}{r_2^2}$$

At $r = r_1$, $\sigma_r = 0$, $\therefore 0 = a + \frac{b}{(2·5r_2)^2}$ $\qquad \therefore b = -6·25 a r_2^2$

$$\therefore 230 = a - 6·25a \qquad \therefore a = -43·8$$

Therefore, at outer surface,

$$\sigma_c = a - \frac{b}{r_1^2} = 2a = -87·6 \ \text{MN/m}^2$$

$$\sigma_l = a = -43·8 \ \text{MN/m}^2$$

Alternatively, set off $\sigma_r = 230 \ \text{MN/m}^2$ at $1/r_2^2$

and $\qquad\qquad \sigma_r = 0$ at $1/r_1^2 (= 1/6·25 r_2^2)$, Fig. 14.10.

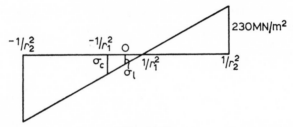

Fɪɢ. 14.10

Then

$$\frac{\sigma_c}{230} = \frac{\dfrac{1}{6·25} + \dfrac{1}{6·25}}{1 - \dfrac{1}{6·25}} = \frac{2}{5·25}$$

$$\therefore \sigma_c = 87·6 \ \text{MN/m}^2$$

and

$$\frac{\sigma_l}{230} = \frac{\dfrac{1}{6·25}}{1 - \dfrac{1}{6·25}} = \frac{1}{5·25}$$

$$\therefore \sigma_l = 43·8 \ \text{MN/m}^2$$

The radial stress at the outer surface is zero, so that

$$\text{tensile circumferential strain} = \frac{(87·6 - \nu \times 43·8) \times 10^6}{E}$$

$$= 3·69 \times 10^{-4} \quad . \qquad . \qquad . \quad (1)$$

and $\qquad$ tensile axial strain $= \dfrac{(43 \cdot 8 - \nu \times 87 \cdot 6) \times 10^6}{E}$

$$= 0 \cdot 918 \times 10^{-4} \ . \qquad . \qquad . \qquad (2)$$

Therefore, from equations (1) and (2)

$$E = \underline{203 \ \mathrm{GN/m^2}} \quad \text{and} \quad \nu = \underline{0 \cdot 287}$$

$$G = \dfrac{E}{2(1 + \nu)} \qquad \text{from equation (13.1)}$$

$$= \dfrac{203}{2(1 + 0 \cdot 287)} = \underline{78 \cdot 8 \ \mathrm{GN/m^2}}$$

4. *A thick cylinder has a length of* 0·25 *m and internal and external diameters of* 0·1 *m and* 0·141 4 *m respectively.*

(*a*) *Determine the circumferential and longitudinal stresses at the inner surface when the cylinder is filled with water under a pressure of* 10 *MN/m².*

(*b*) *How much more water does the cylinder contain than that required to fill it at atmospheric pressure?*

Take E for steel = 200 *GN/m²,* ν *for steel* = 0·3 *and K for water* = 2 *GN/m².*

At $r = 0 \cdot 05$ m, $\sigma_r = 10 \ \mathrm{MN/m^2}, \quad \therefore \ 10 = a + \dfrac{b}{0 \cdot 05^2}$

At $r = 0 \cdot 070 \ 71$ m, $\sigma_r = 0, \qquad \therefore \ 0 = a + \dfrac{b}{0 \cdot 070 \ 71^2}$

$$\therefore \ a = -10 \quad \text{and} \quad b = 0 \cdot 05$$

Therefore, at inner surface,

$$\sigma_c = a - \dfrac{b}{0 \cdot 05^2} = \underline{-30 \ \mathrm{MN/m^2}}$$

and $\qquad\qquad\qquad \sigma_l = a = \underline{-10 \ \mathrm{MN/m^2}}$

Alternatively, the stresses may be obtained from Lamé's line as in Example 3.

Referring to Fig. 14.9, tensile circumferential strain,

$$\varepsilon_c = \left(\dfrac{30}{E} + \dfrac{0 \cdot 3 \times 10}{E} - \dfrac{0 \cdot 3 \times 10}{E} \right) \times 10^6$$

$$= \dfrac{30 \times 10^6}{E}$$

and tensile longitudinal strain,

$$\varepsilon_l = \left(\dfrac{10}{E} + \dfrac{0 \cdot 3 \times 10}{E} - \dfrac{0 \cdot 3 \times 30}{E} \right) \times 10^6$$

$$= \dfrac{4 \times 10^6}{E}$$

∴ volumetric strain on contents of cylinder

$$= 2\varepsilon_c + \varepsilon_l$$

$$= \frac{64 \times 10^6}{200 \times 10^9} = 0.32 \times 10^{-3}$$

Volumetric strain on water at 10 MN/m²

$$= \frac{p}{K} = \frac{10 \times 10^6}{2 \times 10^9} = 5 \times 10^{-3}$$

∴ additional volume of water

$$= \frac{\pi}{4} \times 0.1^2 \times 0.25 \times (0.32 + 5) \times 10^{-3}$$

$$= \underline{10.45 \times 10^{-6} \text{ m}^3}$$

5. *A steel rod, 0·06 m diameter, is forced into a bronze casing having an outside diameter of 0·1 m and thereby produces a hoop tension at the outer circumference of the casing of 35 MN/m². Determine (a) the radial pressure between the rod and the casing, and (b) the rise in temperature which would just eliminate the force fit.*

For steel,　$E = 200$ GN/m², $v = 0.28$, $\alpha = 12 \times 10^{-6}/deg\ C$
For bronze, $E = 110$ GN/m², $v = 0.33$, $\alpha = 19 \times 10^{-6}/deg\ C$
(U. Lond.)

At the outer surface of the casing, $\sigma_r = 0$ and $\sigma_c = -35$ MN/m²,

$$\therefore 0 = a + \frac{b}{0.05^2}$$

and 　　　　　$$-35 = a - \frac{b}{0.05^2}$$

$$\therefore a = -17.5 \quad \text{and} \quad b = 0.043\ 75$$

Therefore when $r = 0.03$ m,

$$p = -17.5 + \frac{0.043\ 75}{0.03^2} = \underline{31.11 \text{ MN/m}^2}$$

Alternatively, set off $\sigma_r = 0$ at $\dfrac{1}{0.05^2}$ and $\sigma_c = -35$ at $-\dfrac{1}{0.05^2}$, Fig. 14.11.

Then 　　$$\frac{p}{35} = \frac{\dfrac{1}{0.03^2} - \dfrac{1}{0.05^2}}{\dfrac{1}{0.05^2} + \dfrac{1}{0.05^2}}$$

$$\therefore p = 31.11 \text{ MN/m}^2$$

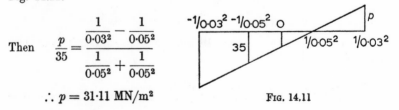

Fig. 14.11

At the surface of the rod,

$$\sigma_c = 31\cdot11 \text{ MN/m}^2 \text{ (see Art. 14.6)}$$

At the inner surface of the casing,

$$\sigma_c = -17\cdot5 - \frac{0\cdot043\ 75}{0\cdot03^2}$$

$$= -66\cdot11 \text{ MN/m}^2*$$

From equation (14.11), shrinkage allowance

$$= 2r_0\left\{\left(\frac{\sigma_c - vp}{E}\right)_{\text{steel}} - \left(\frac{\sigma_c - vp}{E}\right)_{\text{bronze}}\right\}$$

$$= 0\cdot06\left\{\frac{31\cdot11 - 0\cdot28 \times 31\cdot11}{200 \times 10^9} - \frac{-66\cdot11 - 0\cdot33 \times 31\cdot11}{110 \times 10^9}\right\}$$

$$= 48\cdot3 \times 10^{-6} \text{ m}$$

Thus $0\cdot06 \times (19 - 12) \times 10^{-6} \times T = 48\cdot3 \times 10^{-6}$

$$\therefore T = \underline{115 \text{ deg C}}$$

6. *A solid circular shaft has an outer diameter of 0·1 m and is pressed into a uniform sleeve of the same material, 0·12 m, inner diameter 0·099 9 m and outer diameter 0·125 m. If the coefficient of friction at the common surface is 0·3, find the torque which can be transmitted from the shaft to the sleeve. E = 200 GN/m².*

Let the radial pressure at the common surface be p.
Then, for the sleeve,

$$\sigma_r = p \text{ at } r = 0\cdot05 \text{ m,}\dagger \qquad \therefore p = a + \frac{b}{0\cdot05^2}$$

and $\qquad \sigma_r = 0 \text{ at } r = 0\cdot062\ 5 \text{ m,} \qquad \therefore 0 = a + \frac{b}{0\cdot062\ 5^2}$

$$\therefore a = -\frac{256}{144}p \quad \text{and} \quad b = \frac{p}{144}$$

Therefore, at the inner surface,

$$\sigma_c = a - \frac{b}{0\cdot05^2}$$

$$= -\frac{256}{144}p - \frac{400}{144}p = -\frac{41}{9}p$$

Alternatively, this stress may be determined from Lamé's line, as in Example 3.

---

* This may be obtained directly from Fig. 14.11.
† No appreciable error will be introduced by working on the nominal diameter of 0·1m.

At the surface of the shaft, $\sigma_c = p$
Therefore, from equation (14.10),

$$\text{initial difference in diameter} = \frac{0 \cdot 10}{200 \times 10^9}\left(p + \frac{41}{9}\,p\right)$$

$$= 0 \cdot 000\ 1 \text{ m}$$
$$\therefore\ p = 36 \text{ MN/m}^2$$
$$\therefore \text{ normal force between shaft and sleeve} = 36 \times 10^6 \times \pi \times 0 \cdot 10 \times 0 \cdot 12$$
$$= 1 \cdot 356 \times 10^6 \text{ N}$$
$$\therefore \text{ friction force between shaft and sleeve} = 1 \cdot 356 \times 10^6 \times 0 \cdot 3$$
$$= 0 \cdot 47 \times 10^6 \text{ N}$$
$$\therefore \text{ torque transmissible} = 0 \cdot 47 \times 10^6 \times 0 \cdot 05 \text{ N m}$$
$$= \underline{\underline{23 \cdot 5 \text{ kN m}}}$$

7. *A compound cylinder is to be subjected to an internal pressure of* 100 *MN/m². The radii of the inner, common and outer surfaces are respectively* 0·1, 0·1$\sqrt{2}$ *and* 0·2 *m. Determine the shrinkage pressure necessary for the resultant maximum circumferential stress to be as small as possible and determine the value of this stress.*

(a) *Initial stresses.* Let the shrinkage pressure be p.
For the inner cylinder,

$$\sigma_r = p \text{ at } r = 0 \cdot 1\sqrt{2} \text{ m}, \quad \therefore\ p = a_1 + \frac{b_1}{(0 \cdot 1\sqrt{2})^2} = a_1 + 50b_1$$

and $\sigma_r = 0$ at $r = 0 \cdot 1$ m, $\therefore\ 0 = a_1 + \dfrac{b_1}{0 \cdot 1^2} = a_1 + 100b_1$

$$\therefore\ a_1 = 2p \quad \text{and} \quad b_1 = -0 \cdot 02p$$

Therefore, at the inner surface,

$$\sigma_c = a_1 - \frac{b_1}{0 \cdot 1^2} \qquad = 4p$$

For the outer cylinder,

$$\sigma_r = p \text{ at } r = 0 \cdot 1\sqrt{2} \text{ m}, \quad \therefore\ p = a_2 + \frac{b_2}{(0 \cdot 1\sqrt{2})^2} = a_2 + 50b_2$$

and $\sigma_r = 0$ at $r = 0 \cdot 2$ m, $\therefore\ 0 = a_2 + \dfrac{b_2}{0 \cdot 2^2} = a_2 + 25b_2$

$$\therefore\ a_2 = -p \quad \text{and} \quad b = 0 \cdot 04p$$

Therefore, at the inner surface,

$$\sigma_c = a_2 - \frac{b_2}{(0 \cdot 1\sqrt{2})^2} \qquad = -3p$$

(b) Stresses due to internal pressure.

$$\sigma_r = 100 \text{ MN/m}^2 \text{ at } r = 0\cdot1 \text{ m}, \quad \therefore \; 100 = a + \frac{b}{0\cdot1^2} = a + 100b$$

and
$$\sigma_r = 0 \text{ at } r = 0\cdot2 \text{ m}, \quad \therefore \; 0 = a + \frac{b}{0\cdot2^2} = a + 25b$$

$$\therefore \; a = -\frac{100}{3} \quad \text{and} \quad b = \frac{4}{3}$$

Therefore, at $r = 0\cdot1$ m, $\sigma_c = a - \dfrac{b}{0\cdot1^2} = -\dfrac{100}{3} - \dfrac{400}{3} = -\dfrac{500}{3}$ MN/m²

and at $r = 0\cdot1\sqrt{2}$ m, $\quad \sigma_c = a - \dfrac{b}{(0\cdot1\sqrt{2})^2} = -\dfrac{100}{3} - \dfrac{200}{3}$

$$= -100 \text{ MN/m}^2$$

For the resultant maximum circumferential stress to be as small as possible, the resultant stresses at the inner surfaces of each cylinder must be equal, as will be evident from Fig. 14.7,

i.e.
$$-\frac{500}{3} + 4p = -100 - 3p$$

from which
$$p = 9\cdot525 \text{ MN/m}^2$$

Therefore resultant maximum stress $= -100 - 3 \times 9\cdot525$

$$= -128\cdot57 \text{ MN/m}^2$$

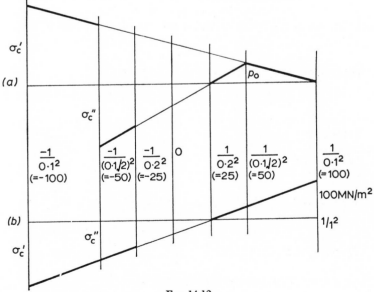

FIG. 14.12

Alternatively, the stresses may be obtained from Figs. 14.12(a) and (b) which represent the Lamé lines for the initial stresses and the stresses due to the internal pressure respectively.

From Fig. 14.12(a), $\dfrac{\sigma_c'}{p} = \dfrac{100 + 100}{100 - 50} = 4$

and $\dfrac{\sigma_c''}{p} = \dfrac{50 + 25}{50 - 25} = 3$

From Fig. 14.12(b), $\dfrac{\sigma_c'}{100} = \dfrac{100 + 25}{100 - 25} = \dfrac{5}{3}$

and $\dfrac{\sigma_c''}{100} = \dfrac{50 + 25}{100 - 25} = 1$

8. *A compound steel cylinder has a bore of 80 mm and an outside diameter of 160 mm, the diameter of the common surface being 120 mm. Find the radial pressure at the common surface which must be provided by shrinkage, if the resultant maximum hoop tension in the inner cylinder under a superimposed internal pressure of 60 MN/m² is to be half the value of the maximum hoop tension which would be produced in the inner cylinder if that cylinder alone were subjected to an internal pressure of 60 MN/m².*

Determine the final hoop tensions at the inner and outer surfaces of both cylinders under the internal pressure of 60 MN/m², and sketch a graph to show how the hoop tension varies across the cylinder wall.   (U. Lond.)

(a) *Initial stresses in inner cylinder.* Let the shrinkage pressure be p.

$\sigma_r = p$ at $r = 0.06$ m, $\therefore p = a_1 + \dfrac{b_1}{0.06^2}$

and $\sigma_r = 0$ at $r = 0.04$ m, $\therefore 0 = a_1 + \dfrac{b_1}{0.04^2}$

$\therefore a_1 = 1.8p$ and $b_1 = -0.00288p$

Therefore, at the inner surface, $\sigma_c = a_1 - \dfrac{b_1}{0.04^2} = 3.6p$

(b) *Stresses due to internal pressure.*

$\sigma_r = 60$ MN/m² at $r = 0.04$ m, $\therefore 60 = a_2 + \dfrac{b_2}{0.04^2}$

and $\sigma_r = 0$ at $r = 0.08$ m, $\therefore 0 = a_2 + \dfrac{b_2}{0.08^2}$

$\therefore a_2 = -20$ and $b_2 = 0.128$

Therefore, at the inner surface, $\sigma_c = a_2 - \dfrac{b_2}{0.04^2} = -100$ MN/m²

Therefore, resultant stress at inner surface
$$= -100 + 3.6p$$

(c) *Inner cylinder alone with internal pressure.*

$\sigma_r = 60$ MN/m² at $r = 0.04$ m, $\therefore 60 = a_3 + \dfrac{b_3}{0.04^2}$

and $\sigma_r = 0$ at $r = 0.06$ m, $\qquad \therefore 0 = a_3 + \dfrac{b_3}{0.06^2}$

$$\therefore a_3 = -48 \text{ and } b_3 = 0.172\ 8$$

Therefore, at the inner surface, $\qquad \sigma_c = a_3 - \dfrac{b_3}{0.04^2} = -156$ MN/m²

Hence $\qquad\qquad -100 + 3.6p = -\dfrac{156}{2}$

from which $\qquad\qquad\qquad p = \underline{6.11 \text{ MN/m}^2}$

(d) *Initial stresses in outer cylinder.*

$\sigma_r = p$ at $r = 0.06$ m, $\qquad \therefore p = a_4 + \dfrac{b_4}{0.06^2}$

and $\sigma_r = 0$ at $r = 0.08$ m, $\qquad \therefore 0 = a_4 + \dfrac{b_4}{0.08^2}$

$$\therefore a_4 = -1.286p \text{ and } b_4 = 0.008\ 229p$$

The resultant hoop stresses in the compound cylinder are then as follows:

Inner cylinder, inner surface: $\sigma_c = -\dfrac{156}{2}$

$$= -78 \text{ MN/m}^2$$

Inner cylinder, outer surface: $\sigma_c = \left(a_1 - \dfrac{b_1}{0.06^2}\right) + \left(a_2 - \dfrac{b_2}{0.06^2}\right)$

$$= -39.6 \text{ MN/m}^2$$

Outer cylinder, inner surface: $\sigma_c = \left(a_4 - \dfrac{b_4}{0.06^2}\right) + \left(a_2 - \dfrac{b_2}{0.06^2}\right)$

$$= -77.3 \text{ MN/m}^2$$

Outer cylinder, outer surface: $\sigma_c = \left(a_4 - \dfrac{b_4}{0.08^2}\right) + \left(a_2 - \dfrac{b_2}{0.08^2}\right)$

$$= -55.7 \text{ MN/m}^2$$

The variation in hoop stress across the cylinder is shown in Fig. 14.13.

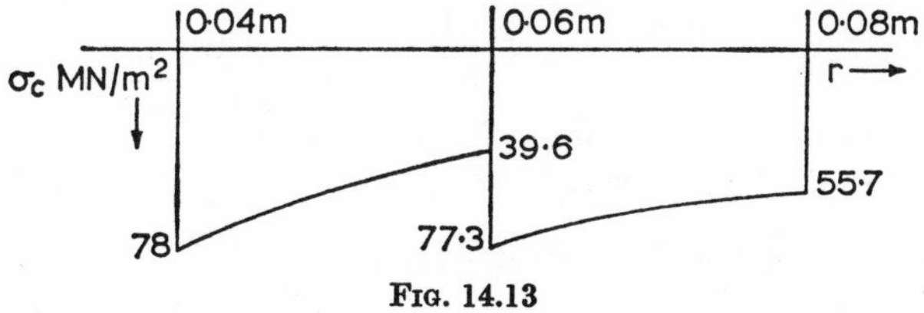

FIG. 14.13

9. *A bronze cylinder of 0·3 m internal diameter and 0·4 m external diameter is surrounded by a closely fitting steel sleeve of 0·45 m external diameter. Calculate the maximum hoop stresses in the steel and bronze when an internal pressure of 30 MN/m² is applied to the compound cylinder, assuming that before the application of this pressure, the contact stress at the common surface is zero.*

For steel, $E = 200 \ GN/m^2$ and $\nu = 0.28$
For bronze, $E = 100 \ GN/m^2$ and $\nu = 0.35$ (U. Lond.)

Let the pressure at the common surface *after* the application of the internal pressure be p. Then, for the inner cylinder,

$$\sigma_r = 30 \ \text{MN/m}^2 \text{ at } r = 0.15 \text{ m}, \quad \therefore \ 30 = a_1 + \frac{b_1}{0.15^2}$$

$$\text{and } \sigma_r = p \text{ at } r = 0.2 \text{ m}, \quad \therefore \ p = a_1 + \frac{b_1}{0.2^2}$$

$$\therefore \ a_1 = -38.6 + 2.285p \ \text{ and } \ b_1 = 1.544 - 0.051 \ 4p$$

Therefore, at the common surface,

$$\sigma_c = a_1 - \frac{b_1}{0.2^2} = -77.2 - 3.57p$$

For the outer cylinder,

$$\sigma_r = p \text{ at } r = 0.2 \text{ m}, \quad \therefore \ p = a_2 + \frac{b_2}{0.2^2}$$

$$\text{and } \sigma_r = 0 \text{ at } r = 0.225 \text{ m}, \quad \therefore \ 0 = a_2 + \frac{b_2}{0.225^2}$$

$$\therefore \ a_2 = -3.76p \ \text{ and } \ b_2 = 0.190 \ 5p$$

Therefore, at the common surface,

$$\sigma_c = a_2 - \frac{b_2}{0.2^2} = -8.52p$$

The diametral strain at the common surface must be the same,

$$\therefore \ \frac{(-77.2 + 3.57p) - 0.35p}{100 \times 10^9} = \frac{-8.52p - 0.28p}{200 \times 10^9} \ *$$

from which $p = \underline{10.13 \ \text{MN/m}^2}$

Therefore, at the inner surface of the inner cylinder,

$$\sigma_c = a_1 - \frac{b_1}{0.15^2} = \underline{-60.8 \ \text{MN/m}^2}$$

At the inner surface of the outer cylinder,
$$\sigma_c = -8.52p = \underline{-86.4 \ \text{MN/m}^2}$$

---

* Neglecting longitudinal stresses. If these are to be taken into account, the compound cylinder must first be treated as a composite bar under external load (i.e. the force on the end plates), as in Art. 1.9.

10. A cylindrical steel container has inner diameter 250 mm and outer diameter 400 mm. If the maximum permissible tensile stress is 140 MN/m², what is the maximum internal pressure it can carry and what will be the tangential stress at the outer circumference due to this internal pressure? (*U. Lond.*)

(*Ans.:* 61·35 MN/m²; 78·65 MN/m²)

11. A steel pipe 100 mm outside diameter and 50 mm inside diameter is subjected to an internal pressure of 14 MN/m², and an external pressure of 5·5 MN/m². Plot a curve showing the distribution of tangential stress across the wall of the pipe. Prove any formula used. (*U. Lond.*)

(*Ans.:* Maximum stress = 8·67 MN/m²)

12. State clearly the assumptions made in Lamé's theory of thick cylinders.

A cast-iron pipe 150 mm internal diameter and 200 mm external diameter is tested under pressure and breaks at an internal pressure of 48 MN/m². Find the safe internal pressure for a pipe of the same material and of the same internal diameter with walls 40 mm thick, using a factor of safety of 4. (*U. Lond.*)

(*Ans.:* 17·3 MN/m²)

13. Find the ratio of thickness to internal diameter for a tube subjected to internal pressure when the pressure is $\frac{5}{8}$ of the value of the maximum permissible circumferential stress.

Find the increase in internal diameter of such a tube 100 mm internal diameter when the internal pressure is 100 MN/m². $E = 200 \, \text{GN/m}^2$; Poisson's ratio = 0·286. (*U. Lond.*)

(*Ans.:* 0·541; 0·094 3 mm)

14. The cylinder of a hydraulic ram supported at the open end is 250 mm internal diameter, and is required to sustain an internal pressure of 20 MN/m². Calculate the necessary thickness of the wall if the maximum shearing stress is limited to 50 MN/m².

Allowing for the effect of the longitudinal stress caused by the pressure on the end of the ram, calculate the increase in diameter due to the application of the 20 MN/m² pressure. $E = 200 \, \text{GN/m}^2$; Poisson's ratio = 0·28. (*U. Lond.*)

(*Ans.:* 36·5 mm; 0·0966 mm)

15. Derive from first principles formulae for the radial and hoop stresses in a thick cylinder at any radius r when subjected to radial pressure.

A thick cylinder of steel having an internal diameter of 100 mm and an external diameter of 200 mm is subjected to an internal pressure of 56 MN/m² and an external pressure of 7 MN/m². Find the maximum direct and shearing stresses in the cylinder and calculate the change of external diameter.

$E = 200 \, \text{GN/m}^2$ and Poisson's ratio = 0·3. (*U. Lond.*)

(*Ans.:* 74·67 MN/m²; 65·33 MN/m²; 0·027 8 mm)

16. A steel tube is 18 mm internal diameter and 3 mm thick. One end is closed and the other end is screwed into a pressure vessel. The projecting length is 300 mm. Neglecting any constraints due to the ends, calculate the safe internal pressure if the allowable stress is not to exceed 150 MN/m². Calculate the increase in the internal volume under this pressure. $E = 200 \, \text{GN/m}^2$; Poisson's ratio = 1/3·5. (*U. Lond.*)

(*Ans.:* 42 MN/m²; 120·6 mm³)

17. Derive formulae for the principal stresses and maximum shearing stress at any point in a thick cylinder subjected to radial pressure.

A steel cylinder is 1 m inside diameter and is to be designed for an internal pressure of 8 MN/m². Calculate the thickness if the maximum shearing stress is not to exceed 35 MN/m². Calculate the increase in volume, due to the working pressure, if the cylinder is 6 m long with closed ends. Neglect any constraints due to the ends. $E = 200 \, \text{GN/m}^2$; Poisson's ratio = 1/3. (*U. Lond.*)

(*Ans.:* 69·3 mm; 0·002 835 m³)

18. A thick steel tube with closed ends, of inside and outside diameters 50 mm and 70 mm respectively, contains oil at a pressure of 1 MN/m^2. The oil is allowed to escape until the pressure in the tube has fallen to 0·75 MN/m^2. Find how much oil has been released per metre length of tube, if bending due to end effects is negligible.

E for steel = 200 GN/m^2; K for oil = 2·75 GN/m^2; ν for steel = 0·25.

(*U. Lond.*) (*Ans.:* 195 mm^3)

19. A bronze sleeve 75 mm external diameter is a sliding fit on a solid steel ram 50 mm diameter. When used in a pump, the external pressure is 30 MN/m^2. Calculate the maximum stresses induced in the steel and the bronze. E for steel = 200 GN/m^2; E for bronze = 90 GN/m^2; Poisson's ratio = 0·35 for both materials. (*U. Lond.*) (*Ans.:* 33·32 MN/m^2; 24·68 MN/m^2)

20. A bronze liner of 50 mm external diameter is to be shrunk on a steel rod of 40 mm diameter. Calculate the maximum radial pressure between liner and rod if the maximum stress in the liner is limited to 120 MN/m^2, also the difference between the liner bore and shaft diameter before shrinking.

E for steel and bronze 200 GN/m^2 and 90 GN/m^2 respectively. Poisson's ratio 0·3 for both steel and bronze. (*U. Lond.*)

(*Ans.:* 26·35 MN/m^2; 0·0605 mm)

21. A ring 12 mm internal diameter has a uniform outside diameter of 40 mm and is 20 mm long axially. An oversize plug is pressed into the ring. If the maximum stress in the ring must not exceed 450 MN/m^2, calculate the maximum difference in diameter of the plug and ring. E = 200 GN/m^2; Poisson's ratio = 0·3. (*U. Lond.*) (*Ans.:* 0·0495 mm)

22. A bronze bush having an outside diameter of 175 mm and an inside diameter of 100 mm is pressed into a recess in a body which is assumed to be perfectly rigid. If the diameter of the recess is 174·95 mm, find the radial pressure produced on the outer surface of the bush and the maximum hoop stress in the bush. Determine also the change in the inside diameter of the bush.

For bronze, take E = 100 GN/m^2 and Poisson's ratio = 0·35. (*U. Lond.*)
(*Ans.:* 17·4 MN/m^2; 51·65 MN/m^2; 0·051 65 mm)

23. If the diameter ratio of a cast-iron hub is 1·75, calculate from first principles what driving allowance should be made on the diameter of the steel shaft on which it is to be forced, when the bursting stress is limited to 24 MN/m^2.

E for steel = 200 GN/m^2; E for cast-iron = 100 GN/m^2; Poisson's ratio = 0·3 for both materials. (*U. Lond.*) (*Ans.:* 0·000 309 6d)

24. A steel cylindrical plug of 125 mm diameter is forced into a steel sleeve of 200 mm external diameter and 100 mm long. If the greatest circumferential stress in the sleeve is 100 MN/m^2, find the torque required to turn the plug in the sleeve assuming the coefficient of friction between the plug and the sleeve is 0·2.

(*U. Lond.*) (*Ans.:* 21·5 kNm)

25. Derive the fundamental formulae for the principal stresses in a thick cylinder under radial pressure.

A solid plug gauge of steel has a diameter of 25·005 mm, and is forced into a ring gauge of the same material, which measures 25 mm inside diameter and 50 mm outside diameter. Its axial length is 20 mm. What is the maximum stress in the ring, and what force is required to slide the plug, assuming the coefficient of friction is 0·3? Take E = 200 GN/m^2. (*U. Lond.*)

(*Ans.:* 25 MN/m^2; 7·07 kN)

26. One steel cylinder is shrunk on to another, the compound cylinder having an inside diameter of 100 mm, an outside diameter of 200 mm and a diameter of 150 mm at the surfaces in contact. If shrinkage produces a radial pressure p_0 at the surfaces in contact, after which the compound cylinder is subjected to an internal pressure p_1, find the ratio of p_0 to p_1 so that the maximum hoop tensions in the two cylinders shall be the same. (*U. Lond.*) (*Ans.:* 0·103)

27. A gun-metal cylinder, 150 mm external diameter and 99·925 mm internal diameter is forced on to a steel cylinder 100 mm external diameter and 50 mm internal diameter. Calculate the maximum resulting stresses in the steel and gun-metal.

E for steel = 200 GN/m²; E for gun-metal = 100 GN/m²; Poisson's ratio = 0·35 for both metals. (*U. Lond.*) (*Ans.:* 55·4 MN/m²; 54·1 MN/m²)

28. A steel cylinder of 100 mm internal diameter and 150 mm outside diameter is strengthened by shrinking another cylinder of the same length on to it. The inside diameter of this cylinder was originally 149·925 mm. Find the external diameter of the outer cylinder so that the contact pressure after shrinking will be 17 MN/m². E = 200 GN/m². (*U. Lond.*) (*Ans.:* 205·4 mm)

29. A steel cylinder 200 mm external diameter and 150 mm internal diameter has another cylinder 250 mm external diameter shrunk on to it. If the maximum tensile stress induced in the outer cylinder is 80 MN/m², find the radial compressive stress between the cylinders.

Determine the circumferential stresses at inner and outer diameter of both cylinders and show, by means of a diagram, how these stresses vary with the radius. Calculate the necessary shrinkage allowance at the common surface.

E = 200 GN/m². (*U. Lond.*)

(*Ans.:* 17·6, 80, 62·5, 80·5, 62·8 MN/m²; 01428 mm)

30. A compound cylinder is to be made by shrinking an outer tube of 300 mm external diameter on to an inner tube of 150 mm internal diameter. Determine the common diameter at the junction if the greatest circumferential stress in the inner tube is to be two-thirds of the greatest circumferential stress in the outer tube. (*U. Lond.*) (*Ans.:* 243·5 mm)

31. A steel cylinder of outside diameter 300 mm and inside diameter 250 mm is shrunk on to one having diameters 250 mm and 200 mm, the interference fit being such that under an internal pressure p the inner tensile stress in both cylinders = 84 MN/m².

Find the initial difference in the nominal 250 mm diameters, and the value of p if E = 200 GN/m². (*U. Lond.*) (*Ans.:* 0·0273 mm; 36·9 MN/m²)

32. A steel spur-wheel ring of 550 mm external diameter is shrunk on to a wheel centre, the original difference of diameters being 0·4 mm. The effective thickness of the ring is 40 mm and of the wheel centre, which may be regarded as a hollow cylinder, 25 mm. Estimate the radial pressure at the common surface. E = 200 GN/m². (*U. Lond.*) (*Ans.:* 11·1 MN/m²)

STRAIN ENERGY; THEORIES OF FAILURE

15.1 Strain energy due to three principal stresses. Fig. 15.1 shows an element of a material which is subjected to three principal stresses σ_x, σ_y and σ_z.

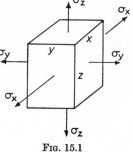

Force due to $\sigma_x = \sigma_x \times yz$.

Strain in direction of $\sigma_x = \dfrac{\sigma_x}{E} - \dfrac{\nu(\sigma_y + \sigma_z)}{E}$

$\therefore$ change in length of side x

$$= \frac{x}{E}\{\sigma_x - \nu(\sigma_y + \sigma_z)\}$$

Fig. 15.1

$\therefore$ work done by $\sigma_x = \dfrac{1}{2} \times \sigma_x \times yz \times \dfrac{x}{E}\{\sigma_x - \nu(\sigma_y + \sigma_z)\}$

$$= \frac{xyz}{2E}\{\sigma_x^2 - \nu(\sigma_x\sigma_y + \sigma_x\sigma_z)\}$$

Similarly, work done by $\sigma_y = \dfrac{xyz}{2E}\{\sigma_y^2 - \nu(\sigma_y\sigma_x + \sigma_y\sigma_z)\}$

and   work done by $\sigma_z = \dfrac{xyz}{2E}\{\sigma_z^2 - \nu(\sigma_z\sigma_x + \sigma_z\sigma_y)\}$

$\therefore$ total work done $= \dfrac{xyz}{2E}\{\sigma_x^2 + \sigma_y^2 + \sigma_z^2 - 2\nu(\sigma_x\sigma_y + \sigma_y\sigma_z + \sigma_z\sigma_x)\}$

This work is stored in the material as strain energy and since xyz represents the volume of the element, strain energy per unit volume,

$$U = \frac{1}{2E}\{\sigma_x^2 + \sigma_y^2 + \sigma_z^2 - 2\nu(\sigma_x\sigma_y + \sigma_y\sigma_z + \sigma_z\sigma_x)\} \quad . \quad (15.1)$$

15.2 Volumetric and shear strain energy. The system of stresses shown in Fig. 15.1 produces (*a*) a change in volume of the element, and (*b*) a change in shape of the element, due to the shear stresses resulting from the unequal direct stresses.

If the three principal stresses are equal, there is no shear stress in the body and the strain is purely volumetric. Thus if $\sigma_x = \sigma_y = \sigma_z = \sigma$, strain energy per unit volume $= \dfrac{1}{2E}\{3\sigma^2 - 2v \times 3\sigma^2\}$

$$= \frac{3(1 - 2v)}{2E}\sigma^2 = \frac{\sigma^2}{2K} \qquad . \qquad . \qquad . \quad (15.2)$$

Since the strain energy is due only to change in volume, it is termed the *volumetric strain energy* (U_v).

The general case of unequal stresses can be resolved into volumetric and shear stresses as follows:

$$\sigma_x = \frac{\sigma_x + \sigma_y + \sigma_z}{3} + \frac{\sigma_x - \sigma_y}{3} + \frac{\sigma_x - \sigma_z}{3}$$

$$\sigma_y = \frac{\sigma_x + \sigma_y + \sigma_z}{3} - \frac{\sigma_x - \sigma_y}{3} + \frac{\sigma_y - \sigma_z}{3}$$

$$\sigma_z = \frac{\sigma_x + \sigma_y + \sigma_z}{3} - \frac{\sigma_x - \sigma_z}{3} - \frac{\sigma_y - \sigma_z}{3}$$

Thus the given stresses σ_x, σ_y and σ_z can be represented by Fig. 15.2, the stresses on element (a) involving pure volumetric strain and those on elements (b), (c) and (d) involving pure shear strain in each of the three co-ordinate planes (see Art. 12.3).

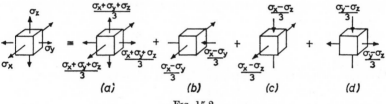

(a)   (b)   (c)   (d)

Fig. 15.2

The volumetric strain energy due to the equal stresses on element (a)

$$= \frac{1}{2K}\left(\frac{\sigma_x + \sigma_y + \sigma_z}{3}\right)^2 . \qquad \text{from equation (15.2)}$$

$$= \frac{1}{18K}(\sigma_x + \sigma_y + \sigma_z)^2$$

The shear strain energy due to the shear stresses on elements (b), (c) and (d) is the difference between the total strain energy and the volumetric strain energy,[*]

i.e. shear strain energy per unit volume,

$$U_s = \frac{1}{2E}\{\sigma_x^2 + \sigma_y^2 + \sigma_z^2 - 2v(\sigma_x\sigma_y + \sigma_y\sigma_z + \sigma_z\sigma_x)\}$$

$$- \frac{1}{18K}(\sigma_x + \sigma_y + \sigma_z)^2$$

[*] This can alternatively be obtained by considering the work done by each of the stresses on elements (b), (c) and (d) due to the resultant strains they produce.

$$= \frac{1}{2E}\{\sigma_x^2 + \sigma_y^2 + \sigma_z^2 - 2\nu(\sigma_x\sigma_y + \sigma_y\sigma_z + \sigma_z\sigma_x)\}$$

$$- \frac{1 - 2\nu}{6E}\{\sigma_x^2 + \sigma_y^2 + \sigma_z^2 + 2(\sigma_x\sigma_y + \sigma_y\sigma_z + \sigma_z\sigma_x)\}$$

$$= \frac{1 + \nu}{3E}\{\sigma_x^2 + \sigma_y^2 + \sigma_z^2 - (\sigma_x\sigma_y + \sigma_y\sigma_z + \sigma_z\sigma_x)\}$$

$$= \frac{1}{6G}\{\sigma_x^2 + \sigma_y^2 + \sigma_z^2 - (\sigma_x\sigma_y + \sigma_y\sigma_z + \sigma_z\sigma_x)\} \quad . \quad . \quad (15.3)$$

15.3 Theories of elastic failure. In a simple tension test, elastic failure is assumed to occur when the stress reaches the elastic limit stress for the material, which will be denoted by σ_0. When a body is subjected to a complex stress system, however, elastic failure does not necessarily occur when the greatest principal stress reaches the value σ_0; the other (lesser) principal stresses in the perpendicular directions may affect the limiting value of the greatest principal stress at failure, which may then be greater or smaller than σ_0.

The effect of the lesser principal stresses at failure depends upon the application, i.e. on whether they are of the same or opposite sign to the greatest principal stress and on whether the material is brittle or ductile. Various theories have been propounded on elastic failure of a material under complex stress and these are usually associated with the name of the originator. Much research has been done on these theories and the most important applications are given after each theory.

Whatever the system of stress applied to a body, it can always be resolved into three principal stresses, as shown in Fig. 15.1 and in the following, it is assumed that $\sigma_x > \sigma_y > \sigma_z$ and that all are of the same sign.

(a) *Maximum Principal Stress Theory (Rankine's Theory)*. Failure occurs when the greatest principal stress reaches the elastic limit stress in a simple tension test, irrespective of the other principal stresses,

i.e.   when $\sigma_x = \sigma_0$.   .   .   . (15.4)

This theory has been found approximately true for brittle materials but not for ductile materials, when rupture takes place on a plane inclined to the plane of greatest direct stress, indicating failure due to shear.

(b) *Maximum Principal Strain Theory (St. Venant's Theory)*. Failure occurs when the greatest principal strain reaches the strain at the elastic limit in a simple tension test,

i.e.   when $\dfrac{\sigma_x}{E} - \nu \dfrac{(\sigma_y + \sigma_z)}{E} = \dfrac{\sigma_0}{E}$

or $\sigma_x - \nu(\sigma_y + \sigma_z) = \sigma_0$.   .   . (15.5)

For like stresses, this theory gives $\sigma_x > \sigma_0$ but this is not substantiated by experiment and the theory finds little general support.

(c) *Maximum Shear Stress Theory (Guest's or Tresca's Theory).* Failure occurs when the greatest shear stress reaches the maximum shear stress at the elastic limit in a simple tension test,

i.e.   when $\dfrac{\sigma_x - \sigma_z}{2} = \dfrac{\sigma_0}{2}$

or $\sigma_x - \sigma_z = \sigma_0$.   .   .   . (15.6)

This theory gives generally good correlation with experimental results obtained with ductile materials.

Care must be taken in applying equation (15.6) to the case of unlike stresses; the maximum shear stress involves the greatest *algebraic* difference of principal stresses.

(d) *Strain Energy Theory (Haigh's Theory).* Failure occurs when the energy stored per unit volume in a strained material reaches the strain energy per unit volume at the elastic limit in a simple tension test, i.e. the maximum energy a body can store without permanent deformation is a fixed quantity, irrespective of the manner in which it is strained.

Thus $\dfrac{1}{2E}\{\sigma_x^2 + \sigma_y^2 + \sigma_z^2 - 2\nu(\sigma_x\sigma_y + \sigma_y\sigma_z + \sigma_z\sigma_x) = \dfrac{\sigma_0^2}{2E}$

or $\sigma_x^2 + \sigma_y^2 + \sigma_z^2 - 2\nu(\sigma_x\sigma_y + \sigma_y\sigma_z + \sigma_z\sigma_x) = \sigma_0^2$. (15.7)

This theory receives good support from experiments on ductile materials, particularly with thick cylinders. It breaks down, however, in the case of hydrostatic pressure ($\sigma_x = \sigma_y = \sigma_z = \sigma$); it predicts failure when $\sigma = \sigma_0/\sqrt{3(1 - 2\nu)}$ whereas, in fact, no failure would occur.

(e) *Shear Strain Energy Theory (Von Mises's Theory).* Failure occurs when the shear strain energy stored per unit volume in a strained material reaches the shear strain energy per unit volume at the elastic limit in a simple tension test; this is similar to the preceding theory but it is assumed that the volumetric strain energy plays no part in producing elastic failure.

Thus $\dfrac{1}{6G}\{\sigma_x^2 + \sigma_y^2 + \sigma_z^2 - (\sigma_x\sigma_y + \sigma_y\sigma_z + \sigma_z\sigma_x)\} = \dfrac{\sigma_0^{2*}}{6G}$

or $\sigma_x^2 + \sigma_y^2 + \sigma_z^2 - (\sigma_x\sigma_y + \sigma_y\sigma_z + \sigma_z\sigma_x) = \sigma_0^2$. (15.8)

The results given by this theory are generally similar to those given by the strain energy theory (see Fig. 15.3). It is more recent and may be regarded as a refinement of the strain energy theory but experimental evidence is not conclusive.

* Obtained by putting $\sigma_y = \sigma_z = 0$ in equation (15.3). This result should not be confused with $\tau^2/2G$ per unit volume, given by equation (1.21); τ is the *shear* stress whereas σ_0 is the *direct* stress.

15.4   Two-dimensional cases. If $\sigma_z = 0$, the five theories of elastic failure reduce to

(a) $$\sigma_x = \sigma_0 \qquad \cdot \qquad \cdot \qquad \cdot \qquad \cdot \qquad . \quad (15.9)$$

(b) $$\sigma_x - \nu\sigma_y = \sigma_0 \qquad \cdot \qquad \cdot \qquad \cdot \qquad (15.10)$$

(c) $$\left.\begin{array}{l}\sigma_x = \sigma_0 \quad \text{(for like stresses)} \\ \text{or} \quad \sigma_x - \sigma_y = \sigma_0 \quad \text{(for unlike stresses)}\end{array}\right\} \quad (15.11)$$

(d) $$\sigma_x^2 + \sigma_y^2 - 2\nu\sigma_x\sigma_y = \sigma_0^2 \qquad \cdot \qquad \cdot \qquad \cdot \qquad (15.12)$$

(e) $$\sigma_x^2 + \sigma_y^2 - \sigma_x\sigma_y = \sigma_0^2 \qquad \cdot \qquad \cdot \qquad \cdot \qquad (15.13)$$

These results are shown graphically in Fig. 15.3; the horizontal axis

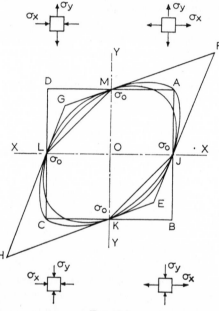

Fig. 15.3

represents σ_x and the vertical axis represents σ_y, tension upwards and to the right, compression downwards and to the left.

For the *maximum principal stress theory*, the boundary within which σ_x and σ_y must lie for no failure is the square ABCD, the limiting value in either direction along OX and OY being σ_0.

For the *maximum principal strain theory*, the boundaries EF and FG represent respectively $\sigma_x - \nu\sigma_y = \sigma_0$ (for $\sigma_x > \sigma_y$) and $\sigma_y - \nu\sigma_x = \sigma_0$ (for $\sigma_y > \sigma_x$), the greater principal stress in each case being tensile. The lines GH and HE represent the corresponding equations when the greater principal stress is compressive.

The *maximum shear stress theory* gives $\sigma_x = \sigma_0$ (for $\sigma_x > \sigma_y$) and $\sigma_y = \sigma_0$ (for $\sigma_y > \sigma_x$) with like stresses; thus, in the first and third quadrants, the boundary coincides with that for the maximum principal stress theory.

For unlike stresses (second and fourth quadrants), $\sigma_x - \sigma_y = \sigma_0$ (or $\sigma_y - \sigma_x = \sigma_0$), where the maximum stress in either case can be tensile or compressive. These equations are represented by JK and LM.

The *strain energy* and *shear strain energy theories* are represented by ellipses with their axes inclined at 45° to OX and OY, the latter ellipse passing through the corners A and C.

Fig. 15.3 shows clearly the following points:

(*a*) the boundary representing the maximum shear stress theory and the two strain energy theories are generally similar;

(*b*) the maximum principal stress theory, usually regarded as only applicable to brittle materials, is nevertheless applicable to ductile materials in the case of like stresses, where it coincides with the maximum shear stress theory;

(*c*) the maximum principal strain theory diverges widely from the other theories in the case of like stresses.

1. *In a piece of material, the stresses on two planes at right angles are: on the first plane 60 MN/m² tension and 20 MN/m² shearing stress; on the second plane 40 MN/m² compression and the complementary shearing stress. On a plane mutually at right angles to both the planes specified, there is no stress. Find the equivalent system of pure shear and pure bulk stress.*

Calculate (a) the total strain energy stored per unit volume, (b) the strain energy stored in volumetric strain and in shear strain. Take Young's modulus and the bulk modulus both as 200 GN/m² and Poisson's ratio as $\frac{1}{3}$.

(U. Lond.)

The principal stresses are given by

$$\sigma = \tfrac{1}{2}\{(\sigma_x + \sigma_y) \pm \sqrt{(\sigma_x - \sigma_y)^2 + 4\tau^2}\} \quad . \quad \text{from equation (12.12)}$$

$$= \tfrac{1}{2}\{(60 - 40) \pm \sqrt{(60 + 40)^2 + 4 \times 20^2}\}$$

$$= 10(1 \pm \sqrt{29}) \text{ MN/m}^2$$

Hence the principal stresses are $10(1 + \sqrt{29})$, $10(1 - \sqrt{29})$ and 0, and the mean stress is $\dfrac{20}{3}$ MN/m².

Resolving the principal stresses as in Art. 15.2,

$$10(1 + \sqrt{29}) = \frac{20}{3} + \frac{20\sqrt{29}}{3} + \frac{10(1 + \sqrt{29})}{3}$$

$$10(1 - \sqrt{29}) = \frac{20}{3} - \frac{20\sqrt{29}}{3} + \frac{10(1 - \sqrt{29})}{3}$$

and $$0 = \frac{20}{3} - \frac{10(1 + \sqrt{29})}{3} - \frac{10(1 - \sqrt{29})}{3}$$

Thus the given stress system is equivalent to a bulk stress of $\frac{20}{3}$ MN/m² and shear stresses in the three co-ordinate planes of $\frac{10}{3}(1 + \sqrt{29})$, $\frac{10}{3}(1 - \sqrt{29})$ and $\frac{20}{3}\sqrt{29}$ MN/m².

From equation (15.1),

$$U = \frac{10^2}{2E}\{(1+\sqrt{29})^2 + (1-\sqrt{29})^2 - \tfrac{2}{3}(1+\sqrt{29})(1-\sqrt{29})\} \times 10^{12}$$

$$= \frac{23 \cdot 3 \times 10^{15}}{6 \times 200 \times 10^9} = \underline{19\ 667\ \text{J/m}^3}$$

From equation (15.2),

$$U_v = \frac{(\tfrac{20}{3})^2 \times 10^{12}}{2 \times 200 \times 10^9} = \underline{111\ \text{J/m}^3}$$

$$\therefore U_s = 19\ 667 - 111 = \underline{19\ 556\ \text{J/m}^3}$$

2. *In a two-dimensional stress system, normal stresses of 20 and 120 N/mm² act on two mutually perpendicular planes in conjunction with a shear stress of 40 N/mm². The stress intensity, judged by the shear strain energy, is excessive. As it was found impossible to reduce the applied stresses, the severity of the shear strain energy condition was reduced by increasing the normal stress of 20 N/mm² to some higher tensile value, X. Find the value of X at which the shear strain energy is least.* (U. Lond.)

The principal stresses are given by

$$\sigma = \tfrac{1}{2}\{(120+X) \pm \sqrt{(120-X)^2 + 4 \times 40^2}\} \quad \text{from equation (12.12)}$$

i.e. , $$\sigma_1 = \left(60 + \frac{X}{2}\right) + \sqrt{5\ 200 - 60X + \left(\frac{X}{2}\right)^2}$$

and $$\sigma_2 = \left(60 + \frac{X}{2}\right) - \sqrt{5\ 200 - 60X + \left(\frac{X}{2}\right)^2}$$

$$\therefore U_s = \frac{1}{6G}\{\sigma_1^2 + \sigma_2^2 - \sigma_1\sigma_2\} \qquad . \qquad . \qquad . \qquad \text{from equation (15.3)}$$

$$= \frac{1}{6G}(19\ 200 - 120X + X^2), \text{ substituting for } \sigma_1 \text{ and } \sigma_2$$

For maximum shear strain energy, $\dfrac{\mathrm{d}U_s}{\mathrm{d}X} = 0$,

$$\therefore X = \underline{60\ \text{N/mm}^2}$$

3. *A thin cylinder of internal diameter 0·3 m is subjected to an internal pressure of 4 MN/m² and to an axial torque of 9π kN m. If the maximum safe stress for the material in simple tension is 150 MN/m² and ν = 0·3, find the required thickness by each of the five theories of elastic failure.*

From Art. (1.4),

$$\sigma_c = \frac{pd}{2t} = \frac{4 \times 10^6 \times 0·3}{2t} \; N/m^2 = \frac{0·6}{t} \; MN/m^2$$

$$\sigma_l = \frac{\sigma_c}{2} = \frac{0·3}{t} \; MN/m^2$$

$$\tau = \frac{\text{torque}}{\text{radius} \times \text{cross-sectional area}} = \frac{9\pi \times 10^3}{0·15(\pi \times 0·3 \times t)} \; N/m^2$$

$$= \frac{0·2}{t} \; MN/m^2$$

Therefore the principal stresses are given by

$$\sigma = \frac{1}{2}\left\{\left(\frac{0·6}{t} + \frac{0·3}{t}\right) \pm \sqrt{\left(\frac{0·6}{t} - \frac{0·3}{t}\right)^2 + 4\left(\frac{0·2}{t}\right)^2}\right\}$$

$$= \frac{1}{2t}(0·9 \pm 0·5)$$

$$\therefore \; \sigma_1 = \frac{0·7}{t} \quad \text{and} \quad \sigma_2 = \frac{0·2}{t} \; MN/m^2$$

(*a*) Maximum principal stress theory:

$$\frac{0·7}{t} = 150 \qquad \therefore \; t = \underline{0·004\ 67 \; m}$$

(*b*) Maximum principal strain theory:

$$\frac{0·7}{t} - 0·3 \times \frac{0·2}{t} = 150 \qquad \therefore \; t = \underline{0·004\ 27 \; m}$$

(*c*) Maximum shear stress theory:

$$\frac{0·7}{t} = 150* \qquad \therefore \; t = \underline{0·004\ 67 \; m}$$

(*d*) Strain energy theory:

$$\left(\frac{0·7}{t}\right)^2 + \left(\frac{0·2}{t}\right)^2 - 2 \times 0·3\left(\frac{0·7}{t}\right)\left(\frac{0·2}{t}\right) = 150^2 \qquad \therefore \; t = \underline{0·004\ 45 \; m}$$

(*e*) Shear strain energy theory:

$$\left(\frac{0·7}{t}\right)^2 + \left(\frac{0·2}{t}\right)^2 - \left(\frac{0·7}{t}\right)\left(\frac{0·2}{t}\right) = 150^2 \qquad \therefore \; t = \underline{0·004\ 16 \; m}$$

* Since the second principal stress is of the same sign as the first, the maximum shear stress is half the difference of the first and third principal stresses, the latter being zero.

4. *A solid round steel shaft transmits a torque of* 20 *kN m and is subjected also to a bending moment of* 10 *kN m. If the torque on the shaft is increased to* 22 *kN m, to what value must the bending moment be reduced if the maximum strain energy is to be the same as that under the initial conditions? Poisson's ratio =* 0·28.

From equation (12.21), the principal stresses are given by

$$\sigma = \frac{16}{\pi d^3}(M \pm \sqrt{M^2 + T^2})$$

$$= k(M \pm \sqrt{M^2 + T^2}) \quad \text{where} \quad k = \frac{16}{\pi d^3}$$

Equating strain energies per unit volume in the two cases,

$$k^2(10 + \sqrt{10^2 + 20^2})^2 + k^2(10 - \sqrt{10^2 + 20^2})^2$$
$$- 2 \times 0\cdot28k^2(10 + \sqrt{10^2 + 20^2})(10 - \sqrt{10^2 + 20^2})$$
$$= k^2(M + \sqrt{M^2 + 22^2})^2 + k^2(M - \sqrt{M^2 + 22^2})^2$$
$$- 2 \times 0\cdot28k^2(M + \sqrt{M^2 + 22^2})(M - \sqrt{M^2 + 22^2})$$

from which $\underline{\quad M = 6\cdot78 \text{ kN m}\quad}$

5. *A circular shaft* 0·1 *m diameter is subjected to combined bending and twisting moments, the bending moment being three times the twisting moment. If the direct tension yield-point of the material is* 350 *MN/m² and the factor of safety on yield is to be* 4, *calculate the allowable twisting moment by the three following theories of elastic failure:* (a) *maximum principal stress theory;* (b) *maximum shearing stress theory;* (c) *shear strain energy theory.*

(U. Lond.)

From equation (12.21), the principal stresses are given by

$$\sigma = \frac{16}{\pi d^3}(M \pm \sqrt{M^2 + T^2})$$

$$= \frac{16}{\pi \times 0\cdot1^3}(3T \pm \sqrt{9T^2 + T^2}) = 5\,090T(3 \pm \sqrt{10})$$

(a) Maximum principal stress theory:

$$5\,090T(3 + \sqrt{10}) = \frac{350 \times 10^6}{4} \quad \therefore T = \underline{2\,790 \text{ N m}}$$

(b) Maximum shear stress theory:

$$5\,090T(3 + \sqrt{10}) - 5\,090T(3 - \sqrt{10}) = \frac{350 \times 10^6}{4} \quad \therefore T = \underline{2\,715 \text{ N m}}$$

(c) Shear strain energy theory:

$$\{5\,090T(3 + \sqrt{10})\}^2 + \{5\,090T(3 - \sqrt{10})\}^2$$
$$- \{5\,090T(3 + \sqrt{10})\}\{5\,090T(3 -- \sqrt{10})\} = \left(\frac{350 \times 10^6}{4}\right)^2$$
$$\therefore T = \underline{2\,755 \text{ N m}}$$

6. *A thick cylinder in which the outside diameter is three times the inside diameter is subjected to an internal pressure of* 80 N/mm². *The material has a yield stress of* 400 N/mm² *and* $v = 0.30$. *Calculate the factors of safety from the five theories of elastic failure.*

From Lamé's line, or otherwise, the principal stresses at the inside surface (the most highly stressed point) are 80 N/mm² (compressive), 100 N/mm² (tensile) and 10 N/mm² (tensile).

Let F be the factor of safety.

(a) Maximum principal stress theory:

$$100 = \frac{400}{F} \qquad \therefore F = \underline{4}$$

(b) Maximum principal strain theory:

$$100 + 0.3 \times 80 - 0.3 \times 10 = \frac{400}{F} \qquad \therefore F = \underline{3.31}$$

(c) Maximum shear stress theory:

$$100 + 80 = \frac{400}{F} \qquad \therefore F = \underline{2.22}$$

(d) Strain energy theory:

$$100^2 + 80^2 + 10^2 - 2 \times 0.3(-100 \times 80 - 80 \times 10 + 10 \times 100) = \left(\frac{400}{F}\right)^2$$

$$\therefore F = \underline{2.75}$$

(e) Shear strain energy theory:

$$100^2 + 80^2 + 10^2 - (-100 \times 80 - 80 \times 10 + 10 \times 100) = \left(\frac{400}{F}\right)^2$$

$$\therefore F = \underline{2.57}$$

7. A piece of material is subjected to three mutually perpendicular tensile stresses of 50, 65 and 80 MN/m². Calculate the strain energy per unit volume. Calculate also the maximum shear strain energy per unit volume and explain the difference between these two strain energies. Poisson's ratio = 0.3 and $E = 200$ GN/m². (*U. Lond.*)   (*Ans.:* 14·14 kJ/m³; 1·46 kJ/m³)

8. At a point in a steel member the major principal stress is 200 MN/m², and the minor principal stress is compressive. If the tensile yield point of the steel is 250 MN/m², find the value of the minor principal stress at which yielding will commence, according to each of the following criteria of failure: (a) maximum shearing stress; (b) maximum total strain energy; (c) maximum shear strain energy. Poisson's ratio = 0.28.

Prove any formula used for (b) and (c). (*U. Lond.*)

(*Ans.:* 50, 104·1, 80·3 MN/m²)

9. At a point in a stressed material the direct stresses on two perpendicular planes are 140 MN/m² tension and 90 MN/m² compression respectively, and the shearing stress on these planes is τ. The yield stress for the material is 250 MN/m².

Find the value of τ at which failure may be expected, according to each of the following theories of failure: (a) maximum principal stress theory; (b) maximum shearing stress theory; (c) maximum shear strain energy theory.

Comment on the difference between the values obtained. (*U. Lond.*)

(*Ans.:* 193·4, 49, 86 MN/m²)

10. A close-coiled helical spring has a wire diameter of 2·5 mm and a mean coil diameter of 40 mm. The spring is subjected to a combined axial load of 54 N and a torque acting about the axis of the spring. Determine the maximum permissible torque if: (a) the material is brittle and ultimate failure is to be avoided. The criterion of failure is the maximum tensile stress, and the ultimate tensile stress is 1·2 GN/m²; (b) the material is ductile and failure by yielding is to be avoided. The criterion of failure is the maximum shear stress and the yield in tension is 0·9 GN/m². (*I. Mech. E.*)   (*Ans.:* 1·692 N m; 1·665 N m)

11. Derive a formula for the total strain energy per unit volume of a material subjected to three principal stresses.

A torque of 1·5 kN m is transmitted by a cylindrical tube 100 mm external diameter and of uniform thickness 2·5 mm. If the elastic limit of the material under simple tension is 250 MN/m², calculate the factor of safety when the criterion of failure is (a) maximum shearing stress, (b) maximum shear strain energy.
(*U. Lond.*)   (*Ans.:* 3·04; 3·51)

12. A mild steel shaft is subjected to a torque of 2·5 kN m and to a bending moment of 1·5 kN m. Calculate the equivalent torque on the shaft and necessary diameter for a maximum shearing stress of 80 MN/m²: (i) according to the maximum shearing stress theory, (ii) according to the strain energy theory. Poisson's ratio = 0·3. (*U. Lond.*)   (*Ans.:* 2·915 KN m; 57 mm; 59·4 mm)

13. In a solid circular shaft, subjected to a bending moment of 2 kN m and a twisting moment of 1·5 kN m, the total strain energy must not exceed that produced by a simple tensile stress of 80 MN/m². Find the minimum diameter of the shaft, if Poisson's ratio is 0·325. Derive from fundamentals the expression used for total strain energy. (*U. Lond.*)   (*Ans.:* 66·8 mm)

14. A hollow cylindrical brass beam, of inner and outer diameter 50 and 75 mm respectively, sustains on a certain cross-section a pure bending moment of 2 kN m and an axial torque. If a factor of safety of 3 is required, what is the maximum torque that may be transmitted along the shaft if failure is reckoned to have occurred when the shear strain energy per unit volume has reached a value corresponding to a simple tensile stress of 200 MN/m²? (*U. Lond.*)

(*Ans.:* 1·1 kN m)

15. A shaft of diameter 100 mm is subjected to a bending moment of 5 kN m. Find the value of the maximum torque which can be applied to the shaft for each of the following conditions: (a) maximum direct stress not to exceed 120 MN/m²; (b) maximum shearing stress not to exceed 60 MN/m²; (c) maximum shear strain energy per unit volume not to exceed that induced by simple shear of 80 MN/m².
(*U. Lond.*)   (*Ans.:* 17·92, 10·66, 14·32 kN m)

16. Show how to find the total strain energy per unit volume in a piece of material subjected to pure shearing stress combined with a simple direct stress.

A solid circular shaft is required to carry a twisting moment of 6 kN m and a bending moment of 2 kN m. Determine the diameter on the assumption that the total strain energy per unit volume is not to exceed that in material under a pure shearing stress of 30 MN/m². $E = 200$ GN/m² and Poissons ratio = 1/3·5.
(*U. Lond.*)   (*Ans.:* 100·7 mm)